FOOTSTEPS
Profiles of Remarkable Health Care Leaders
2018 REVISED EDITION

Stephen E. Gordon, M.D., M.B.A.
Editor-in-Chief

Lauren M. Frasca, M.B.A and Eric Idsvoog, B.A.
Profile Editors and Head Writers

Rushika Fernandopulle, M.D., M.P.P.
Executive Editor

EDITORS OF THE ORIGINAL EDITION
Benjamin J. Hartman, M.D. *Associate Editor, Administration*
Sally Aaron, M.B.A., *Associate Editor, Business Careers*
Azita Hamedani, M.D., M.P.H., *Associate Editor, Medical Careers*
Marya L. Besharov, Ph.D., M.B.A., *Managing Editor*

(Continued on next page)

A Project of the Harvard Interfaculty
Program for Health Systems Improvement

Senior Writers
Sarah Berkson, Adam Block, Doris Huang, Erica Hutchins, Fang Ko,
Elana Light, Stephanie Mayer, Priya Nalkur, Maya Nambison,
Teddy Pasquali, Sara Schulman, Joanna Yeo

Interviewer–Writers
Jennifer Chen, Talia Eini, Julia Glueck, Tim Greene, Kiran Gupta,
Cait Koss, Michelle Levine, Elinathan Ohiomamba, Dalia Rotstein,
Joel Thomas, Tap Van Geel, Johanna Visuri

Term Editors
Anna Gallardo, Editor (Spring 2002)
Claire Healy, Assistant Editor (Fall 2002)
David Rosenthal, Assistant Editor (Fall 2002)

Editorial Consultants
Naomi Westwater Weekes
Amanda M. Teo
David P. Taylor

Introduction
Andrew Iliff

Indexing, Proofreading & Fact Checking
Crystal Myler; Victor Shopov (indexing)

Karla Pollick
Executive Director, Harvard Interfaculty Program for Health Systems
Improvement, 2004–2011

Design and Production
Marc Kaufman
Digital Design Group (www.ddgdesign.com)

ISBN: 0-9787306-1-5
Library of Congress Card Number: 2007936879
Printed in Canada by Webcom, Toronto, Ontario

Table of Contents

PREFACE TO THE 2018 EDITION

The origins of this book date back to the summer of 2002 when, after moving back to Cambridge to start a post-baccalaureate program, I met up with Rushika Fernandopulle, with whom I had worked at The Advisory Board Company. He was the newly appointed executive director of the Harvard Interfaculty Program for Health Systems Improvement, a program designed to bring together the talent and resources across Harvard University towards the common goal of improving health care systems. He told me about discussions he had been having with some Harvard undergraduates about the lack of advice for people pursuing less traditional paths in health care, especially as health care leaders. Students knew the hoops and hurdles of how to get into medical school, but what if they wanted to do more than just practice medicine? What if they wanted to influence policy, run a hospital, serve in government, or lead an insurance or pharmaceutical company? Those paths were less clear.

It was a time of growing concern both about the rising cost of health care in the United States as well the quality of care delivered, and there were increasing numbers of students interested in joining the effort to improve health care. But they wanted good advice. They weren't looking for "how to" guides on getting into a particular type of graduate program; those were already available. Rather, these students sought a more fundamental sort of guidance: How do you decide what matters most to you? How do you develop a useful skill set knowing your interests might take you very far from your current path? And how much worrying and planning should one actually do, anyway—particularly when so much of how one's career turned out seemed determined by random events and good luck.

With these questions in mind, we decided to start asking some influential health care leaders how their *own* careers started, and what advice they had to offer. We enlisted a team of 30 or so undergraduates, recent graduates, and graduate students to start thinking about these questions and interviewing people. The process began by interviewing prominent people in our own backyard, at Harvard. This initial effort included some of the greatest minds in health care systems and policy, such as David Blumenthal and Harvey

Fineberg. They each lent their powerful networks to this effort and put us in touch with a virtual who's who in American health care at the time. We used these introductions to expand our scope, and soon we were traveling around the country interviewing senior leaders across every part of the health care system. Back in Cambridge, we had a team of students who were writing up transcripts and turning them into brief profiles. We were fortunate to receive some additional funding from Bunny Ellerin and the Harvard Business School Health Care Alumni Association, which helped fund an early version of the book that year focused exclusively on business careers.

As the academic year drew to a close, we realized that while we had interviewed more than 100 people—and had several hundred pages of transcripts—we were nowhere near doing justice to the richness those interviews contained. They were filled with dozens and dozens of incredible stories, insights, and advice: beautiful articulations of people's truest motivations, remarkable stories of unexpected opportunities, and deep struggles with figuring how one could best maximize their impact on society, and so much more. The narratives felt worthy of significantly more in-depth and robust presentations than we initially had been able to do.

Over the next few years, Lauren Frasca and I continued to work on gradually turning the existing material into finished in-depth profiles. In 2004, we took what we had completed and put out an early version of this book, entitled *Footsteps: Profiles of Forty Health Care Leaders,* which was printed in limited quantity and distribution. Many of the real gems in the current volume were not included, however, and the hope of continuing to work on them and eventually putting out a "final" version remained.

In the years that followed, the lives of those helming the project got very busy. Graduate school, residencies, weddings, family and personal illnesses, and the birth of new children all became new realities. Rushika, who had supported the effort through his leadership at the Harvard Interfaculty Program for Health Systems Improvement, moved on to start building what would eventually evolve into Iora Health. In his place, Karla Pollick—a gifted organizer and motivator—continued to encourage us to complete a final version, and made herself widely available to do whatever she could to help. Her efforts resulted in a partnership with the American College of Physician Executives, (since renamed the Association for Physician Leadership) through which we published a 2007 edition of the book focused mostly on physician leaders, entitled *At the Top of Their Game: Profiles of Successful Healthcare Leaders.*

Sadly, much of the best material we created still had not made it into any of these editions, and remained on the hard drives of our writers and editors. We felt the project was still incomplete. At the same time, we felt the heart of this book—the *why* of people's early career decisions, those decisions that launched them on their trajectories—was timeless, and very relevant to students and young professionals today.

Therefore, starting in 2012 we gave it one last push. Working closely with Eric Idsvoog, mostly in our free time, we started to update every profile. We also got back in touch with the people profiled whose careers had significantly evolved, which not surprisingly were the vast majority. To our delight, everyone seemed delighted to see this project resurface. Many commented on how surprised they were by how accurate the underlying themes of their profiles remained, despite the years that had passed.

And so, a decade and a half after the project's inception, and with greater breadth and scope than we could have imagined at the start, we are pleased to finally present these gems of insight from one generation of health care leaders to the next.

I hope you enjoy reading it as much as we enjoyed creating it.

— STEPHEN E. GORDON, M.D., M.B.A.
BOSTON, MA
JANUARY 2018

Preface to the Original Edition

"Excellence is a better teacher than mediocrity. The lessons of the ordinary are everywhere. Truly profound and original insights are to be found only in studying the exemplary."

—Warren G. Bennis

This book grew out of a series of conversations with students and junior faculty members at Harvard University in the course of building a new health policy group called the Harvard Interfaculty Program for Health Systems Improvement. The goal of this new endeavor was to leverage resources both from across the University's many silos (business, medicine, law, economics, etc.) and from the "real world" to address some of the most difficult but important issues facing the U.S. health care system. In addition to sponsoring a number of more traditional research projects to fill gaps of knowledge, we asked students and faculty how we could better help them work in this area. Over and over again, we heard that although they wanted to dedicate their careers to helping address these important issues of how to deliver and finance health care, they needed more guidance on how to best do so.

We decided the best way to help guide students in this area was to help them learn, as Warren Bennis suggests above, from the exemplary; to expose them to the career paths, decisions, and advice of truly remarkable leaders in health care. We were fortunate to find an exemplary young leader ourselves in Stephen Gordon who built a team of over 80 students and young professionals to identify, approach, and interview a truly phenomenal group of leaders from a wide variety of perspectives within health care, and then write, edit, and rewrite (often many times) the profiles you are about to read.

We are extremely grateful to the dozens of senior leaders, both those whose profiles are included in this volume, and those whose are not, for taking the time out of their extremely busy schedules to speak with us, and for their candor and willingness to share both their successes and failures in an effort to help others learn from them. Individually, each profile can teach a lot; collectively, they provide a powerful tool to help understand how to influence change and to craft one's own path of leadership within health care.

Our hope is that the publication of this volume marks not the end of this project but simply a milestone in it; we already have much more valuable material than could fit within these covers, and many more leaders we wish to learn from. We welcome any comments or suggestions on this book, as well as support for continuing this valuable work in the future.

— RUSHIKA FERNANDOPULLE, M.D., M.P.P.
HARVARD INTERFACULTY PROGRAM FOR HEALTH SYSTEMS
IMPROVEMENT
CAMBRIDGE, MA
2004

Acknowledgements

A great many people contributed to this book and its predecessors over the years, and it would be impossible to thank all of them. Please know I am grateful to each of you for your contribution.

I am indebted to the health care leaders profiled in this work for opening their calendars to our interviews as well as opening their hearts and memories during our conversations. My thanks, as well, to those we interviewed for this project but whose profiles were not included in this final edition. Several of their profiles were included in previous editions of this work.

Among those who supported this effort since the beginning is David Blumenthal. As the chair of the Harvard Interfaculty Program for Health Systems Improvement, he agreed to fund this project and provided guidance at several stages for which I owe him greatly. I am also indebted to Karla Pollick, who took over as Executive Director for the Program for Health Systems Improvement in 2004, and encouraged the completion of this final edition with an effort beyond all reasonable expectation. My gratitude also goes to Harvey Fineberg. In addition to helping define the vision for this book in its early stages, he opened up a vast network of senior health care leaders to us through his connections. Thank you as well to Bunny Ellerin, head of the Harvard Business School Health Care Alumni group, who provided funding to a very early edition of this work.

A very special thank you to Lauren Frasca, who stayed involved with this project long after we stopped having the means to pay her for her time, and who personally wrote or edited many of the profiles in this book. Likewise, I owe much gratitude to Eric Idsvoog, who stepped in as an editor for the ACPE edition in 2007 and continued on with revisions through the very end. He has contributed in one way or another to every page in this book, including many profiles he authored himself. A special thank you as well to Benjamin Hartman, Sally Aaron, Marya Hill-Popper Besharov, and Azita Hamedani, who—along with Lauren Frasca—served as the team of editors who oversaw most of the initial work of conducting the interviews and drafting profiles.

I would like to thank David Sclar for making the original suggestion of writing a book on career paths in health care outside strictly clinical medicine or biomedical research. Also thanks to Anna Gallardo, for serving as the initial editor, and Claire Healy, David Rosenthal, and Michelle Levine for their involvement early on. My thanks to Doris Huang and Joanna Yeo for their student leadership, as well as to Amy Trenkle and Hyunsook Song for all of their help in managing the administration of the project in its early phases.

The following people also contributed in various ways and deserve thanks: Sarah Berkson, Diana Barnes-Brown, L. Robert Burns, Bette McClay, Aneesh Chopra, Anne Claiborne, Zoe Cohen, Frank Connors, Malcolm Cox, Wil Cunningham, Maggie Delissio, Miriam Donaldson, Maria Fernandopulle, Stan Finkelstein, Howie Forman, Amanda Fulmor, Jean Gauthier, Adina Gerver, Elizabeth Gordon, Cristina Gutierrez, Alexandra Hallen, Jared Hopkins, Mike Houseman, Gail Jacobs, Sam Joffee, Anissa Kalinowski, June Kinney, Adam Kirsch, Julie Lane, Sharon Levin, Stephanie Meyer, Lee Ann Michelson, Jacqueline Murphy, Priya Nalkur, Eugene Ng, Wendy Netter, Amy Ojena, Teddy Pasquali, Mark Pauly, Andrew Resnick, Jill Rubin, Bijan Salehizadeh, Ann Schiff, Cindy Schwartz, Sara Schulman, Ilana Shatz, Vijay Shredder, Christa Smith, Ian Spatz, Zachary Stillerman, Jean-Phillippe Talmon, Jessica Teplow, Felix Tollinche, Audrey Walton, Ben Williams, and Frank Williams.

My sincere thanks to Marc Kaufman at Digital Design Group in Newton, Massachusetts, for demonstrating more kindness and patience in seeing this through to the end than anyone could reasonably have expected; to Amanda Teo, my wife, for her encouragement and editorial skills on several occasions; to Crystal Myler, who brought renewed energy and substantial skill to the final weeks of production; and to Naomi Westwater Weekes for her help in pushing things through at the end. Finally, many thanks to Andrew Iliff who authored the introduction.

Finally, my greatest thanks is reserved for Rushika Fernandopulle. As executive director of the Harvard Interfaculty Program for Health Systems Improvement in 2002, Rushika invited me to take on this project, opened up his network across health care, and provided ongoing guidance and funding. Without him, this book would never have been created.

—SEG

How to Read this Book

This book contains a wealth of combined experience in health care spread across more than 500 pages. While we have only included material felt worthy of inclusion, we recognize that you may lack the time (or interest!) in reading it cover-to-cover. With that in mind, we have added some tools to help you tailor your approach, and still get what you want from the material.

First, in addition to the standard table of contents on page i, we have included a *thematic table of contents* starting on page xvii. This table of contents allows you to filter profiles by certain variables—specifically type of training, role, and sector of the health care system. For example, a reader considering pursuing an MBA might want to read through everyone with an MBA, regardless of role or sector, to get a sense of the work of MBAs in health care. Another reader might be considering switching from research into pharmaceuticals, and may want to read through everyone in in the pharmaceuticals, biotechnology and medical devices category, regardless of their training or role. We hope that you find this a helpful tool in creating a customized reading list for you that is most specific to your interests.

Second, in addition to a regular index (of places, names, etc.) on page 473, we have compiled a *thematic index* starting on page 489. This is designed to allow exploration of a wide range of concepts across the profiles. For example, a physician considering leaving clinical practice could look up "leaving clinical medicine" under "career changes" and find 8 specific places in the book where this is discussed. Another reader might be struggling to achieve a satisfactory work-life balance, and could look up "work-life balance" under "life style of profiles" and find 14 places where this is specifically discussed. In total, this index identifies more than 500 themes.

A Note on Variation in Length

The profiles in this book range significantly in terms of length and depth of analysis. This does not reflect anything about the profiled person's career—or our interest in it. Rather, this simply reflects *when* during the course of the project we interviewed them. At the beginning of the project, we started with short profiles mostly written by undergraduates. As the project went on, we conducted increasingly detailed interviews—often by the editors—and wrote up increasingly analytical profiles.

A dozen or so of these later profiles, which are particularly in-depth, might be considered "featured" profiles. These profiles are typically ten or more pages, and include sections dedicated to discussion of various themes woven throughout the profile. Included in this group are the profiles of Don Berwick, David Blumenthal, David Cutler, Arnold Epstein, Harvey Fineberg, Raymond Gilmartin, John Iglehart, Anula Jayasuriya, Arthur Kleinmann, Paul Levy, Fitzhugh Mullen, Joseph Newhouse, Nancy Oriol, and Gail Wilensky.

A NOTE ON CURRENCY OF POSITIONS

Efforts have been made to update as much of the information about each profiled leader as possible. To the best of our knowledge, the positions listed in this book were up-to-date as of the end of 2016. That said, we apologize in advance for any inaccurate information that has been inadvertently included, or accurate information that has been inadvertently omitted.

Thematic Table of Contents

Please note that these lists are not meant to be exhaustive, but rather represent some starting points for readers interested in specific topics.

BY DEGREE

Doctorates

Physicians

Law Degrees (J.D.)

Masters in Business Administration (M.B.A.)

Masters in Public Health (M.P.H.)

Masters in Public Policy (M.P.P.)

BY ROLE

Clinical Researchers

EXECUTIVES AND MANAGERS

PRACTICING PHYSICIANS

PROFESSORS

WRITERS AND EDITORS

NON-PROFIT (NON-PROVIDER) ORGANIZATIONS

PHARMACEUTICAL, BIOTECHNOLOGY, MEDICAL DEVICES

PROFESSIONAL ASSOCIATIONS

PUBLIC HEALTH

UNIVERSITY APPOINTMENTS AND ACADEMIC AFFILIATIONS

INTRODUCTION

This book is—decidedly—not a career guide: it will not tell you how to get into medical school, nor how to become a health care CEO. This book is about why people choose these goals—the motivations for pursuing careers in health care and the fulfillment found by some leaders in this field. It is about the values they hold and how these values shape their careers.

This book is a collection of stories of how people's careers unfolded, and the choices and principles that guided them. The bulk of the interviews was conducted over a decade ago, yet the insights and experiences detailed here remain timelessly relevant. While some of these interviews have been published in earlier versions, this volume is the most complete and wide-ranging collection, covering an immense array of careers, roles, and personalities. Anyone contemplating a career anywhere in health care will find something here that speaks directly to the challenges and opportunities that they confront, both now and as their career evolves.

The central question posed in the interviews is how people find meaning and satisfaction in their work—how they have balanced varied interests and personal goals. Working in health care involves tradeoffs and sacrifices. On the whole, people doing comparable jobs in other fields confront less heartache, earn higher compensation, and participate in less frustrating systems. So why do they do it? Most importantly, why do they *keep* doing it, and how do they balance the diverse priorities and opportunities that working in health care presents?

In this introduction we examine four central themes: the core motivations that drive the leaders profiled in these pages; the dilemmas and opportunities of combining different elements of the health care landscape in a single career; the balance between planning and serendipity in charting a career path; and the challenge of shifting careers to, and within, different areas of health care and beyond.

MOTIVATIONS

This is a book about why health care professionals do what they do. Not surprisingly, many physicians find the role physicians can play in individual people's lives to be immensely satisfying, including the satisfaction of providing care during some of the most important and meaningful moments of people's lives.

> I've always been astonished what a privileged opportunity medicine provides for the doctor to enter the life-world of the patient, and the lived experience of suffering. To make sense of that lived experience, you really have to know the context of the person.

—Arthur Kleinman, psychiatrist and professor of anthropology and social medicine

> What I did as an oncologist was to engage in a very intimate relationship with another human being who was facing the gravities of the threat of cancer. You'd walk that journey with them, and you'd tell patients, "You know, we're going to go to a dark and scary place here... You focus on the light at the end of the tunnel, and I'll focus on the journey."

—Andrew von Eschenbach, former FDA commissioner

> I still believe that taking care of sick people is the most important thing you can do, and I find our health care system obscene because it is set up to shunt aside the sickest and neediest among us. I think that society sees itself increasingly as a giant market, and the measure of all things is money. I'm certainly a missionary about that—I think there are things a lot more important than commercial gain.

—Marcia Angell, professor of social medicine

Even for health care professionals who work primarily outside of the clinic or hospital, caring for patients remains central. A physician by training, Howard Koh continued treating patients even as his career took him into public health and government roles. Caring for patients was grounding, informing his work as a health commissioner. Anula Jayasuriya, trained as a physician but best known for her work as a venture capitalist, likewise sees the experience of caring for patients as formative:

> What I think is wonderful about medicine is that you can give, and you give directly to people. In most other professions you are at least once removed. It is an important part of my identity and I am privileged to have had the training.

Many of our interlocutors[1] set their sights on having a broader impact than a purely clinical career typically allows. Some care for a particular community. Harris Berman, longtime CEO of Tufts Health Plan in Boston, was inspired by his work in the Peace Corps to think in these terms: "I liked the

---

1   Throughout the introduction the term "interlocutor", "profilee" and "profiled leader" are used interchangeably.

concept of taking care of a population, and figuring out what a population needed." Donald Abrams, an oncologist who treated early HIV/AIDS patients, most of them young gay men, remembers feeling grounded in the bond he shared with that group:

> It was hard to draw the line between them and me. But that's what kept me there, kept me buoyant and uplifted. It was such a challenge; it was exciting. And it was my people—my community.

Others, motivated by concerns about social justice and inequality, promote care for the neediest:

> From the very beginning what I was interested in was seeing that people who need health care get it. If there's something we have a cure for and we don't help people, I just think that's outrageous. That people die from a condition that's not controlled is outrageous, and disproportionately, the people who don't get help are low-income, uninsured, minority populations—all of the barriers stand in their way.

> —*Karen Davis, former president, The Commonwealth Fund*

Such motives often lead to careers in non-profit institutions. Yet many of our interlocutors in the private sector share their non-profit peers' sense of social purpose. Jayasuriya, for example, defines her success as an investor in terms of "having chosen, backed, and contributed to the success of several companies that have significant impact on human health."

Working on health care policy can achieve a broad impact, but it can also be frustrating. This is in part because, unlike the person-to-person work of clinical care, policymakers and advocates are often several degrees removed from those whom they seek to help. Arthur Kellermann and James Mongan admit that their work at times felt like "tilting at windmills" or "running around in circles." Arnold Epstein, whose career has unfolded at the crossroads of medical research and health policy, says that the link between the two is "long and tenuous." In a similar vein, Davis acknowledges that in some policy work, "you can never be sure of the difference made by your own work," in part because its impact unfolds over years, rather than days or hours as is often the case in the clinical setting.

Another motivation for many interlocutors is the magnitude of their impact: it matters not just how many people are affected by their work, but also how great the effect is. Angell ascribes the satisfaction of editing a leading journal in part to the degree of its influence: "You can have a huge impact at the *New England Journal of Medicine*. I am at heart a secular missionary, and that's a place for missionaries."

Across the board, the interlocutors emphasize the importance of doing work that feels meaningful, in whatever way most matters to you. Kellermann remembers a turning point early in his career when, in support of his research on gun violence—then, as now, a marginalized topic in public health research—a mentor urged him simply to "follow your heart, do the stuff that really matters, and don't let anyone talk you out of it." Venture capitalist Tom Dickerson cautions, "Whatever you end up doing, remember that you have to go into the office every day and do it from nine to five. You'd better like it."

Another powerful motivation, distinct from the common thread of caring for patients, is the satisfaction of creativity and building new things.

> For me, a large part of the thrill is looking at the vast array of medical/research technologies—I have always loved being at the leading edge of technical advance. A lot of people can look at technology and be enamored of it. The skill—and the thrill—is being able to do the thought experiment of predicting which technology can actually be made into a product, and actually both make returns for the investors and be valuable, in people's hands, in a timeframe that matches an investment fund's lifecycle. That is the trick.

> *—Anula Jayasuriya, venture capitalist*

This drive to create can even operate to the exclusion of other core development functions.

> I am motivated by the ability to create—that's what gets me going, the creativity that goes into picking ideas and building them into businesses. I always need to have more then one venture going on because, if the business is successful, at some point the businesses get where they're beyond the creative phase. They go into the management phase, and that's where I like to step out of the role as CEO and take a more passive one, or see new ownership. I don't want to give up my creative energy.

> *—Steve Hochberg, venture capitalist*

Many of those profiled are driven by the imperative to teach and mentor the next generation of physicians and health care leaders.

> Teaching gave me the greatest satisfaction. I love it. You have these really bright kids and you work with them, and mentor them, and create long-lasting relationships. I'm still in touch with a lot of the kids from there. I remember when I was at MIT teaching—I literally remember walking into 77 Mass Ave., looking up at the columns thinking, "I can't believe they're letting me do this." It was such a kick and such a privilege.

> *—Paul Levy, former hospital CEO*

Combining Interests

The second major theme that emerges from these profiles is the imperative to integrate different interests and disciplines in a single career.

My career was always going to have two sides to it. It was going to have a humanities-social science side—I wasn't sure if it was going to be history or anthropology or what exactly—and the medical side, but I didn't know how it would come together.

—Arthur Kleinman, professor of anthropology, psychiatry and social medicine

Such an approach entails challenges—in addition to the multiple "start-up" costs of engaging in multiple disciplines, shifting between fields can result in a loss of career momentum, at least initially. But many profilees view this as a virtue. Epstein, who has served in a number of leadership roles across academia, policy and government, explains:

More than most people, I really like the combination and the transition intellectually, emotionally, between different activities. If I have the choice of great diversity in widespread challenges and the opportunity to move across disciplines or combine them versus feeling like I have extraordinary competency in one area—I'll take the former.

The broad consensus is that synthesizing distinct interests is a major strength, allowing a much broader analytical approach. Koh, who, like Epstein, is a physician with extensive experience in high-level government positions:

The medical model is usually very specialized. In the medical model, one studies diseases or organs or very narrow parts of the medical universe. In public health, one considers issues in their entirety and looks at the impact of policy, sociocultural factors, education and behavior as well as biology.

For Donald Berwick, combining different disciplines required sustained effort:

I constantly tried to have my cake and eat it too. My tactic was to try to find how to have both. I like the Kennedy School and medical school, or clinical work and policy work. It's that unwillingness to give up one for the other probably also played a large role…perhaps a longer-standing personality trait of optimism, or stubbornness, or a reluctance to choose. What the Kennedy School did was take vague ideas I had had about evaluating practices and gave them a sharp intellectual edge… By giving me the tools, it made it possible for me to have my cake and eat it too.

While such a "dual degree" approach has become more common in recent years, for several of the interlocutors here it was a path-breaking decision. Harvey Fineberg recalls the conversation with the dean of his medical school when he explained that he wanted to get a Masters in Public Policy. The dean looked puzzled:

So after awhile he said, "Let me get this straight—you're thinking about taking off a year?" And I said, "That's right." And he said, "And you're not going to go into a laboratory?" And I said, "No, actually, I had been thinking about going into this program in public policy." And he said, "public policy"—and then looking through my records—"but your record here isn't all that bad!"

Several interlocutors describe the credibility that cross-disciplinary qualifications can confer, including when non-clinical leaders engage with physicians. Robert Galvin recalls a conversation he had with Jack Welch, the legendary CEO of GE, where Galvin's responsibilities had significantly expanded. Galvin was now managing a sizable budget, and Welch said to him: "I can't believe I'm giving a doctor a billion dollars to manage…at least you have an MBA."

Others observed that while an MBA can be helpful, it is not essential. As Peter Slavin explains: "Some of the best managers I've ever met in health care never spent a day in business school, a school of public health, or a public policy school. They just have a natural feel for it." He also notes that over time credentials matter less than accomplishments and reputation.

Several interlocutors argue that health care should be lead by physicians, who are guided by the experience of direct patient interaction.

> I wish we could sign doctors up to be the CEOs of every hospital and insurance company, and in elected positions—then maybe we'd have laws and policies that were better informed.
>
> —*Nancy Oriol, medical school dean of students*

For Jack Rowe, a geriatrician by training who eventually became the CEO of health insurer Aetna, this was a crucial motivation for moving into the business side of health care:

> There are a lot of people who started asking me why I went to the "dark side." One of them said to me, "Why did you go work for a managed care company?" And I said, "Well, what do you think their problem is?" And he said, "Their problem is they just don't have people there who understand us doctors and health care." And then he said, "Ohhh, I get it."

At the same time, the decision to leave clinical practice and direct engagement with patients is extremely difficult.

> I went into medicine to see and treat patients. Through everything I've done in my leadership and managerial career, I have always been able to have the satisfaction of knowing that some aspect of my job or the decisions I make would at least in part impact patients. It's just the human interaction—the conversations you have with patients, how you do or don't make a difference in their lives—*that* I miss.
>
> —*Jane Henney, former commissioner of the FDA*

PLANNING AND SERENDIPITY

The third major theme concerns the balance between career planning and serendipity. Again and again, people talk about the remarkable role that chance has played in their careers. Virtually no one in this book has seen their career unfold precisely as they planned—indeed, they have tried to stay open to new opportunities by not over-planning.

> Everybody worries an enormous amount about directing his or her career and taking control of it, but the reality is that stuff just happens sometimes over which you have no control. The game is as much recognizing the unexpected opportunity and seizing it as it is actually planning it out.

—Tom Dickerson, venture capitalist

Howard Berman describes identifying and taking advantage of opportunities as a learned skill: "If you ask most people, 'How did you get into what you do?' it usually starts with 'Well, it's a funny story,' which means it wasn't what they planned. I try to tell people, 'Don't over-plan. Just take the opportunities as they come, and things will sort themselves out.'" Rowe agrees:

> One thing I would say is that I think it's important to be opportunistic. That is kind of a bad word—and people think that's bad—but I think it's good. I think an opportunist is a guy who steals home plate from third base when the pitcher throws the ball at the catcher's head. And if you sit there on third base and don't steal home, you are not being opportunistic and you're not taking advantage of the opportunities in front of you. You're not serving anybody well.

Fineberg, whose career has spanned a startling variety of roles in public health, academia, and government, quotes President Eisenhower's saying that "plans are useless, but planning is essential," Maryann Fralic elaborates:

> I think it is wrong to so precisely plan a career. If you are focused only on the track that you are on, you will miss seeing other opportunities. You will be busy looking ahead only at what your goal is, and although peripheral things may be happening that are really quite wonderful, you will never see them— you will not recognize them. Allow for some serendipity.

Angell suggests that women in particular have had to pursue non-linear careers:

> My career path was very crooked. It was not a straight line. That has to do mainly with the fact that women, when I started out, had to seize the moment. They had to watch for opportunities because there was not a clear-cut career track for them. I did seize opportunities, and they turned out to be unusual ones.

Joseph Newhouse believes he could not have planned his career as it unfolded: "When I was in graduate school, if someone would have told me I would ultimately become a professor of health policy and management, I would have thought they were hallucinating."

Serendipity takes many forms. For Kellermann, each conversation holds the potential to change a life's course:

> One of my basic philosophies is that happenstance conversations often play very pivotal roles in people's lives. I've been lucky enough to meet truly great people in medicine over the course of my career, people who pass by and leave me nuggets of wisdom. Sometimes I feel like Forrest Gump. What you'll find with a lot of careers is, it's not navigating across the lake, it's shooting the rapids. Chance encounters with exceptional patients and exceptional people have bumped me in one direction or another as I have gone down this stream—I only half comprehend where it's taking me or what I'll do when I get there.

For Berwick, discomfort can be a signal that a change of course is in order, if one musters the courage to confront rather than dismiss the discomfort:

> I showed up for the first day [of a course], and I was just very uncomfortable. On noon of day two I left—flew home early. I just thought it was garbage...I had quite a sleepless night, and in the morning, I had this kind of sudden insight. The reason for my discomfort was not really that it was garbage, but rather that it was the first time I had ever really heard a theory that I could understand about how quality happens, and it made almost everything I was doing theoretically incorrect. Which was very, very difficult for me to realize—it had to do with my whole career, not just my current job. And so I went back to D.C., and went to the last day of the course.

Kleinman describes his embrace of an even more extreme embrace of serendipity:

> The day classes began, as I was driving up Palm Drive, I made my decision to go to medical school. I actually made it in a funny way: it's the first right turn you make as you get on Palm Drive, and a car actually swerved in front of me, and I had to go to the right. I said to myself, "Well, it feels right, it was natural to happen, so I might as well go there."

The conflicting demands and imperatives of a successful career can be extremely challenging, entailing significant sacrifices.

> My greatest regrets are the times when I was first starting out, and I was so motivated to create, but I had too many balls in the air. I was juggling too much, and I was too stressed. That rubs off on your home life. Modulating the amount

of new projects I take on has always been the most difficult thing for me.

—*Steve Hochberg, Venture Capitalist*

Oriol frames the roads not taken in terms of a profound appreciation for the path you are on: "Anything that I love, but am not doing right now, I miss. But since I also love what I am doing now, and I know that you can't do everything all of the time, I have no regrets."

Besides regrets, career transitions can have concrete consequences, including the challenge of repeatedly starting over:

> One of the things that is difficult about entering industry after extensive academic training is that you are older than your professional peers. It's a little disheartening. The other thing that's a negative is that you start at the bottom of the ladder several times in succession. Medicine is a hierarchy—you go through it, and then you step off and start again at zero in another field. As they teach us in business school, there is an opportunity cost.

—*Anula Jayasuriya, Venture Capitalist*

Berman, on the other hand, notes the influence you have when you come into a new position as an expert: "When you make a mid-career change, you come to your new position as an expert. And as the new leader, you have a license to drive change. It can be a very exciting opportunity." Others note that for them the exact opposite—their *lack* of expertise, and therefore fresh eyes—was the source of their strength. Levy explains a conversation between himself and the Dean of the Harvard Medical School earlier in his career: "Dean Martin and I hit it off, and he said, "Why don't you come join me as dean for administration?" and I said, "How about because I don't know anything about medicine?" He said, "Well that's perfect, because I want someone with a fresh perspective."

The converse career shift, made by several interlocutors, is the move into health care from an outside field. Often this transition is made to lead a large healthcare organization, in which management skill and experience are prerequisites.

> Managing an institution is not really health policy…it is mostly about people: getting people to work together, nurturing them, organizing them, stimulating them, and helping them think through their problems. It's a lot of coaching. You have to be a real people person to be good as a manager. Much of it is managing yourself in relation to other people—knowing what to say, when to say it.

—*David Blumenthal, President of The Commonwealth Fund*

Such leadership skills may be more important than extensive experience within the field of health care.

The president didn't care how much I knew about health care. What he cared about was whether I could manage a large, complex agency, through both the political and the budgetary processes. He knew that I had a background in science and that I knew enough about health care—but he was much more concerned with getting someone who could manage HHS.

—*Donna Shalala, former U.S. Secretary of Health and Human Services*

Some profiled leaders felt that being a "newcomer" to health care conferred some advantages:

My perspective as a newcomer in the industry gave me the ability to ask "why?" It also allowed me to be proactive, and also to work with scientists on the "so what?" questions that needed to be asked to ensure that our programs and initiatives will make a positive difference in people's lives.

—*Mara Aspinall, biotech industry executive*

Such career transitions inevitably entail leaving other work behind, however, which can be a challenge in itself.

I tell all of the people that I train that life is like a trapeze act, and you swing from one ring to another. When you reach out for that next ring you think is going to take you to a greater height, you've always got to be prepared to let go of the other one. You've got to be able to let go if you want to reach out.

—*Andrew von Eschenbach, former director, National Cancer Institute*

Finally, while this is a book about the impact of careers in health care, several interlocutors emphasized the importance of work-life balance and maintaining a sense of perspective.

You really need balance. There are times in your career when your personal life has to be first, and other times when the career is first. There's a time to devote to family, there's a time when your career is the most important, there's a time when your husband's schedule is, when your children's activities are—you need to bend around that. In our family it was always give and take.

—*Maryann Fralic, consultant and professor of nursing*

Furthermore, true success depends on maintaining a dynamic equilibrium between work and other priorities.

There are decisions that need to be made at each major stage in one's life. Don't assume that your work/family balance decision today will be the same one that you want to make a year from now. In addition, while many focus balance issues on having and caring for young children, there are many other times that decisions need to be made—including illness and caring for older parents.

—*Mara Aspinall, biotech industry executive*

Others note that the most impactful careers are marathons, not sprints.

> I don't think I advanced any faster than I would have if I worked 70 hours a week. At the end of the day, it's about maintaining some sense of perspective that it's okay to not kill yourself, because those last ten hours don't really add that much to your career, they really detract a lot from your personal life.

—*Tom Dickerson, venture capitalist*

An effective career depends on understanding that the best way to accomplish your ambitions may not be the most heroic, and is certainly not solitary. As Maryann Fralic says, "Anybody who believes they're just great and that's how it happened—that's nonsense."

> There comes a point in time when you realize that you personally are not going to cure cancer, that the cure to cancer is going to depend upon a team, with everybody contributing. Then, as a member of that team, you decide that you're not going to play anymore. You're going to coach. There has to be a decision then as to what's more important: you scoring a touchdown or you doing something that helps the team win.

—*Andrew von Eschenbach, former director, National Cancer Institute*

Some interlocutors highlight the need for patience, recognizing that life will place demands on you that may trump career plans, at least temporarily.

> Careers are really important, but they're not the most important thing in life. If you have to put them on hold for a while or restructure and rebuild them, there's time. But there's not time to go back and fix broken relationships with family or with friends, or to lose your integrity. Careers can be set aside for a time if you need to. You can come back and redirect them, or watch them bounce even higher than they've been before. And some of those other things, unless you're paying attention to them all the time, you can never restore.

—*Jane Henney, former commissioner of the FDA*

Finally, several interlocutors caution against indulging in regret.

> I think forward, not backward. I'm always wondering, "What can I do now, what looks like a good challenge for tomorrow?" And certainly there are times when I say, "I can't stand this anymore." Academic medicine can be frustrating, and I sometimes long for the concrete rewards of my days as a builder. But the uncertainty of tomorrow draws me. And because I don't believe that I know where some other path might have taken me anyway, how can I have regrets?

—*Nancy Oriol, medical school dean of students*

LEADERSHIP PROFILES

Donald I. Abrams

Chief, Hematology-Oncology, San Francisco General Hospital
Professor of Clinical Medicine, UCSF

San Francisco in the early 1980s was home to some of the very first cases of the newly emerging AIDS epidemic. As a young gay physician at the time, Donald Abrams was concerned about this both personally and professionally, and so he became a leading researcher on the disease in its early years. In this profile he discusses what this has meant to him, and how, ultimately, the same things that drew him to the care of HIV/AIDS patients have since led him to move towards other fields.

EDUCATION & TRAINING

1968–1972	A.B., Brown University
1973–1977	M.D., Stanford University
1977–1980	Resident, Internal Medicine, Kaiser Foundation Hospital (San Francisco)
1980–1983	Fellow, Hematology-Oncology, University of California-San Francisco
2002–2003	Fellow, Program in Integrative Medicine, University of Arizona

CAREER PATH

1984–1988	Assistant Clinical Professor, Department of Medicine, Cancer Research Institute, UCSF
1988–1992	Associate Professor of Clinical Medicine, Department of Medicine, UCSF
1992–	Professor of Clinical Medicine, UCSF
1995–2000	Treasurer, President, Gay and Lesbian Medical Association
2003–	Chief, Hematology-Oncology Division, San Francisco General Hospital
2006–2008	Director of Clinical Programs, Osher Center for Integrative Medicine, UCSF

SELECTED PUBLICATIONS

Abrams DI, et al. "Persistent diffuse lymphadenopathy in homosexual men: Endpoint or prodrome?" *Annals of Internal Medicine.* 100:801–808, 1984.

Abrams DI, et al. "Short-term effects of cannabinoids in patients with HIV-1 infection." *Annals of Internal Medicine.* 139:258–266, 2003.

Abrams DI, et al. "Physician-assisted suicide and patients with human immunodeficiency virus disease." *NEJM.* 336:417–421, 1997.

From the beginning of the epidemic—when I was one of the few doctors in the world who was caring for HIV/AIDS patients or even knew anything about the disease—I never stopped my work. Whenever I went home I would be with my friends who'd say, "Well, what did you learn today? What are we going to do?" And then my friends started getting sick... and I was just always at work. But a career in medicine is just that, it's a career. If you're looking for a nine-to-five job, you've got the wrong career path.

—Donald Abrams

As a young, gay physician in San Francisco during the early 1980s, Donald Abrams found himself in the midst of the earliest stages of the AIDS epidemic as it was unfolding within his own community. An oncologist with an interest in immune disorders, Abrams began seeing patients, most of them gay men, with symptoms for which no known diagnosis could fully account. Abrams's efforts on behalf of these patients made him a leader in the early research on and treatment of HIV/AIDS. He has devoted much of his career to fighting the disease, not only in the clinic and the lab but also as advocate for its victims and as an educator within the medical community. He has traveled throughout the world as a lecturer on HIV/AIDS, and has served as president of the Gay and Lesbian Medical Association.

FORECASTING A CAREER IN MEDICINE

Abrams cannot point to any specific moment when he decided to go into medicine: "I don't remember a time when I didn't want to be a doctor, and I don't remember why that was." He also remembers the difficulty he had reconciling his own plans with the expectations of parents, teachers, and other mentors:

I know my parents wanted me to be a rabbi, but my temple folded after my bar mitzvah, so I took that to be a bad sign. Then I took a vocational test in high school and it said that I was best suited to be, not a certified public accountant, but a junior certified public accountant. So that was disturbing. The next time I took the test I tried to fake it so I could get a better career opportunity.

Despite this career forecast, Abrams was accepted to the Brown University Master of Medical Science Program in 1968, with the expectation that he would graduate from Brown's newly founded medical school in 1976. He decided to spend the summer of his junior year abroad working as a nurse in a hemodialysis unit at Sint Lucas Ziekenhuis in Amsterdam. "When I got there I said, 'It's a big world out here. Do I really want to stay in Providence for the rest of my career?'" After some soul-searching and a road trip from Amsterdam to Athens and back again, Abrams decided that he did not, in fact, want to spend even the next five years in Providence. He applied to other medical schools, and was ultimately accepted at Stanford.

A Rotation Abroad

Stanford's research in the 1970s was concentrated on the study of lymphoma and lupus, two diseases that feature the lymphocyte (white blood cell) as a key player. Abrams's interest in these illnesses would continue throughout his career.

After his first year at Stanford, Abrams was awarded a California State Fellowship that covered four years of medical school tuition. Unrestricted by financial concerns, Abrams was able to spend his fourth of five years in medical school abroad in London pursuing clinical clerkships. Abrams saw his time in London as an opportunity to explore his intended specialty of psychiatry. Before he arrived in London, he made a stop in Boston at McLean Psychiatric Hospital to work in the borderline personality unit, where the first seeds of doubt about psychiatry were planted in him: "It was hard for me to understand the psychiatric illness of the patients because they seemed very similar to young people that I was in school with. The blur between who was staff and who were patients also confused me a bit."

Abrams's next rotation was in London at the Maudsley Institute of Psychiatry, where he worked in a psychoanalytic group that applied the teachings of Melanie Klein:

> Anytime a patient said "two," that meant breasts, and any time they said "three" that meant the penis. And so we sat there listening to all of these patients talk and then we would go to patient care conferences. And at the Maudsley Institute they had the electric shock people, and the people that believed in giving drugs, and then the people like us who thought that everything could be arranged if you figured out where the patient's twos and threes came from. What really disturbed me was the fact that what we call "depressed" in the United States, they called "situational adjustment reaction" in England, and things that we called "psychotic," they called "depressed." So it seemed to me that—in a country that spoke the same language we did—the fact that we didn't agree on what these diagnoses were was off-putting to me. I felt that if I was going to devote my career to something in medicine, I wanted something that was a little more concrete than that.

A MOVE TO SAN FRANCISCO: FINDING A RESIDENCY

Abrams decided not to return to Palo Alto when he came back from England: "I met an Israeli ballet dancer who moved back to the States with me and he thought Palo Alto was really too dull and boring and very homogenous." Instead, and against the advice of Abrams's advisors at Stanford, he and his partner relocated to more diverse San Francisco. Abrams's advisors warned him that he might have a difficult time matching for an internship and residency because he had spent so little of his time in medical school actually on the Stanford campus. With that in mind, Abrams applied to programs all over the state of California and ended up matching with his fourth choice, Kaiser Foundation Hospital in San Francisco:

> So I went to Kaiser, which at that time in 1977 was a rare bird as a health maintenance organization. I remember, having been trained at Stanford and other rarified environments, that the first time I saw a patient with a stroke at Kaiser, I didn't even know what was happening because I had never seen a stroke. At Stanford you saw such bizarre and unusual things that you never really saw bread and butter medicine.

A number of factors steered Abrams toward oncology at Kaiser. He had lost three of his four grandparents at an early age: "Something got instilled in me during my infancy to fear loss of people I love and to fear death. So I was attracted to patients who were at that transition point in their lives, and I was interested in watching them handle it." His previous exposure to cancer and lupus at Stanford was helpful, but what really made it an easy transition was meeting chief of medicine and rheumatologist Jeffrey Fessel, who would eventually become one of Abrams's most influential mentors. Fessel was working on treatment for autoimmune diseases, such as lupus: "He felt that the one way to sort of turn off autoimmune diseases was to give patients large doses of steroids, like decadron. I thought, 'Boy, maybe there is another way to deal with this disease.'"

In 1979, while still focusing primarily on lupus patients, Abrams and his colleagues began to see large numbers of gay, male patients coming to Kaiser with swollen glands. The patients initially saw hematologist Lee Wilkinson, another great mentor of Abrams, to make sure they did not have a lymphoma or a cancer of the immune system. After ruling this out, Wilkinson referred them to Abrams, his resident:

> Lee knew that I was gay and he started referring all of these young gay guys with swollen glands to me so I could try to figure out what was going on. I ran a lot of blood tests and biopsied a number of these guys and found out that they didn't have lymphoma. Their lymph nodes were just very highly reactive because their bodies were responding to something. So I told the

patients, "Listen, I think you're living too much in the fast lane. You're having too many sexual partners, too many sexually transmitted diseases, and using too many recreational drugs. Why don't you slow down a little bit and see if these lymph nodes go away."

At the time, Abrams did not understand the enormous importance of what he was seeing—the emergence of HIV/AIDS in the United States:

> I didn't appreciate that this was a really big thing—to have this whole new disease happening. It was strange and bizarre and on the forefront of a giant new problem that would encompass the rest of my career. If I had been in perhaps a more academic setting than Kaiser, I might have written a paper describing this syndrome of benign reactive lymphadenopathy in gay men. But I didn't and no one pushed me to—I just thought, "Oh, this is normal. This is what happens when you do medicine. You get new challenges."

Working alongside both Wilkinson and Fessel, Abrams wanted to stay at Kaiser even after his residency was completed, but when he approached Fessel with the idea, he received a resounding no: "Fessel said to me, 'We're not interested in bringing on people who can't give to the program more than the program has given them,' which meant that he wanted me to go and do a fellowship."

While flipping through the *New England Journal of Medicine*, he stumbled upon a fellowship in plasmaphoresis:

> Plasmaphoresis is when you clean the blood through a machine and take off antibodies that the patient makes. This seemed like I might have found an alternative to Jeffrey Fessel's high dose decadron (a steroid) that he was giving all these women with lupus. I thought it would be really neat.

At the last minute, Wilkinson approached Abrams to let him know that he had recommended him for a hematology-oncology fellowship at the University of California-San Francisco (UCSF). Abrams was accepted to the program in 1980.

THE VARMUS LAB

During the first year of his fellowship, Abrams encountered a young female patient with a bizarre leukemia. The patient ultimately died, and immediately afterwards, her father came in with an even stranger leukemia. Abrams was intrigued, and thought that the leukemia had to be either environmentally or virally induced. He chose virally induced malignancies as the topic of the presentation he was required to give to his peers at the end of the year. A group of physicians and researchers attended, including Harold Varmus (who received the 1989 Nobel Prize for work with retroviruses along with Michael Bishop[1]). Varmus enjoyed the presentation enough to invite Abrams to spend the second year of his fellowship working in his microbiology lab.

Before he started his new position, Abrams traveled to Seattle during his summer break to learn about bone marrow transplant. On the way to the airport, he heard a startling news broadcast:

> I'm in the car driving and I hear something about an epidemic of cancer in gay men. I said, "Whoa! What's that?" I wondered what they were talking about but I couldn't find any more information about it. I got to Seattle—I wasn't particularly out professionally at that time—but I started running around to everybody I met and said, "I'm Donald Abrams, I'm a visiting fellow, do you know anything about this epidemic of cancer in gay men?" And nobody knew what I was talking about.

On his return from Seattle, Abrams met Paul Volberding, who did know what he was talking about. Volberding worked with Jay Levy, one of the future discoverers of the AIDS virus. He was about to begin the clinical treatment of the first case he had seen of Kaposi's sarcoma, which became known as "the gay cancer." He asked Abrams to join him.

Abrams concurrently began working in the Varmus lab, and at a clinic set up for patients with this yet-unnamed disease. Before he knew it, two hundred patients were coming to him to be studied for lymphadenopathy in the cancer clinic at UCSF: "I started taking my lymph nodes and pieces of Kaposi's sarcoma and other tissues from these patients and looking for a retrovirus in them." Abrams was frustrated by the laboratory work, at which he felt inept: "Every time I tried to make RNA, I would work on it for weeks and go to the refrigerator, take out the film—and there was nothing there." Still, he was continually fascinated by these patients, on both a personal and intellectual level:

> It was quite strange because here I was, a 31-year-old gay man, and I had two hundred gay men who were between 25 and 35 with swollen glands. It was hard to draw the line between them and me. But that's what kept me there, kept me buoyant and uplifted. It was such a challenge; it was exciting. And it was my people—my community.

NAMING AIDS, AND WORKING WITH ITS PATIENTS

Abrams ran his studies out of the cancer clinic at UCSF. In 1983, the university decided that Abrams would move his practice over to San Francisco General Hospital (SFGH) in order to combine his work with that of Paul Volberding, who had just received a grant from the NIH to study Kaposi's sarcoma. Abrams was told that the move would be good for his career, but he felt that the decision was largely based on the university's fear of the new disease, and partly on "some inherent homophobia that went unexpressed."

Whatever the reason, Abrams was not happy about the move: "I sort of went over there kicking and screaming. In fact, I said 'I am not going over to that clinic in that building where the elevator has graffiti in it.' And Dr. Volberding painted the elevator so I would come." Despite his fears that they wouldn't, Abrams's patients came with him.

In 1983, Volberding, Constance Wofsy and Abrams established the UCSF AIDS/Oncology program at the SFGH. It was one of the first HIV/AIDS facilities in the nation. The AIDS virus had finally been named, though it was not yet part of the American vernacular. The three physicians and their support staff made it their mission to care for patients with the disease, disseminate information, and conduct research. AIDS became even more personal to Abrams in 1989 when his partner passed away because of the disease. Abrams withdrew slightly from his clinical activities and focused on his research.

In 1996, the SFGH's new chief of medicine asked that hematology be brought into the AIDS/Oncology program and, "rather then call the program the AIDS/Oncology/Hematology program, which is a long thing to say when you answer the telephone," the doctors decided to change the name to the Positive Health Program (PHP). PHP provided HIV/AIDS, oncology and hematology services. It has been ranked as the top facility in the nation for AIDS care by *U.S. News and World Report*. Abrams worked tirelessly to make the division "self-supporting on research grants for studies relevant to the population we serve." In 2003, the hematology/oncology division was made a free-standing division in the department of medicine, separate from the PHP program.

AN INVISIBLE MINORITY

Abrams believes that his work advocating for gay men, and in particular gay men with HIV/AIDS, has defined his career. He has held positions as treasurer and president of the Gay and Lesbian Medical Association, and also as chairman of the Community Consortium, a group of physicians dedicated to the treatment of HIV/AIDS patients. Rewarding as these activities have been, they have also been difficult: "To be gay and professional is a little rough, but not as rough as it would be if I were in Boise or Cleveland, maybe even Boston." Even in the "tolerant and accepting" environment of San Francisco, Abrams remembers not feeling totally comfortable until he was officially on the faculty at UCSF. He believes that health care is a traditionally conservative field, and often when Abrams is asked to give interviews or serve on committees, he feels he is seen "not as Donald Abrams, but as a member of the gay male community." He experienced this when he was called to serve on an FDA anti-viral advisory committee:

In Washington…I knew I was there as a representative of the gay community. Friends of mine who were AIDS activists and would attend those meetings would say to me, "You really did more for us than anybody could have even imagined, sitting up their in your blue blazer and gray flannel pants and white shirt and red tie, just like the rest of them. And just saying—as if you were saying you were right-handed—that you're gay." It really personalized homosexuality for people who still called it homosexuality.

Abrams feels that he has been able to serve as a role model for other gay men and women in health care. He also believes that, as part of an "invisible minority," he has been able to promote other minorities to positions where they, too, can serve as role models.

LIVING ON THE EDGE: SOLAR ECLIPSES AND INTEGRATIVE MEDICINE

As a pioneer in the work on HIV/AIDS, Abrams has had the opportunity to travel all over the world to lecture on the topic. He remembers that during the period of the disease's emergence, he was one of the first doctors to do so: "I have had the opportunity to travel to the point where I am a current 2.5 million mile United Airlines flyer!" He and his partner Clint, a macrobiotic chef, often use those flyer miles to chase solar eclipses as a hobby: "We've been doing it since 1994. We're flying over Antarctica this November to intercept the path of totality for our first in-the-air eclipse. It's been fabulous."

In 2002, Abrams began to increasingly direct his research interests to alternative and complementary therapies for HIV/AIDS and cancer patients. With a grant from the National Center for Complementary and Alternative Medicine, he studied oyster mushrooms as a lipid lowering treatment for patients with hyperlipidemia secondary to AIDS treatment. Attributing this shift in focus to his desire to be on the cutting edge at all times, Abrams notes: "I'm constantly reinventing myself. It's important to keep me stimulated. I always like to be multi-tasking; I can never sit still."

True to his word, but to the surprise of much of the medical community, Abrams gave up involvement with HIV/AIDS research and treatment in 2006 to devote more of his time to integrative medicine. With the development of more effective retroviral drugs by 2006, HIV had been transformed from an acute into a chronic and more manageable disease. The pressures that motivated him during his early years of involvement with the disease, Abrams explains, were no longer there for him in the same way:

HIV care doesn't grab me and doesn't move me and doesn't excite me or challenge me the way it used to. So I, in fact, will be seeing my last HIV clinic on August 8, and I will no longer be doing HIV research or care. I'm happy for the patients, fortunately, that you can see them and say, "I'll see you in 4 months. Here's your lab slip. Here's your prescription refill." But for me, that doesn't speak to my need to be a healer, and it doesn't excite me the way it did at the very beginning, when there was so much uncertainty.[2]

In 2006, Abrams became director of clinical programs for UCSF's Osher Center for Integrative Medicine, a position he served in through 2008. He has researched and written about medical marijuana, assisted suicide, and what he calls, with a touch of understatement, "a lot of other pretty interesting things." Abrams still often finds himself pushing the envelope in the eyes of other medical professionals—an aspect of his career of which he remains very proud.

Note

1   A profile of Michael Bishop can be found on page 78.

2   Quoted in Ronald Bayer and Gerald Oppenheimer, "Pioneers in AIDS Care—Reflections on the Early Years," *New England Journal of Medicine* 355 (2006): 2275.

Marcia Angell

Former Editor-in-Chief, *New England Journal of Medicine*
Senior Lecturer, Social Medicine, Harvard University

Starting medical school at a time when women were still only a small fraction of medical students, Marcia Angell began her career feeling very much that she was forced to fit into what she perceived to be a man's world. In this profile she discusses these struggles, as well as how her initial participation in editing a medical textbook eventually led her to a long and distinguished career in medical publishing and later as an author. She also shares her thoughts on journalism's impact on the field of health care, and on the ethical motivations behind her career in journalism and in teaching.

Education & Training
1956–1960	B.S., James Madison University
1963–1967	M.D., Boston University School of Medicine
1967–1968	Intern, Mount Auburn Hospital (Cambridge, MA)
1968–1969	Resident, Internal Medicine, University Hospital (Boston)
1977–1978	Resident, Pathology, Mount Auburn Hospital
1978–1980	Resident, Pathology, New England Deaconess Hospital (Boston)[1]

Career Path
1979–1988	Deputy Editor, *New England Journal of Medicine*
1988–1999	Executive Editor, *New England Journal of Medicine*
1999–2000	Editor-in-Chief, *New England Journal of Medicine*
2000–	Senior Lecturer, Department of Global Health and Social Medicine, Harvard Medical School

Selected Publications

Robbins SL, Angell M. *Basic Pathology*. Philadelphia: WB Saunders, 1971, 1976, 1981.

"Women in medicine; beyond prejudice." *NEJM*. 1981; 303:1527-8.

Science on Trial: The Clash of Medical Evidence and the Law in the Breast Implant Case. New York: WW Norton & Co., 1996.

"The Journal and Its Owner—Resolving the Crisis." *NEJM*. 1999; 341:752.

"Is Academic Medicine for Sale?" *NEJM*. 2000; 342: 1516-8.

The Truth About the Drug Companies: How They Deceive Us and What To Do About It. New York: Random House, 2004.

"The Epidemic of Mental Illness: Why?" *New York Review of Books*. June 23, 2011.

"The Illusions of Psychiatry." *New York Review of Books*. July 14, 2011.

My career path was very crooked. It was not a straight line. That has to do mainly with the fact that women, when I started out, had to seize the moment. They had to watch for opportunities because there was not a clear-cut career track for them. I did seize opportunities, and they turned out to be unusual ones.

—Marcia Angell

As editor-in-chief of the *New England Journal of Medicine*, Marcia Angell occupied one of the most influential positions in medicine. She earned this position after a long career in medical publishing that began in part as a compromise between her love for clinical medicine and her desire to make time for her children. A self-described "secular missionary," Angell used her medical and scientific training, her editorial acumen and her relentless skepticism to maintain the *Journal's* leading role in the profession. Since stepping down as editor-in-chief in 2000, Angell has refocused her career on teaching and on her own writing. She has published essays on topics including medical ethics, palliative care, and medical law. In 1996, she published her first book for the general public, *Science on Trial: The Clash of Medical Evidence and the Law in the Breast Implant Case*, and was named one of the 25 most influential Americans by *Time* magazine in 1997. Her argument for reform in the pharmaceutical industry, *The Truth About the Drug Companies: How They Deceive Us and What to Do About It*, was published in 2004. Two essays on the development and marketing of psychiatric drugs, published in the *New York Review of Books* in 2011, were selected for inclusion in the 2012 volume of *The Best American Essays*.

CHOOSING MEDICINE

When Angell was a child, one of her favorite books was her family's copy of the *Red Cross Manual*. Even at a young age, the idea of studying illness and practicing medicine attracted her: "I thought that taking care of people who were sick and making them well was the best thing anyone could do." During Angell's childhood in the 1950s, however, there were many barriers for women who wanted to be physicians. Most of the women she knew were housewives, and she had few role models in the working world, much less in medicine. She recalls that her parents expected her to work after college for a year or so, and then to leave her job upon getting married.

When Angell started high school, she found herself drawn to biology. "Because of this, my mother suggested that I could be a medical technician, and I assumed that that is what I would be. But deep down, I still wanted to be a doctor." In preparation for her career as a medical technician, Angell secured her first summer job as a secretary assistant in the virology department at the University of Buffalo. It was 1956, and the lab was handling the diagnostic work on a series of polio epidemics. Angell was fascinated:

> Instead of staying in the office to do secretarial work, I would wander into the lab and try to find work there. I got very interested in their world. The scientists were largely Ph.D.s in virology, and they had no interest in doctors. To them, doctors were people who had alligators on their shirts and played golf. If you were an intellectual and interested in science, you got a Ph.D.

Angell felt that after this experience she had "crossed a barrier in her own mind," and despite social and familial pressures to the contrary, she became determined to pursue an advanced degree and a profession. The critical choice left before her was whether to pursue a Ph.D. or an M.D. Because of the strong influence of her lab colleagues, she began her college career at James Madison University as a biology major, with the intention of pursuing a Ph.D. and a research career. Still, she kept feeling drawn back to medicine. In her senior year, Angell finally made the decision to go to medical school. Looking into the requirements needed for admission, she found that the suggested major was chemistry. She quickly loaded up on chemistry classes, and graduated with a double major in chemistry and math, and a minor in biology.

But first, Angell applied for and received a Fulbright to study microbiology in Germany. When she returned to the United States, the idea of moving back into her parents' home did not appeal to her. Instead, she moved to Boston with a friend. At this point, her parents decided that she was "getting too unconventional," and refused to pay for her schooling if she lived in Boston. Angell moved anyway, and worked for two years as a research assistant at the Massachusetts Institute of Technology to save $1,500 to cover her first semester of medical school at Boston University. "My parents, who were skeptical of the whole enterprise, changed their minds after two years. They became my greatest champions."

MEDICAL SCHOOL: "A MAN'S WORLD"

Angell's friends and family grew to accept her desire to be a physician, and by the time Angell began her studies in 1963, medical schools no longer officially discouraged women from becoming doctors. There were, however, fewer than ten women in her class of 80, and Angell spent much of medical school feeling that she was living in "a man's world." Angell felt that the inconveniences imposed on female doctors sent a subtle yet insidious message that they were not yet fully welcome. For instance, the hospital dressing rooms had two sections: one for the doctors (presumed male), and one for the nurses (presumed female). Daycare and pregnancy leaves did not yet exist and it was not socially acceptable for a man to stay home with children.

> The first day of medical school, a guy came up to me and asked, "Why don't you just become a nurse?" Another one said, "I hate to see a woman in a man's pants." During rotations, a group of us would stand there and be called "gentlemen," even though it was clear that one person in the group was not a gentleman: me. More generally, we were taught in psychiatry that morning sickness was a psychological rejection of the baby, and dysmenorrhea a rejection of the female role, and pernicious nonsense like that.

During her second year at Boston University, Angell took a pathology class taught by Stanley Robbins—a class that transformed Angell from "a good student into a great one, at least in that class." Angell read the textbook, authored by Robbins, and was enthralled by both the subject material and the scientific writing style:

> I did much of my reading in the bathtub. I would put a board over it and prop my book up there. When I started the Robbins text, I went through three or four chapters, and was just fascinated by it. The bathwater became cold and my roommates were knocking on the bathroom door wondering what was going on. All I could think was, "This is a good book."

During the course, Robbins was working on the next edition of the book. In order to craft the text in a way that was more accessible to its audience, he worked in collaboration with his students. He asked Angell to read the chapters as he wrote them and give him feedback. Despite her fears that Robbins might be offended by her boldness, she took a risk: she did a paper edit on some chapters. Far from being offended, Robbins was pleased.

After graduation, Angell went on to the Mount Auburn Hospital in Cambridge, Massachusetts for an internship, and then to University Hospital in Boston to do her residency in internal medicine. During her second year of residency, Angell married and was confronted squarely with the sexism that, up until that point, had largely taken the form of a less overt social rejection. She became pregnant and had to leave her residency:

> One of the most insidious things about sexism or racism or any -ism is that the victims absorb some of the attitude, too. When I grew up I thought in a marriage a man should be the boss—I really thought that. There was a part of me that thought that I was going to medical school because I wanted to

go, but men were going there to choose their profession—and that they had more entitlement to be there. So, on the one hand I was angry and it did make me determined to hang in there, but on the other hand, I wasn't as angry as I should have been when my daughter was born and I was essentially let go without any discussion.

Angell planned on taking four months off after her daughter's birth, and then going back to finish her residency. A month after her termination from University Hospital, Robbins approached her about creating an entirely new, more clinically oriented textbook, which would later become known as the "Baby Robbins." Once involved in this project, with one child and another on the way, Angell's four-month hiatus stretched into eight years.

THE NEW ENGLAND JOURNAL OF MEDICINE

Angell made raising her children her first priority for the next few years, although while they napped, she continued to work on the first and second editions of "Baby Robbins." As her children grew, however, her desire to re-immerse herself in medicine became stronger. She considered pursuing nephrology because of a long-time interest in the kidneys and the range of diseases they are involved in. But one night she was struck with what she calls the reality of her situation:

> My husband was away, and my six-year-old child was sick and had been vomiting and screaming all night. The next morning, my younger child was up and ready to boogie. I thought, "If I had to go and take care of patients today, I just couldn't do it." That night, I finally formulated the question which would influence much of my professional life: "How can I juggle both a career in medicine and motherhood?"

To achieve a balance between work and family life, Angell needed something like a typical, nine-to-five day, so she could work while her children were at school and be available for them nights and weekends. Unfortunately, neither internal medicine nor nephrology satisfied those requirements, but pathology did. It was less interesting to her than other subjects, but it was practical: "If one of my children was sick and I couldn't get to work I wouldn't feel like I was letting anyone down in a major way. I mean, if you're going to do an autopsy it doesn't matter so much if it's now or this afternoon." Furthermore, she had already written a textbook on the subject. Still, she knew from the start that it was not how she wanted to spend the rest of her career:

> The interest in medicine, for me, was patients—being with patients, talking to them, figuring out what was wrong with them. In pathology, you were figuring out what was wrong with them, but only in tissue samples or after the fact. But it came down to patients or my children, and I chose my children.

Before her pathology residency was finished, however, Arnold Relman, who had been the head of nephrology when Angell was in medical school, presented her with an inviting proposal. Relman had worked with Angell and Robbins on a paper about a kidney disease that was published in the *New England Journal of Medicine (NEJM)* in 1968, and she had stayed in touch with him during her initial leave from medicine. In 1977, during her residency in pathology, Relman had become *NEJM*'s editor-in-chief. At the time, the *Journal* was relatively understaffed. Thinking that Angell would be a perfect addition, Relman asked her to join the group.

Angell had never considered publishing as a viable career option, and was somewhat reluctant. She had enjoyed the writing and editing she did with Robbins through the years, but she viewed it as a sideline, and had her sights set on practicing medicine. Still, she considered the offer. In the end, she agreed to spend half of her final year of residency working at the journal, to see if her interest in writing would last:

> I knew that I probably didn't want to spend my whole life in pathology, so I split my time. The idea was that at the end of the year, I would sit down and decide if I wanted to do journalism or pathology, and Bud would decide if he was going to give me a job or not.

At the end of the year, the decision was easy. "There was no doubt in my mind that staying at the *Journal* was what I wanted to do. I loved being there." She left pathology and joined the editorial staff full-time as assistant deputy editor.

A SECULAR MISSIONARY AT HEART

Angell found her work as an editor stimulating. She enjoyed the pressure of putting out a weekly journal and reveled in the immediate satisfaction that it gave her: "The *Journal* is like taking care of patients—you get a fairly quick return on what you are doing. Every Thursday you have it there, in your hand." She also loved the variety of writing and editing that *NEJM* required. She fondly recalls the fact that her seven in-boxes were always full, her phone was always ringing, and no day was ever the same as the one before:

> Editing the *Journal* is one of the most influential jobs in medicine—there's no question about that. It's a wonderful job. You have an eagle's-eye view of all of medicine; you know about everything out there. You're not just publishing research results, you're publishing health policy, medical economics, medical ethics—the journal is everywhere that health care is involved. So if you are interested in writing, medicine, philosophy, and ethics—which I am—it's all there in that one job. You can have a huge impact at the *NEJM*. I am at heart a secular missionary, and that's a place for missionaries.

In addition to her work at *NEJM*, Angell began teaching at Harvard Medical School in the Department of Social Medicine, where she became a senior lecturer in 2000.

The MMS Crisis

In 1999 a major conflict arose between the journal and its owner, the Massachusetts Medical Society. The MMS wanted more control of the "brand" and had plans to use it to increase revenues in ways Angell and others on the editorial staff considered inappropriate. Jerome Kassirer, who had taken over as editor-in-chief from Arnold Relman in 1991, opposed this shift. After voicing his opinions on the matter, Kassirer was asked by the MMS to resign. Angell recalls: "Kassirer was fired in 1999 by the MMS and it was a big brouhaha. There was a very public outcry of dismay that he was fired for commercial reasons."

After Kassirer's departure, Angell was offered the position to be his successor—a move that was supported by many staff. She would only consider accepting the position if she was given full editorial independence and total control of the brand. The MMS had little choice but to accept her terms. Towards the end of her one-year contract as temporary editor-in-chief, the MMS considered her candidature to fill the position permanently. Angell would stay only if the conditions of her original contract were kept. The MMS declined to extend the conditions, and Angell resigned. Angell believes that she has stood by her principles throughout her career: "To be able to say that at my age is the achievement I am proudest of."

Working as a Medical Journalist

Angell's ability to relate to people in a familiar manner allows her to communicate well—and communication has allowed her to be an effective physician as well as a good writer and professor. She insists that this skill cannot be learned in a classroom, and is the result of experience:

> Good teachers, writers, and doctors all have experience. A good teacher is one who is in a student's head and understands what exactly he or she is having trouble with. Writing an editorial takes the same talent, because if you get ahead of your readers, you will alienate them. A good doctor has the same necessary appreciation for his or her patients.

Angell believes that students should not concentrate solely on the educational background required for medical school, "and certainly not if they wanted to be the editor of the *NEJM*." She also thinks that those who go into medicine are better off if they enter the field late rather than early, and major in something broader then pre-medical courses. Angell points out that there is one absolute requirement for aspiring science writers and editors:

To be an editor of a medical journal requires thoroughgoing skepticism. You shouldn't believe anything unless there is evidence for it. No matter whether the author has a Nobel Prize, no matter how distinguished, you shouldn't accept conclusions on his or her say-so alone.

Angell teaches the faculty seminar at Harvard University in the Division of Medical Ethics, and gives occasional lectures. Her latest book, *The Truth About the Drug Companies: How They Deceive Us and What to Do About It* (2004), argues for reform in the pharmaceutical industry. Angell describes the disproportionate amount of money spent by large pharmaceutical companies on marketing as opposed to research and development, as well as the network of suspect relationships among pharmaceutical companies, doctors, universities and politicians that keep prices high for patients and profits high for drug manufacturers. Angell's work in this book, which has been continued in several contributions to the *New York Review of Books*, is yet another example of the missionary influence that compelled her work at *NEJM* and still motivates her today.

I still believe that taking care of sick people is the most important thing you can do, and I find our health care system obscene because it is set up to shunt aside the sickest and neediest among us. I think that society sees itself increasingly as a giant market, and the measure of all things is money. I'm certainly a missionary about that—I think there are things a lot more important than commercial gain.

Note

1.   The New England Deaconess Hospital merged with Beth Israel Hospital in 1996 to form Beth Israel Deaconess Medical Center.

MARA G. ASPINALL

Executive Chairman, GenePeeks
Chief Executive Officer, Health Catalysts
Former President, Genzyme Genetics

Mara Aspinall's career has been shaped by a series of bold transitions between sectors. Now an established biotech executive, Aspinall discusses in this profile how a wide range of non-health care experiences prepared her for the challenges of her current role, as well as how her non-medical background allows her to challenge traditional thinking about drug discovery and diagnostic development. She also shares her thoughts about being a female executive. Her story weaves together a de-sire to achieve broad impact, a challenging and diverse career, and a commitment to community involvement.

EDUCATION & TRAINING
1979–1983	B.A., Tufts University
1985–1987	M.B.A., Harvard Business School

CAREER PATH
1983–1985	Associate Consultant, Bain & Co.
1987–1990	Consultant, Bain & Co.
1990–1997	Director of Client Services and Marketing, Hale and Dorr, L.L.P.
1997–2003	President, Genzyme Pharmaceuticals, Genzyme Corporation
2001–2007	President, Genzyme Genetics, Genzyme Corporation
2008	Sabbatical for research on personalized medicine and physician behavior, Dana-Farber Cancer Institute and Harvard Medical School
2009–2011	President and CEO, On-Q-ity
2011–2014	President and CEO, Ventana Medical Systems, Inc. and Global Head, Roche Tissue Diagnostics
2014–	CEO, Health Catalysts

A selected list of Mara Aspinall's service positions and publications can be found on the last page of this profile.

From the basic level, biotech is about attacking disease at the root cause; that is the future of health care. There will always be symptom management, but if you want to cure a disease, you need to attack it at the core.

—*Mara Aspinall*

When Mara Aspinall joined Genzyme in 1997 she had to embark on a crash course in biology and chemistry. Originally interested in politics, she studied international relations and Chinese in college and went on to earn her M.B.A. at Harvard. She then joined Bain as a consultant, and followed up on this experience with a stint as a law firm executive. By the time she joined Genzyme, Aspinall had learned what it required to adapt to new and challenging situations. While her career has undergone a series of bold transitions between sectors, it has been constantly informed by the ideals that shaped her early interests in politics and community activism.

Aspinall's initial pursuits lay far away from anything to do with health care or medicine. Encouraged by her parents, as an undergraduate at Tufts University Aspinall followed her intellectual passions instead of focusing on a specific career: "I had the freedom and the nerve to study what I enjoyed in college." In retrospect, this decision is still one that she emphatically supports.

Aspinall's first career aspirations were actually grounded in politics, rooted in her firm desire to impact society in a positive way. Working on various political campaigns in high school and college fostered this interest, and her early experimentation with politics also allowed her to recognize at a young age that one of her greatest skills was galvanizing a group of people around a single goal. She recalls her first political canvass:

> In my first year of college, I organized a letter-writing campaign to support continued federal funding of student loans. This was the Reagan era in the 1980s, and the federal government was planning to reduce student loan funding. In one month, we collected and sent more than two thousand letters for then Massachusetts Senator Paul Tsongas to emphasize the strong support he had from college students in voting for continued funding. I saw how much impact we could make. I also realized that my skills were more

oriented toward achieving impact through a "one-to-many" approach versus a "one-to-one" approach.

This realization ultimately influenced her decision to pursue further education to develop her management skills. After spending two years as an associate with Bain & Company, a management consulting firm, she applied to and attended Harvard Business School to earn her M.B.A.: "The M.B.A. offered me the best long-term way to learn how successful companies and executives impact industries and individuals. It enabled me to gain new insights on best practices around the world on how to effect positive change."

After completing her M.B.A., Aspinall returned to Bain & Company:

> My decision to go into consulting, and Bain in particular, was to give me a broad exposure to a number of different industries and how they work. In addition, it also gave me the ability to learn from some of the best and brightest business leaders. It was a tremendous boost in translating the theory learned in business school into realistic and practical strategies for success in an operating company. It also gave me a hands-on ability to recognize the day-to-day challenges that come in working in "the real world."

BUILDING A SKILL SET

During her tenure at Bain, where she specialized in the field of information technology, Aspinall was first exposed to health care as an industry. The resulting combination of skills—expertise in information technology and a broad understanding of health care issues—would prove useful to her throughout her career:

> My largest clients were in the information field. Today, more and more of health care is related to information, whether it be research data or patient test results. This experience gave me a high level of comfort in those industries as well as an understanding of the importance of technology, both software and hardware, in helping the health care industry to move forward.

After three years of refining her analytical and management skills, Aspinall was ready to move from consulting into an operating role. In 1990, she accepted a position as director of client services for Hale and Dorr, a legal firm known for its work with entrepreneurs and initial public offerings. In this position, Aspinall crafted a strategy to help the firm better serve its clientele through technology. She was able to take an active role in the daily operations of the legal firm's business, thanks to a trend in the legal sector toward hiring business leaders to help run large corporate law firms:

> It gave me the opportunity to work and focus on one operating business, not just consult. It was a tremendous opportunity. It allowed me to build my own team, articulate the strategy, and then implement it. I had the privilege of

building a team of fourteen professionals (from two), and of creating a role-model organization for law firms across the U.S.

Aspinall spent seven years with Hale and Dorr, after which she began to push her career in a new direction. She looked at management positions with many of the new internet companies thriving in the late 1990s. She also spoke with the leadership team at Genzyme. Aspinall was attracted to the biotech firm's working environment: "I was captivated by the people I met at Genzyme, their commitment to patients and their professionalism." Genzyme's atmosphere and Aspinall's interest in health care were both important factors in her decision to work at Genzyme, but the greatest influence on her decision was the opportunity that a management position with Genzyme provided:

> I wanted to take one additional step in my career. I had gone from consulting to working in a staff position in a professional services company, and I was ready to move to a general management position with P&L responsibility. It was the next logical step in my career.

MOVING INTO THE BIOTECH WORLD

Aspinall started with Genzyme in 1997 as vice president of corporate development, and soon became president of Genzyme Pharmaceuticals, one of Genzyme Corporation's divisions. Based in Cambridge, Massachusetts, Genzyme (now called Sanofi Aventis) is a leading biotechnology firm that specializes in diagnostics and therapies for rare genetic disorders and chronic diseases. Aspinall's academic background was in the social sciences, so she spent months studying the natural sciences on her own. Once she became comfortable with the subject matter, she began to enjoy the challenges of understanding this diverse and quickly changing field: "Biotech is not a field in which you can know everything and rest on your laurels. It gave me tremendous respect for what I did and did not know."

Although her career path was not originally oriented toward health care, Aspinall stresses that her diverse training and experience has benefited rather than handicapped her as a biotech executive. In a field where she is surrounded by scientific minds, Aspinall finds that her unique perspective and experience give her the open-mindedness and non-traditional approaches necessary to address issues in creative ways. She can often identify problems that scientists overlook or offer alternative solutions:

> My perspective as a newcomer in the industry gave me the ability to ask "why?" It also allowed me to be proactive, and also to work with scientists on the "so what?" questions that needed to be asked to ensure that our programs and initiatives will make a positive difference in people's lives.

Aspinall found her colleagues to be a talented and directed group of people. When asked about perceptions that health care is a poorly managed industry, she disagrees and faults the structure of the industry itself:

Health care is a relatively young industry. Doctors have been around for a long time, but health care as a business industry is a new concept. Biotech is brand new, and the pharmaceutical industry has emerged as a powerhouse since after the Second World War. Health care needs to begin thinking of itself as an integrated industry. We need to work less in silos, which to me says that the drug companies, diagnostic companies and service providers need to work with the providers early to show how their products are going to impact patients effectively and efficiently.

Under Aspinall's management, Genzyme's genetics and pharmaceuticals divisions generated multiple years of double-digit growth in revenues and profits.

PERSONALIZED MEDICINE

During her tenure at Genzyme Aspinall became increasingly interested in the power of personalized medicine. Personalized medicine is the field which tries to calibrate and customize the treatment of diseases, including cancer, to the genetics of specific patients. In 2008 Aspinall went on sabbatical from Genzyme to work on the implementation of personalized medicine at the Dana-Farber Cancer Institute and Harvard Medical School. Shortly thereafter, in 2009, she was recruited to become president and CEO of On-Q-ity, a new company focused on transforming cancer care through the implementation of personalized diagnostics. Then, in 2011, she was recruited as president and CEO of Ventana Medical Systems, a member of the Roche Group, and the leading provider worldwide of tissue-based tests for diagnosing cancer. In 2014, she worked to make diagnostics a more prominent and distinct academic discipline, helping to launch the International School of Biomedical Diagnostics, a collaboration between Arizona State University and Dublin City College.

COMMUNITY AND CAUSES

Even before she worked at Genzyme, Aspinall was involved in the health care community as a board member of the Boston-based Dana-Farber Cancer Institute and chairman of the Massachusetts chapter of the American Cancer Society. To this day, she continues to use her leadership skills for positive impact by promoting cancer prevention as well as early childhood education: "I've taken a lot of risks in my career, making time to focus not only on my day-to-day activities, but also to be an active participant in community programs and initiatives." Her words underscore the balancing act needed to develop both a corporate career and significant community commitments. She considers this role in terms of career, impact, and development:

> It was important for me to make an impact, especially in the cancer community and early childhood education. My volunteer work gave me an opportunity to focus on other things when I had a long day or week. It's nice to have something in the community to focus your energy on. From a development point of view, I've learned a tremendous amount. I've learned to work with a diverse group of people who face different challenges than those I see at work. I'm grateful for all the time that people took to teach me, and hopefully I was able to give a little of that back.

On Being an Executive, Who Happens to be Female

As a female executive in a predominantly male corporate culture, Aspinall admits that "it's still a challenge for women to be perceived as being as committed to their careers as their male counterparts," but she feels that women are better represented in biotech and health care management than in other industries. Still, she notes that she is often asked questions that her male counterparts are not expected to have to answer: "It annoys me when I am asked at cocktail parties, 'Do you work?' when men are not asked the same question. It's assumed that they work outside the home." Now, Aspinall makes a point of turning that question around and asking the men she meets, "Do you work?"; this has garnered her a reputation for her outspokenness on the issue.

Aspinall believes that choices between family and career must be addressed by both men and women; she and her husband have coordinated their professional lives to ensure fulfillment of their professional and familial responsibilities. In discussing balance, she prefers the term "decision" rather than "sacrifice," because she believes that choices between family and career are deliberate and self-directed. She also notes that not every decision needs to last forever:

> There are decisions that need to be made at each major stage in one's life. Don't assume that your work/family balance decision today will be the same one that you want to make a year from now. In addition, while many focus balance issues on having and caring for young children, there are many other times that decisions need to be made—including illness and caring for older parents.

On Career Development

Drawing on her own experiences, Aspinall advises aspiring health care leaders to "take risks, particularly early in [their] career. It's much harder to do so later on." She also suggests focusing on the experiences different positions will give you and not just which industry they are in:

> You should be guided by the type of experience you want. The industry, while important, is certainly not the only issue to consider, especially in the beginning of your career. You must decide, do you want a small, entrepreneurial company experience? Or do you want to learn from a large company? Look less on industry and more on function and type of atmosphere that you want to be a part of.

HEALTH CARE-RELATED ACADEMIC AND COMMUNITY SERVICE

1994–1999	Chairman of the Board and Director, American Cancer Society, Massachusetts
1997–2010	Trustee, Executive Committee; Chairman and Trustee, Science Committee, Dana-Farber Cancer Institute
2000–	Co-Chair, Early Education for All
2004–2011	Director, Personalized Medicine Coalition
2008–	Advisory Board member, Harvard Business School Healthcare Initiative
2009–	Lecturer on Health Care Policy, Harvard Medical School
2009–	Steering Committee on Professional Transformation, College of American Pathology
2009–	Co-Founder and Director, European Personalized Medicine Diagnostics Association
2012–	Founder and Director, DxInsights
2014	Co-Founder, International School of Biomedical Diagnostics, Arizona State University and Dublin City University

SELECTED PUBLICATIONS

Michael Kipp, Robert Hunter, and Mara Aspinall. "Market Crossroads: Fertile Ground for Board Development." *Corporate Governance* 2.2 (2002): 13–15.

Mara Aspinall and Richard Hamermesh. "Realizing the Promise of Personalized Medicine." *Harvard Business Review* 85.10 (Oct. 2007): 108–117.

"Personalized Medicine and Pathology—Friend or Foe?" *Archives of Pathology & Laboratory Medicine* 133.4 (Apr. 2009): 527–528.

"The Explosion of Genetic Testing: Opportunities and Challenges." Harvard Business School Case. Oct. 2009.

"Plavix: Drugs in the Age of Personalized Medicine." Harvard Business School Case. Nov. 2010.

James Crawford and Mara Aspinall. "The Business Value and Cost–Effectiveness of Genomic Medicine." *Future Medicine* 9.3 (May 2012): 265–286.

Charles D. Baker

Governor of Massachusetts
Former President and CEO, Harvard Pilgrim Health Care, Inc.

Encompassing a wide variety of roles in the public and private sectors, including eight years in state government and a decade at the helm of one of New England's most successful health insurance providers, Charles Baker has spent his career at the intersection of government, public policy and buisness. In this profile, he discusses the challenging but rewarding transitions between these different worlds, and the different kinds of problems he has had to address in each. He also discusses the turnaround that he helped to engineer at Harvard Pilgrim Health Care, and the particular satisfactions he derives from working in the health care sector.

Education & Training

1975–1979	A.B., Harvard College
1984–1986	M.B.A., Northwestern University

Career Path

1986–1988	Consultant, Touche Ross & Co.
1988–1991	Co-Director, Pioneer Institute for Public Policy Research, Inc.
1991–1992	Undersecretary, Health & Human Services, Massachusetts
1992–1994	Secretary of Health & Human Services, Massachusetts
1994–1998	Secretary of Administration and Finance, Massachusetts
1998–1999	President and CEO, Harvard Vanguard Medical Associates
1999–2009	President and CEO, Harvard Pilgrim Health Care, Inc.
2009–2010	Massachusetts Gubernatorial Candidate
2011–2013	Executive in Residence, General Catalyst Partners
2013–2014	Massachusetts Gubernatorial Candidate
2015–	Governor of Massachusetts

I've never had any specific long-term career goals; I've just wanted to do something that was important, and I wanted it to make a difference. But I've never had a career path that said what I wanted to be when I grew up. On my business school application, I said I wanted to be the CEO of a major public or private entity at some point. But that's the only time I've aspired to anything in particular.

—*Charles D. Baker*

Charles Baker began his career intending to be a journalist. After graduating from Harvard University as an English major he spent several years trying to use his writing skills to find steady work. He held jobs with various newspapers, but found that securing a steady job as a reporter was extremely difficult: "It was the late 1970s and everybody thought they were going to be the next Bob Woodward. So it was a very hard field to break into. I got close a couple of times, but I never quite made it through." Changing course, Baker accepted an offer to be the communications director of a small trade association called the Massachusetts High Technology Council. There, he explains, "I did a lot of writing—it was a communications job, so I wrote newsletters, and I wrote press releases. I developed messages, wrote speeches, and generated stories for the folks who were overseeing the organization." He enjoyed the writing aspect of the job, but after three years, felt limited in his career trajectory.

Hoping to increase his skill set and marketability, Baker applied to business school at Northwestern University, where he earned an M.B.A. at the Kellogg School of Management, concentrating in public/non-profit management. He explains his decision in terms of a desire to be versatile:

The reason I went to business school was because I'd majored in English as an undergrad so I didn't really have any background in accounting, finance, management, and operations. I didn't want to get pigeonholed into being just a communications guy because my fear was that that's all I would be. If I'd stayed at the High Tech Council, I'd be a great communications person, but I would never have gotten out of there. I had been hanging out with a bunch of high-technology executives, and I really liked the idea of being a manager— any type of management seemed like a really interesting deal.

While Baker would eventually satisfy his desire for a management role, a series of positions that gave him an invaluable breadth of experience were nearer on the horizon.

FROM BUSINESS TO GOVERNMENT

Shortly after receiving his M.B.A., Baker returned to the Boston area and went to work for Touche Ross & Co. as a consultant. The Boston office of Touche Ross, Baker explains, "had a big government consulting practice," and it was the range of experience such a practice might afford him that drew Baker to the position:

> I thought—correctly, as it turned out—that by joining that firm in their Boston office I would be exposed to a number of different problem-solving activities in a number of different states. Over the next couple of years, I worked on state government projects in Texas, Massachusetts, New Jersey, and New Hampshire.

These projects turned out to be the best possible preparation for Baker's later work in government: "Interestingly, most of the work involved health and human services stuff—an area I later became quite familiar with during my time in state government."

As he gained exposure to health care, Baker began to experience aspects of the health care sector that he found frustrating—feelings he has held on to across his career:

> I felt the same way I feel now: health care is the most under-managed and under-led sector of the economy, and that's because it doesn't like strong managers and strong leaders. It's funny to have this huge sector in the economy that really doesn't like strong management. It rejects it like a bacterial infection.

While the business culture of the health care sector did not at first appeal to Baker, he nevertheless arrived at a deep appreciation of the sector's importance both economically and for people's everyday lives:

> The other thing I learned spending time around the health care sector was that it's really important, and it touches other sectors of the economy in many ways. It also has a tremendous personal impact on almost everybody at one time or another.

Baker left Touche Ross in the summer of 1988 to start the Pioneer Institute, an independent, non-profit public policy research institute, with two other colleagues. As one of two co-directors, Baker handled operations, fundraising, and public relations, while his partner managed the research agenda and recruited researchers. Over the next two years, the institute published a series of independently authored monographs, and held a number of educational forums on health care, insurance, and education issues. During this period of time, Baker developed solid relationships with various members of the business and political communities, and was eventually referred to then gubernatorial candidate William Weld as a valuable source of advice on health care policy.

THE WELD ADMINISTRATION

Weld and Baker hit it off the first time they met, and talked a lot about various policy issues throughout the course of the 1990 gubernatorial campaign. Shortly after winning the election, Weld asked Baker if he would be willing to serve in his administration. Baker agreed, and in 1991, he was appointed undersecretary of the Executive Office of Health and Human Services. During Baker's tenure at Health and Human Services, Massachusetts significantly reformed its Medicaid and cash assistance programs, expanded its public health programming, and streamlined its facility systems. In 1994, Baker became secretary for administration and finance. In this role, he worked to re-structure the state's pension system, reduce the size of county government, re-write many of the commonwealth's regulations, and modernize its purchasing functions.

During his time in government, Baker learned the nuances and realities of how health care policy and administration within a government context differed from the private sector. The sense of common mission that he had often enjoyed in the business world had given way to a more contentious political environment:

> In business, if you say "This is where we're going and this is why," everybody says, "Ok, let's go." In government, if you say "This is where we're going and this is why" everybody says, "Well, let's have a hearing and talk about it" or "over my dead body you're going to do that." In most private organizations you sort of get up every day and say, "What are we trying to do today?" and everybody agrees. But government can't do that because there are so many points of view, and everything is done in the bright eye of the public.

Baker thought hard about how to adapt to this new environment, and came to see it as a new kind of challenge:

> I think it's much more of a communicative and administrative job, because the bullets come from every direction. Nobody has to say ok. They can just say no, and you have to figure out a way to make them say yes. That can be a lot of work.

One thing that Baker liked about these positions was the manageable size of local and state government, compared to the federal government, which he describes as "a foreign planet that doesn't feel remotely real" because of its enormous scale. He found working in state government rewarding, although he notes the significant pay cut and huge increase in responsibility this entailed. This was a sacrifice, but on the whole, he regards his choice as overwhelmingly positive:

> The best part was that the issues were important and the people were really smart. It's like working on a puzzle; it's very stimulating because there's no easy way to get anything done. It's both relationship-driven and analytical. I try to be good about having people make a decision on the merits and not the personality. If the personality *is* involved, you want it to be in a good way. You never want someone to deep-six something because they were mad at you for something else.

CHANGING ROLES AND ENTERING THE NON-PROFIT SECTOR

Baker stopped working for the government in the fall of 1998 when he was offered a position as president and CEO of Harvard Vanguard Medical Associates, a non-profit physicians' group that served about 300,000 Massachusetts residents. Simultaneously, he was also offered an administrative position at North Shore Medical Center, a 579-bed hospital outside of Boston. In some ways North Shore seemed like the best option: "It would have been really interesting and fun, filled with people who I like and admire." But Baker also believed strongly in the managed care movement, and Harvard Vanguard would allow him to be involved in that movement in a way that North Shore, a hospital rather than a managed care organization, would not. "From a values point of view," Baker explains, "they were in a very different place."

Harvard Vanguard, at the time, was closely affiliated with Harvard Pilgrim Health Care, a non-profit HMO which had originally been part of the same organization. Six months after Baker arrived at Harvard Vanguard, Harvard Pilgrim issued its preliminary 1998 year-end financial report which showed enormous losses, and shortly after the board of directors removed the chief financial officer and the chief executive officer. Since Harvard Pilgrim provided insurance for the majority of Harvard Vanguard's patients, if Harvard Pilgrim failed, Harvard Vanguard would likely fail as well. It was subsequently decided that the best course of action would be for Baker to join Harvard Pilgrim. Had it not been for the financial emergency posed by the Harvard Pilgrim crisis, Baker believes he would have stayed at Harvard Vanguard. He appreciated "the care-giving, clinical side more than the enabling, financial side." That said, in the end, he feels he was able to have a greater impact by accepting this position.

Running an HMO

It was initially a difficult transition to move from a small and tightly knit group of colleagues in the governor's cabinet to managing a few thousand staff members across a large HMO. Having to cope with Pilgrim's pressing financial challenges, however, gave him a sense of community in his new position: "I had a leadership group and staff that felt like they went through it together and accomplished a lot and have really strong feelings about who they work for and what they've done."

The year Baker was appointed CEO, HPHC lost $227 million. The team that Baker built to deal with the crisis developed a tremendous amount of camaraderie and commitment, perhaps more so than in any other place he had worked. They were willing to embrace the trials of a complicated company turnaround. To keep this team united, and Harvard Pilgrim up and running, Baker's days at HPHC were focused on communicating the strategy and vision of the organization:

> Most of my time was spent keeping our employees and our key constituents up to speed on what we're doing, and why—and soliciting their feedback whenever I could. If a typical week is sixty hours, I'd spend ten hours on email and the phone, ten hours on giving or preparing either internal or external presentations, and ten to fifteen hours meeting with senior management, and then ten to fifteen hours talking with or meeting with constituents, accountants, brokers, trading partners, suppliers.

It is in this sort of leadership position that Baker has found himself most comfortable and fulfilled. Baker believes it is not just leading an organization, but specifically leading an organization with a social mission, that has brought him his greatest satisfaction.

> Intellectual satisfaction is important, but not as much as emotional satisfaction. I would be bored out of my mind if I was doing something that I thought was intellectually complicated but didn't seem to have any kind of social purpose.

In July of 2009, Baker stepped down from his position at Harvard Pilgrim in order to devote himself full time to a bid for the Republican nomination for the 2010 gubernatorial race in Massachusetts. Baker won the nomination, but lost the general election to incumbent Governor Deval Patrick in a hard-fought race. In 2011, Baker joined the venture capital firm General Catalyst Partners in Cambridge, Massachusetts. In September 2013, he announced that he would again run for the office of governor of Massachusetts. Baker won the Republican nomination and then the general election, taking office in 2015.

Harris A. Berman

Dean, Tufts University School of Medicine
Former Chief Executive Officer, Tufts Health Plan

A physician by training, Harris Berman has spent his career at the intersection
of health care administration and public health, including almost two decades as
the head of one of New England's largest non-profit health insurance companies.
In this profile, Berman describes how his role as a physician for the Peace Corps
sparked a lifelong interest in health care management and influenced a career
defined by helping more people gain access to quality health care. With a natural
tendency toward leadership and entrepreneurship, Berman helped to create one
of the first prepaid insurance plans in New England for his health care practice.
He describes the evolution of his career in terms of his ability, as an executive and
administrator, to make a systemic impact on the health care of large groups of
patients.

EDUCATION & TRAINING

1956–1960	A.B., Harvard College
1960–1964	M.D., Columbia University College of Physicians and Surgeons
1964–1965	Intern, Medicine, New England Medical Center (NEMC), Boston
1967–1968	Resident, Medicine, Harvard Medical Service, Boston City Hospital
1968–1969	Resident, Medicine, NEMC
1969–1971	Fellow, Infectious Diseases, NEMC, and Tropical Public Health, Harvard School of Public Health

CAREER PATH

1965–1967	Senior Physician, United States Peace Corps (India)
1971–1986	Executive Director, Co-Founder and Medical Director, Matthew Thornton Health Plan
1986–2003	Chief Executive Officer, Tufts Health Plan
2003–	Professor (2003–) and Chair (2003–2008), Department of Public Health and Family Medicine, Tufts University School of Medicine
2004–2008	Dean of Public Health and Professional Degree Programs, Tufts University School of Medicine
2008–2011	Vice Dean, Tufts University School of Medicine
2011–	Dean, Tufts University School of Medicine

ADDITIONAL INFORMATION

Tufts Health Plan:	www.tuftshealthplan.com
Tufts School of Medicine:	www.tufts.edu/med

I think health care is a great profession. I was delighted when one of my daughters decided she wanted to
go into medicine. It will always be important work,
and there will always be meaningful work for doctors. But health care is complicated and it takes a lot
more than doctors to run it. There's lots of opportunity for people, whether they come at it from a business point of view, a patient care point of view or
a policy point of view. They're all important to the
system.

—Harris Berman

Inspired at a young age by President Kennedy's advocacy of universal
health care, and later by his own early experience as a physician for the Peace
Corps, Harris Berman has spent his career as a leading innovator in the managed care movement since the movement's beginnings. After founding one
of the first managed care organizations in New England, Berman served as
chief executive officer of Tufts Health Plan from 1986 to 2003. As CEO of the
$2 billion not-for-profit health plan with 2,300 employees, Berman managed
relationships with the plan's 18,000 private practice physicians and 83 hospitals. During his seventeen-year tenure, Berman grew the plan's membership
from 60,000 to nearly one million by focusing on improving the quality of
its policies, care, programs, and products.

EARLY EXPERIENCES: MEDICAL SCHOOL AND THE PEACE CORPS

Berman was interested in management and business at an early age. His
father was a businessman, so he "learned a lot about business at the dinner
table, and worked in business in the summers." He had always wanted to be a
doctor too, so he struggled with a difficult decision: "For a while at Harvard
College, I was torn: did I want to go to medical school or did I want to go
to business school?" Berman decided to enroll at the Columbia University
College of Physicians and Surgeons, and in 1964 he earned his M.D. After
completing his program, Berman jumped at the chance to work as a physician for the recently established Peace Corps. The experience "really shaped
my thinking about how I wanted to practice medicine, what I wanted to do,"
he reflects. It was a great opportunity for someone right out of an internship
to be able to practice both medicine and public health.

Berman spent two years working as a physician in India and Nepal, and
later in Western Samoa and Fiji. He soon discovered that "it wasn't just a

matter of taking care of the ill Peace Corps volunteers who would walk into my office…but it was a matter of planning for a population of 1,500 volunteers, placed all over the Indian subcontinent, and exposed to illnesses and conditions unlike any they had previously encountered." These were special population-level issues that most doctors would not have faced:

> How do we keep the volunteers healthy? What do we do in case of medical and surgical emergencies, disasters, even deaths? We had a number of serious accidents, people scattered all over what was then a country with a pretty rudimentary health care system and rudimentary communications; you couldn't call from one side of the country to the other, or even if you could, the static was so bad, you frequently couldn't hear.

Berman left the Peace Corps with a desire to learn more about the infectious diseases that he saw abroad, an interest in public health, and the need to manage something more than just a one-person practice:

> I liked the concept of taking care of a population, and figuring out what a population needed. When I left the Peace Corps and finished up my residency training, I wanted to get away from academia and really get out into the community and practice. I also wanted to manage things. I wanted to think in terms of "How do you take care of a population?"

FOUNDING THE MATTHEW THORNTON HEALTH PLAN

While still in medical school, Berman had already begun to realize some of the shortcomings of the existing health insurance model:

> In the 1950s and 1960s, what we had was just health insurance, mostly dominated by the "Blues," and it was really more catastrophic insurance than anything else. For instance, insurance companies did not cover deliveries of babies because pregnancy wasn't an "illness."

Berman envisioned a plan that would make medical care more accessible:

> I felt that people would be better off if they had complete insurance coverage and could go to the doctor early on, rather than spending a lot of money out of their pocket first, or worrying whether they could afford the care. And we thought, for the doctors, it was a better way of care because the doctors would know that they could do whatever needed to be done for the patient, and not worry about whether or not the patient could afford it.

Kennedy and Nixon were engaged in the presidential debates of 1960 at the time: "Kennedy was making his pitch for universal health insurance, and we all thought that was the right direction."

When Berman returned to his fellowship in infectious diseases at the New England Medical Center after his time in the Peace Corps, he met another resident, James Squires:

> We were both from New Hampshire, and we were both going to finish in a couple of years, at about the same time. He mentioned that he was interested in going back to New Hampshire and starting a practice and maybe some sort of prepayment mechanism. We clicked immediately. We ended up starting a health plan in New Hampshire right out of our residency, called the Matthew Thornton Health Plan, and we both ran that and practiced medicine.

It took Berman and Squires two years to form the not-for-profit health plan and the practice. They hired a Wharton business school graduate to run the plan, and several other doctors to help them carry the patient load. Berman became very involved in running the plan. Although at first he served as the medical director of Matthew Thornton, he found himself becoming more and more occupied with the business side of the practice. "I carried a full load on the clinical side and sort of did the administration between things or at lunch time or evenings."

After the company experienced difficulties in keeping a permanent executive director, Berman decided to take on the position. Although he was hesitant—everyone who had held the position before had been a business school graduate—he remembers feeling reassured after attending a talk by Kellogg Business School professor Ed Hughes, who said that "business schools exist to teach skills that entrepreneurs are born with." The increasing difficulty of balancing patient care with his administrative duties also made the shift into full-time administration seem like a good choice:

> After fifteen years of practicing medicine, I began to realize that the patients I was seeing often were recovering from some illness that one of my partners had seen them for, because I wasn't available when they got sick. I realized this may be fine for me, but it wasn't really in my patients' best interests that I wasn't providing continuous care.

Berman came to miss the direct, visible impact that doctors have on their patients: "There are very few professions that I know of where you get the immediate gratification that you do in practicing medicine. You go home at the end of the day and you realize, 'A couple times today, I really helped somebody.'" Shifting to an administrative role, however, eventually led Berman to his position as CEO of Tufts Health Plan, where he was able to make a difference in the greater health care system, and therefore to many more patients.

The Matthew Thornton Health Plan eventually became part of Blue Cross, and today is owned by Anthem Blue Cross. Founding the health care plan was an important turning point in Berman's career because he stepped away from only treating individual patients: "I got interested in the system and how you make the system work."

MAKING A FRESH START WITH TUFTS

After several years as executive director of Matthew Thornton, Berman accepted an offer in 1986 to become CEO of Tufts Health Plan in Boston:

> When you make a mid-career change, you come to your new position as an expert. And as the new leader, you have a license to drive change. It can be a very exciting opportunity.

When Berman became CEO, he devoted a lot of time to "just wandering around and getting a feel for what was going on." He spent at least three hours each day talking with people who were networking for jobs, entrepreneurs that wanted to know how they could shape their products for the managed care environment, and students who were interested in management. The time spent with people in the organization led to good relationships, which was particularly satisfying with regard to his managment team:

> I've been very proud of the fact that I, unlike the leaders of many organizations, don't have a lot of management turnover. Most of the people on my management team have worked with me for at least ten years. I let them do their jobs and that's why I don't lose people. I trust them and empower them.

Berman saw great potential for company growth at Tufts. One of his great accomplishments was growing the not-for-profit plan over seventeen years from 60,000 members to nearly one million—an organization sizeable enough to help keep the for-profit health plans out of the Tufts Health Plan market:

> Boston and Minneapolis are the only two markets in the country not dominated by for-profit health plans. And in Minneapolis, it's because it's legislated, it's illegal to operate a for-profit plan there. In Boston, the success of the not-for-profits achieved the same effect. This gives me a lot of satisfaction.

His persistent belief in the potential for prepaid plans and universal coverage helped to make room in the health care system for the HMO movement:

> It was an interesting challenge to work with doctors who, for the most part, were in a health plan not because they wanted to be, but because they had to be. I felt like I had participated in the creation of this change, this evolution in health care of what became known as HMOs. I now took on the challenge of helping private doctors who hadn't become a part of that change to do so belatedly.

For Berman, one of the most disappointing aspects of his job is the fact that he has worked in an industry that has been so negatively viewed in the public eye:

I've 2,300 employees here who are trying to do the right thing everyday—trying to make sure people get the care they need, and yet, to listen to politicians, you'd think we're some sort of evil conspirators. It's just not the case. That's been a disappointment. For years I've joked that when I retire, if people asked me what I used to do, I would just say, "I was a doctor," and leave it at that.

He has also been frustrated that the health care sector has not lived up to his early hopes: "I've found it fascinating to see the public policy issues involved here, and the gridlock we've been in for 40 years, not being able to provide universal coverage."

RETURNING TO ACADEMIA

Berman retired from Tufts Health Plan in 2003 and became professor and chair of the department of public health and family medicine at Tufts University School of Medicine, a position quite different from his prior work: "It has always been fun to assume new challenges," he says of his new role. Proving his love of new challenges, in 2008 Berman took on the role of vice dean of Tufts Medical School, and in 2011, at the age of 73, was appointed to serve as the medical school's dean. Reflecting on his career at the time of his appointment in an article in *Tufts Now*, Berman stated:

> Looking back, I've had a few careers, which has really been fun. Aside from the Peace Corps, where it all started, I've practiced medicine for 15 years and started an HMO in New Hampshire. Then I moved on to running a large organization, the Tufts Health Plan, which grew into a $2 billion enterprise. I was the CEO of that and learned a lot about running a business on the job. And then, coming to academe, I've had to learn a whole different way of thinking. Yet leadership is leadership. It's really about how you relate to people—the people who are your team, the people you serve. I've taken a lot of comfort in how easily leadership skills are transferable from venue to venue.[1]

When asked for career advice, Berman encourages students to be introspective and figure out who they are and what they like as they choose a career. Above, all, Berman emphasizes that one should never be too rigid about planning for the future:

> If you ask most people, "How did you get into what you do?" it usually starts with "Well, it's a funny story," which means it wasn't what they planned. I try to tell people, "Don't over-plan." Just take the opportunities as they come, and things will sort themselves out.

Note

1   B. Morgan, "Harris Berman Named Medical Dean," *Tufts Now*, Oct. 6, 2011.

Donald M. Berwick

Senior Fellow and President Emeritus, Institute for Healthcare Improvement
Former Administrator, Centers for Medicare and Medicaid Services

A pediatrician by training, Donald Berwick has become one of the world's leading experts on quality improvement in health care. His story provides an exceptional example of a career integrating multiple interests and disciplines. In this profile, Berwick discusses the early experiences that led him to question traditional thinking about quality improvement and to look beyond health care for solutions to health care's problems. He also discusses the creation of IHI.

EDUCATION & TRAINING
1964–1968	A.B., Harvard College (Social Relations)
1968–1972	M.D., Harvard Medical School
1968–1972	M.P.P., JFK School of Government, Harvard University
1972–1973	Intern, Internal Medicine, Massachusetts General Hospital
1973–1979	Resident and Fellow, Pediatrics, Boston Children's Hospital

CAREER PATH
1974–1980	Instructor in Health Services, and Member of the Center for the Analysis of Health Practices, Harvard School of Public Health
1979–1996	Pediatrician, Harvard Community Health Plan (HCHP)
1980–1985	Acting Research Director (1980–1983) and Director of Quality Assurance (1980–1985), HCHP; Associate Director, Institute for Health Research (Harvard and HCHP) (1983–1985)
1985–1989	Vice President, Quality-of-Care Measurement, HCHP
1987–1991	Principal Investigator, National Demonstration Project on Quality Improvement in Health Care
1991–2010	President and CEO, Institute for Healthcare Improvement
2010–2011	Administrator, Centers for Medicare and Medicaid Services, Department of Health and Human Services
2012–	Senior Fellow, Institute for Healthcare Improvement
2013–2014	Massachusetts Gubernatorial Candidate

SELECTED PUBLICATIONS

Berwick DM, Godfrey AB, Roessner J. *Curing Health Care: New Strategies for Quality Improvement.* San Francisco: Jossey-Bass, 1990.

Brennan T, Berwick DM. *New Rules: Regulation, Markets, and the Quality of American Health Care.* San Francisco: Jossey-Bass, 1996.

Berwick DM. *Escape Fire: Designs for the Future of Health Care.* San Francisco: Jossey-Bass, 2004.

Berwick *DM. Promising Care: How We Can Rescue Health Care by Improving It.* San Francisco: Jossey-Bass, 2013.

When one is clear and constant in one's purpose, when fear does not control the atmosphere (and thus the data), when learning is guided by accurate information and sound rules of inference, when suppliers of services remain in dialogue with those who depend on them, and when the hearts and talents of all workers are enlisted in the pursuit of better ways, the potential for improvement in quality is nearly boundless.[1]

—*Don Berwick*

The plenary session of the Institute for Healthcare Improvement's annual quality forum can feel as much like a rock concert as a meeting of four thousand hospital managers. As IHI's co-founder and CEO Don Berwick emerges to give his annual address—which he is known to work on for several months in advance—he is greeted by chants of "Don! Don! Don!" What started as a small institute dedicated to quality improvement in health care has become a bona fide movement, and health care leaders at all levels from across the nation have joined in the cause, finding insight, inspiration, and above all reassurance that they are not alone in their struggles to improve health care quality.

Founded in 1991 and based in Boston, IHI is a not-for-profit organization leading the effort to improve health care throughout the world. The Institute aims to develop and implement innovative concepts for improving patient care. Thousands of health care providers, including many of the finest hospitals in the world, participate in IHI's groundbreaking work. Berwick himself is considered by many to be the world's leading thinker on quality improvement in health care.

Origins of Interest in Medicine

Berwick grew up in Moodus, a rural farm town in Connecticut. His father was a local physician, a general practitioner who had set up his medical practice right after the war in 1946. His mother was a town activist and homemaker; she developed ovarian cancer when he was fourteen, and died within a year. Berwick knew from a young age that he wanted to follow in his father's footsteps:

I don't remember any age when that wasn't the case. It was an excellent model. He was a very devoted and beloved doctor in town. And it just seemed like a great kind of work to do. In a small town everyone has roles, very vivid roles within the community. My father was one of only two doctors in town, so this was sort of an obvious and attractive career for me.

Berwick recalls that his father, a widely respected but intimidating man, agreed with the prevailing view at the time that medicine was highly physician-centered, and that physicians had both the answers and the authority to make health care decisions—a point of view that Berwick would, in time, depart from in his own emphasis on "patient-centered" care.

Berwick graduated from high school in 1964 in a class of 53 people and set off for Harvard University—the first student from Moodus to do so. On his first day of freshman biology at Harvard, he met Ann Greenberg, a young woman from Rhode Island, and the two became lab partners. She thought that "he was funny and great at explaining things...and would be a great partner." Eleven years later the two of them were married.

Berwick entered college as a pre-med, and knew he would devote a good chunk of his studies to the required basic sciences. But he had also, in part through involvement in student government and debating competitions during high school, developed a strong interest in government, public policy, and the social sciences. These interests led him to complete his pre-med requirements while majoring in "social relations," a mixture of psychology and sociology. While this major held Berwick's interest, it never caused him to seriously contemplate a career other than medicine:

> I toyed from time to time with politics or law as an option, and international law. I was in a freshman seminar with a wonderful professor named Roger Fisher, who is the guy who wrote *Getting to Yes*, and he organized a group of students to write a book on international conflict, which we did, and that attracted me into international political science, which remains an interest— but I never really wavered from pre-med.

In 1968, as Berwick was graduating from Harvard, he was informed that he was to be drafted into the army for Vietnam, and as a result turned down a traveling fellowship to head straight to Harvard Medical School.

LEARNING THE TOOLS FOR IMPROVEMENT

Like most medical students, Berwick immersed himself deeply in the basic sciences during his first two years. During his second year, however, he decided to join the Kennedy School of Government's newly founded joint M.D.-M.P.P. program.[2] HMS had just implemented the "new curriculum," which gave him a lot of electives, so he got permission to spend his entire third year of medical school at KSG, allowing him to complete the joint program in only four years. It was, Berwick explains, both a continuation and an intensification of his earlier interest in government and policy:

It was just an amazing experience—absolutely a turning point in my commitment to work on policy as an ongoing concern. There were a few things that made the KSG experience particularly influential in my thinking. First, since the program was in development, the senior-most faculty members at the KSG were our teachers—so I had Richard Neustadt, Fred Mosteller, and Francis Bator—the absolutely cream of the crop senior faculty in government and policy. So it was amazing exposure to the best minds at the school. And since they sat in on each other's lectures they were all there all the time, which made it a highly integrated experience.

Berwick's courses at KSG, in economics, decision theory, and statistics, among other things, proved invaluable in his future work: "I had analytic methods that were relevant to looking at health care differently." Before attending KSG, Berwick says, his interests in political science and medicine seemed difficult to integrate: "When I was in one I was missing the other." The program at KSG, with its commitment to interdisciplinary work on health policy, showed him that this did not have to be the case:

Health policy hadn't quite been formulated in the set of disciplines the way it now has. There were a few people at HMS who were leaders at the time, such as Rashi Fein in economics and Paul Denson at the Center on Health Policy. But I really had to go to the Kennedy School to find the depth of discipline that turned out to be so important to me.

BEARING WITNESS TO PROBLEMS IN HEALTH CARE

In 1972, after graduating from HMS, Berwick began his internship in medicine at Massachusetts General Hospital. In many ways, MGH was an ideal place to do a residency: "I have never been in a better, more excellent institution than MGH—it remains the pinnacle of my experience clinically." Yet as time went on, Berwick became dissatisfied with aspects of his work that seemed intrinsic to the way health care was done, not just at MGH but everywhere:

I became aware that I was frustrated with a lot of the work—in particular a lot of the geriatrics. It seemed sort of futile to me—the immense amount of technology and effort going into people really at the end of their lives.... It was wasteful. A lot of invasive stuff going on with people who needed something different.

It has remained one of Berwick's core beliefs that considerable resources are not only wasted, but are used in a manner that is hurtful to patients at the end of their lives.

Dissatisfied with internal medicine, Berwick decided to change residency programs. "I had always liked kids. I had been a camp counselor for years and years, and really knew that children were special to me," he explains. So in the middle of the year, he interviewed at Children's Hospital in Boston and was accepted for a pediatrics residency beginning in his second year.

At Children's, Berwick also continued to develop the interest in behavioral science that he had cultivated in his social relations major at Harvard: "I was very interested in the psychiatric and psycho-social aspects of pediatrics, so a lot of my concerns in my pediatric training were in that—learning how to deal with the emotional and psychological side of illness." His experience at Children's would remain with him in later years as he developed his vision of patient-centered care.

Another lasting lesson from this period stems from Berwick's involvement with the care of a young child with cerebral toxoplasmosis who was accidentally over-medicated. While the error did not cause the boy's death, the experience taught him "how good people with good intentions in health care can unknowingly do bad things." This would later become one of the pillars of Berwick's thinking about the sources of error in health care.

By this time, Berwick was already envisioning a career very different from that of his father, who had been in full-time non-academic practice:

> I knew I probably wanted to be in academia and doing some research as part of my work. I guess I imagined myself continuing to see patients, but my models were at that time of people who were doing that part-time while they were pursuing research.

While Berwick harbored this ambition to do research throughout his residency, he recalls being too focused on the daily details of practicing medicine to think much about it: "You are very much learning how to be a doctor—not thinking in system terms at that point." He nevertheless made at least one attempt, a study of the decision theory behind the management of heart attacks that would build on his work at KSG—but it remained only an attempt: "I had a data collection sheet set up and I was ready to do a study in the ED…. I never actually pulled it off. I was thinking that way, but I wasn't actually able to execute it."

It was during this period that Howard Hiatt, Berwick's most influential mentor, began to play a significant role in his career. Hiatt had served as his advisor on a paper Berwick was writing on one of Hiatt's own proposals for a community-based health care system:

> I disagreed a bit on the approach, but he was very respectful and helpful. Soon after I graduated from HMS he took the job of being the dean of the [Harvard] School of Public Health, and he approached me towards the end of my internship and asked me if I would be interested in coming to the HSPH to help set up some programs that he envisioned in health policy and quantitative methods in health services research.

After completing his pediatric residency, Berwick went to HSPH and became the assistant to the dean, and also joined the school's Center for the Analysis of Health Care Practices (CAHP), which Hiatt had established. He took a leave from HSPH in 1977 to go back to Children's Hospital for a year of senior residency followed by a year in a general pediatrics fellowship, and returned to HSPH in 1979 as a junior faculty member. He continued to spend half of his time at HSPH and half at Children's, where he taught and served as director of consultations for the pediatrics service.

In the midst of so much professional growth and change, Berwick's personal life had also been transformed. In 1976, eleven years after the two had met in freshman biology, Berwick married Ann Greenberg; nine months later they had their first child.

THE BEGINNING OF THE SEARCH FOR A BETTER SYSTEM

After completing his residency, Berwick began practicing as a pediatrician in 1979 with the Harvard Community Health Plan, one of the most creative health plans in the then-nascent HMO movement. In the 1990s, HMOs became best known for cost-containment, and the resulting tension between many HMOs, their patients, and those patients' physicians became the subject of considerable debate and satire. In the early 1970s, however, the HMO movement was quite different:

> It was totally a vision from inside the system, started by great leaders in medical care like Robert Ebert, the dean of HMS at the time, and Joseph Dorsey, Robert Biblo and H. Richard Nesson. They knew that you could organize a system that would do far better—that could be both less expensive and less wasteful, and much better for patients. This is the original vision of managed care which was an extremely compelling one...very, very positive.

HMOs, explains, Berwick, were meant to be an "integrated and thoughtful and preventive-oriented" alternative to the chaotic, wasteful, and crisis-oriented care that had evolved into the norm.

The Harvard Community Health Plan (HCHP) was started in 1969 as a classical staff-model HMO, which was quite different from what HMOs later became: "It was a delivery system that happened to be an insurer, not an insurer that happened to handle the delivery of care." Berwick was attracted to the organization because its ethos corroborated the lessons of his own clinical experience:

> The leaders of HCHP—these were people I deeply agreed with. They were people who knew as I did that what I had been observing in hospitals was this disorganized and extremely overdone care—just sort of order every test you could think of, do whatever you want to the patient. People believed that this

was good medicine, but I didn't, and I found a resonance in the value system that I was observing.

In 1980, Gordon Moore and Tom Pyle, HCHP's medical director and CEO, respectively, asked Berwick to direct HCHP's research arm and join the pediatrics unit, as well as fill an opening for director of quality assurance. The core of the work involved evaluating clinical practices and clinical decision analysis, work for which Berwick was well prepared thanks to his time at KSG. He had studied decision theory there, and later taught courses on decision analysis at HSPH with Hiatt, Harvey Fineberg (page 166) and Milton Weinstein. He had also recently co-authored a study of strategies for dealing with cholesterol in children that made extensive use of decision analysis.[3]

MEASURING THE QUALITY OF CARE

A year later, in 1981, HCHP suffered significant financial losses due to misestimating hospital utilization, and as a result its management team became very focused on cost-containment. The management structure was reconfigured so that the medical director, Gordon Moore, reported directly to Tom Pyle, the CEO.

Concerned about the potential impact on quality, the plan's board established the office of vice president for quality-of-care management. Gordon Moore and Tom Pyle asked Berwick to take on this role:

> They wanted a kind of internal watchdog. If I accepted the vice presidency, I would be given support to measure the quality of care in the organization, as a counterweight to the deep concerns about cost at that time. The budget was unlimited—anything I thought I needed I would get.

While there was nothing new about measuring quality, this was the first time it had been so closely tied in with the plan's strategic direction. "They needed to do it as part of their plan to cut costs, to make sure they were cutting costs in the right places," Berwick explains.

Berwick took on this expanded role, and continued his academic work at HSPH as part of the Center for the Analysis of Healthcare Practices. Shortly thereafter, in 1984-1985, the center's original funding had sunset, and it did not receive any additional support. Berwick therefore proposed that HCHP adopt the center. The resulting entity was the Institute for Health Research, and Howard Frazier, the director of CAHP, became the new director, with Berwick its associate director. Berwick's research job was now to run the institute (along with Frazier), even as he was measuring quality of care for HCHP.

GROWING INTERNAL CONFLICT

Over time, Berwick grew increasingly frustrated with his work at HCHP. Measuring the quality of care did not seem to be contributing to quality improvement, and his efforts were, to say the least, not widely appreciated by the health plan's staff—as many of Berwick's anecdotes from this period attest:

> I remember touring one week and going to the internal medicine department at Kenmore center, and giving them these feedback forms. I began handing out these sheets, and a doctor in the back—a friend of mine, in fact—stood up, walked up to me, crumpled her sheet of feedback, threw it at me and walked out of the room. That was the kind of experience I was having.

Berwick understood her reaction. Measuring patient dissatisfaction without at the same time providing suggestions about how to alleviate it was bound to create frustration, especially for doctors and nurses already working as hard as possible to keep up:

> I knew what she was feeling. Here I was telling her that the patients were dissatisfied with the waiting room, that they waited too long or the magazines were not up to date, and she was basically saying, "How the hell can I do anything about this? This isn't in my control—why are you bothering me?"

At the same time, Berwick knew that even if laying blame upon individual workers was counterproductive, the underlying problems were important. He experienced this on a personal level when his wife, who had visited one of the plan's clinics for an x-ray, experienced a ridiculously long wait. She urged Berwick to focus on eliminating such useless wait-periods, and he did just that:

> So we began a measurement system for waiting in x-ray departments all over the plan. Patients got a form stamped when they came in and again when they got their x-ray, and then that stack of forms was sent to my office and my staff subtracted the times and then calculated the waiting times for each center.

One month, Berwick noticed that one of the centers had a sudden improvement, from a mean wait-time of close to an hour to about two minutes. He sent a letter of congratulations, and after seeing it remain low for another month or two he decided to visit the clinic:

> I remember speaking to the administrator who ran the technical functions, and I said, "How did you do this?" And she said, "It's very simple to do that. I lied. Every day we just take a bunch of your tickets and we stamp them two minutes apart and we send them off."

And I asked, "Well why did you do that?" And she said, "Because you were making my life harder. This makes my life easier. And by the way...who are you to think that I am not doing everything I can to shorten the waiting times? I've been here ten years, I've been doing that every day of my life—so you just add trouble to me."

In another instance, Berwick recalls having lunch with a good friend, a senior manager of one of the clinics experiencing difficulties. Berwick suggested some things he might try, and his friend became furious: "He just exploded at me. He said, 'We are friends, we are trying to have lunch, and here you are telling me all this shit. Can't you just get off my back?'"

Berwick was torn: his work was gaining national recognition for putting a spotlight on very real health care problems, yet he felt that measuring problems stopped painfully short of solving them:

> That was the period when I got more and more frustrated. We clearly had probably the best measurements in the country at that point—I was speaking all over the country about what we were doing, it caught many people's attention partly because it was such a big program—but it wasn't very satisfying. Over those years I began noticing that the measurements weren't changing—nothing seemed to be improving, at least not quickly. And the organization didn't really welcome the measurements. So it was a very negative period in which intellectually it was interesting to learn how to measure, but affectively very much of a downer.

Looking Beyond Health Care for Answers

Beginning in about 1985, Berwick channeled his frustration into an effort to look beyond the health care sector itself for solutions to its problems. This change in his thinking was brought about by a couple of key events. One was a conversation with HCHP's CEO:

> I went to Tom Pyle and told him I didn't think things were going too well on the measurement front, and I wanted to quit the quality function. And he said that maybe before I got too frustrated I should go look at other industries—NASA for instance—and study how they approach this problem.

Berwick began by examining quality at a hotel he was staying at during a conference in Princeton. He noticed that the rooms at this hotel were consistently spotless, whereas HCHP's clinics were often quite messy, and so he spent a few hours with their housekeeping service understanding how they worked. He also arranged to meet with quality executives from the Gillette Corporation, NASA, and AT&T, whose Bell Laboratories were well known for their quality control processes. AT&T's senior quality executive, A. Blanton Godfrey, met with Berwick and soon became a close collaborator.

The second event was a meeting with Hospital Corporation of America's vice president for quality, Paul Batalden, who invited Berwick to HCA's Nashville headquarters to speak about his work with HCHP:

> I went down to their headquarters and spoke. He was cordial, but I was talking strictly about measurement, and he said, "I know what you are doing, but you really need to study the work of this guy Deming."

The way to do this, he told Berwick, was to enroll in one of Deming's four-day seminars in Washington, D.C. "I didn't have any idea what he was talking about," Berwick recalls, "but I said I would do it."

W. Edwards Deming is known as the father of the Japanese post-war industrial revival, and was a leading thinker on quality in the U.S. Trained as a statistician, he had assisted the U.S. military during World War II with improving the quality of war materials; after the war, he was invited by Japan's industrial leaders to help them remake the world's image of Japanese products. The rest is history: "Japanese" came to signify not a cheap imitation, as it often had in the first half of the century, but rather an innovative, high-quality product. Berwick took Batalden's advice, and went to Washington for Deming's course:

> I showed up for the first day, and I was just very uncomfortable. On noon of day two I left—flew home early. I just thought it was garbage.

> I had quite a sleepless night, and in the morning, I had this kind of sudden insight. The reason for my discomfort was not really that it was garbage, but rather that it was the first time I had ever really heard a theory that I could understand about how quality happens, and it made almost everything I was doing theoretically incorrect. Which was very, very difficult for me to realize—It had to do with my whole career, not just my current job. I also suddenly understood what Batalden was trying to tell me. And so I went back to D.C., and went to the last day of the course.

Back at the course, Berwick took the opportunity to meet Deming over dinner with a group of attendees. He recalls that Deming was abrupt—"he didn't answer a single question I asked—he absolutely ignored me"—but in retrospect he understands why: "I was so far from understanding what he was talking about, I really wasn't worth his answering—I wouldn't have even understood his answers."

FROM MEASURING TO IMPROVING:
THE NATIONAL DEMONSTRATION PROJECT

As Berwick's philosophy developed, so did his aims at HCHP. He had been charged with measuring quality and outcomes, but this no longer seemed like the right way to improve quality:

> I changed tactics at HCHP, and began instead to try to teach Deming's theory, even though I didn't fully understand it. I began drifting bit by bit from what I was hired to do. I was hired to inspect, but a core part of Deming's theory was away from inspection. And so the more I taught the more uncomfortable I became.

This change in thinking—focusing on improvement over measurement—became one of the core tenets of Berwick's quality movement, and led to a reorientation of his entire career. Measuring quality and assigning blame did not seem nearly as fruitful as focusing on the root causes of problems and finding ways to solve them.

The second part of this shift in thinking followed from Pyle's initial suggestion to look at quality improvement at NASA and elsewhere: in place of measurement—a process inherently internal to a given system—one could benefit greatly by looking outside of the system for answers. In 1986, Berwick partnered on a new venture with Godfrey, who by then had left AT&T to join the Juran Institute, a consulting firm focused on quality improvement. They set out to conduct an experiment asking the question: "Can the tools of modern quality improvement, with which other industries have achieved breakthroughs in performance, help in health care as well?"[4] They selected a group of 21 quality leaders from outside of health care and assigned each one of them to a different hospital, where they would make observations with the aim of formulating a plan for quality improvement.

Funded by the Hartford Foundation through a senior program officer, Richard Sharpe, but still hosted through HCHP as part of its research arm, the experiment was called the National Demonstration Project on Quality Improvement in Health Care (NDP). The participants reconvened one year later, and every hospital presented what they had learned. Sharpe, sufficiently impressed with the results, suggested that they continue and expand the project, and gave them an additional $600,000 for work over the next three years.

With the additional funding, Berwick and Godfrey proposed running courses for health care managers on what they were finding—lessons from non-health care industries on improving quality in health care and process improvement strategies—as well as annual summits for people involved in these efforts. Joined by Jane Roessner, they also published the findings of the NDP in their 1990 book, *Curing Health Care*.[5]

THE BIRTHDAY CLUB AND THE BIRTH OF IHI

In 1989, Berwick decided to end his involvement with HCHP and started focusing solely on the NDP:

> I had to make a choice. I was not really doing what they paid me to do, which

was to come up with more and more systematic measurements of quality. And I did not believe in doing that.

To supplement his lost income from HCHP, Berwick began working as a consultant with a few hospitals to implement process improvements developed in the NDP. Among the hospitals was Dartmouth-Hitchcock, which soon thereafter hired Paul Batalden as a professor, allowing Berwick to collaborate with him more frequently. Berwick and Batalden began holding a series of informal gatherings for a diverse group of colleagues in health care and quality improvement to discuss what they were learning. The group met every few months at the O'Hare Airport in Chicago, and included people such as Jim Roberts (then of the JCAHO, the hospital accreditation organization), Vinod Sahney (of the Henry Ford Health System) and John Ware (formerly of RAND, then at Tufts New England Medical Center in Boston). Since the group's first two meetings fell on the birthdays of two members, they called themselves "The Birthday Club."

Back at the NDP, the courses they had starting teaching were proving exceedingly popular, with a two-year waiting list for enrollment. Since they charged tuition, however, they were not spending the additional money Sharpe had given them—in fact, they were making a profit, and by 1991 they had accumulated $600,000 in the bank. Sharpe, confident in the movement Berwick and his partners were starting, told him to keep the money for further projects so long as it helped them achieve their original purpose.

Berwick and his partners used this encouragement to turn the NDP into a permanent entity. The NDP and its funding were still being hosted by HCHP, but this had become only a technicality. In 1991, then, Pyle was asked to turn the money over to a new organization, which was incorporated as the Institute for Healthcare Improvement. Sharpe agreed to give the institute another round of funding for an endowment, and "The Birthday Club" became IHI's first board of trustees.

After the IHI: Federal and State Government

In 2010, President Barack Obama asked Donald Berwick to serve as the administrator of the Centers for Medicare & Medicaid Services (CMS). The nomination happened just after the passage of the Patient Protection and Affordable Care Act, the most sweeping health care reform in a generation. Berwick's appointment was thus caught up in the broader controversy surrounding the president's health care reform. Critics also repeatedly cited comments had made praising aspects of the U.K.'s health care system as evidence that he favored the implementation of a more "socialized" health care system. When Republicans in Congress promised extensive delays in Berwick's confirmation, President Obama chose to bypass the confirmation process and make a recess appointment. After nearly twenty years leading the IHI, Berwick stepped down to accept the new position at CMS, in which he served through the end of 2011.

After his time in Washington, Berwick returned to the IHI as a senior fellow, and soon began a new chapter in his career when he declared his candidacy to become governor of Massachusetts in June of 2013. Running for the Democratic nomination, Berwick advocated a single-payer health care system for Massachusetts. In September 2014, he lost the primary to Martha Coakley.

PRINCIPLES OF DONALD BERWICK'S CAREER
CONTINUOUS IMPROVEMENT AS AN IDEAL IN HEALTH CARE

In 1989, with the NDP well under way, Berwick began to realize how significant the project's results might be. It was his longtime mentor, though, who finally prompted him to formulate and publish what he had learned: "I had an informal chat with Howard Hiatt, and I was describing what I thought I was learning, and he said 'You really need to write that up'—and so I did." Berwick published his ideas in the *New England Journal of Medicine* under the title "Continuous Improvement as an Ideal in Health Care." Writing the article allowed Berwick to crystallize his best ideas and, in a way, to feel their full force for the first time himself:

> Nothing in my experience has ever quite matched that. It was completely fortuitous. I just was thinking in a way that apparently synchronized with a lot of other concerns in the country. That paper was without any doubt the turning point in my career.

In the article, Berwick accepted that even well-meaning, competent workers will make mistakes, and advocated a focus not on measuring these errors, but rather on organizing systems that are robust to them. These ideas were revolutionary at the time—they did not yet have wide acceptance in the medical community, and this was long before the public would learn about them from reports like the Institute of Medicine's *To Err is Human* (2002).

Berwick's article powerfully articulates the central ideas of his philosophy of quality improvement. In its opening lines, he asks the reader to imagine two assembly lines, each monitored by a different foreman. Foreman 1 is intent on accurately, minutely measuring the errors of his workers, and threatens to replace anyone who underperforms. Foreman 2, who represents the model Berwick prefers, has a rather different point of view:

> "I am here to help you if I can," he says. "We are in this together for the long haul. You and I have a common interest in a job well done. I know that most of you are trying very hard, but sometimes things can go wrong. My job is to

notice opportunities for improvement—skills that could be shared, lessons from the past, or experiments to try together—and to give you the means to do your work even better than you do now. I want to help the average ones among you, not just the exceptional few at either end of the spectrum of competence." (CI)

The rest of the article walks through the key ideas that follow from this new approach: a move away from blame, the power of good people to improve, and the need for changing systems rather than people.

THE BAD THEORY OF BAD APPLES

The first idea in Berwick's philosophy is to focus on improvement rather than measurement, or assigning blame. As he explains it, there are different schools of thought in quality improvement, and the one that focuses on measurement and blame—based on what he calls the "Theory of Bad Apples"—has prevailed in health care:

> Those in health care who espouse the Theory of Bad Apples are looking hard for better tools of inspection. Such tools must have excellent measuring ability—high sensitivity and specificity, simultaneously—lest the malefactors escape or the innocent be made victims. They search for outliers—statistics far enough from the average that chance alone is unlikely to provide a good excuse. (CI)

This theory, however, has not succeeded to any real extent, and a better theory for quality improvement exists:

> The Theory of Bad Apples let American industry down for decades. It took some visionary theorists, many of them statisticians, in companies with great foresight to learn that relying on inspection to improve quality is at best inefficient, and at worst a formula for failure. The Japanese learned first—from American theorists, ironically—that their were far better ways to improve quality, and the result is international economic history.... What Japan had discovered was primarily a new, more cogent, and more valid way to focus on quality. Call it the Theory of Continuous Improvement.... (CI)

The virtue of this theory is not just that it avoids tension in the workplace of the sort Berwick had experienced at HCHP, though this is important. Nor does Berwick deny that there are indeed bad apples: "When we have garbage—bad doctors, bad nurses, bad hospitals—we ought to find them, shut them down, throw them out, fire them. That will make the system a tiny bit better" (CI).

A tiny bit—but only a tiny bit, and this is Berwick's point. The most compelling reason to shift quality improvement efforts away from a focus on bad apples is that bad apples account for so small a fraction of errors; the vast majority of bad events in medicine are legitimate human errors made by well-intentioned and competent practitioners. Berwick traces the origin of this idea back to his residency, and particularly to his involvement with the over-medicated cancer patient at Children's, when he became aware of "good people unintentionally doing bad things."

RELYING ON GOOD PEOPLE:
THE POWER IN THE MIDDLE OF THE BELL CURVE

The theory of bad apples attributes error to malice or incompetence, and tries to root out the workers supposed to be responsible; on this theory, everyone is a suspect, and what matters is not so much getting better as just getting by—doing just well enough to escape the censure of regulators. The theory of continuous improvement has a different point of view: it assumes that the vast majority of workers want to do better, and seeks to harness this desire to improve quality. Reestablishing respect for health care workers is thus a fundamental goal for Berwick, because quality improvement depends on it:

> Physicians, hospital employees, and health care workers, like workers anywhere, must be assumed to be trying hard, acting in good faith, and not willfully failing to do what they know to be correct. (CI)

The conviction that assigning blame is more often than not counterproductive reverberates throughout Berwick's writing on the health care system. Even in his most stringent critiques, he emphasizes the system itself as the major problem, and seeks to persuade those involved in it to re-imagine their roles vis-à-vis that system:

> It's not that we don't have capable executives and committed boards. It's that the capable executives are still devoted to maintaining the *status quo*. And the hospital boards—I don't know if this should appear in print—but they're sort of out to lunch. They're good-hearted. They care about the organizations that they are stewards of; they respect the managers and the doctors. But they don't understand that they have a duty to cause change. And without executive and board leadership, I'm not sure we're going to get off the dime.[6]

While Berwick has high expectations for health care leaders, he has consistently argued that improving quality means focusing on the middle of the bell curve, rather than on the small number of under- and over-performers at either end. The power of the continuous improvement approach stems from the fact that smaller systematic improvements, if they take place across the middle of the curve that includes the overwhelming majority of workers, can achieve far more than drastic efforts directed at the curve's ends. The idea is at once democratic in spirit and statistically powerful, and Berwick is quick to credit health care workers at all levels for the inherent will to do better that underlies such statistics:

The reservoir—the latent will in the workforce to do better—is absolutely overwhelming. It's like drilling for oil. There is so much pent-up need in the health care workforce—and I include here not just doctors, but nurses, pharmacists, respiratory therapists, managers—to really do better. It's so easy to get there once you decide to. It's a constant source of energy to find that people want to be better at what they do. (G)

The movement Berwick has created reflects this underlying principle. Just as continuous improvement focuses on the mass of people in the middle, IHI focuses on the people in the middle as well—not in terms of quality, but in terms of power. The IHI National Quality Forums are attended not primarily by the most senior executives, but by middle-level managers—the people who, by sheer volume, can make real change in health care.

Berwick's faith in the average worker differs not only from the suspicious search for bad apples, but also from the traditional economic view of workers as profit-maximizers, motivated primarily by financial incentives. While such incentives are often proposed as a way to improve health care outcomes, Berwick finds them largely inappropriate: "When someone shows up and says, I'll pay you ten bucks more to do a good job, [employees] feel not helped out, not incentivized. They feel insulted. And they ought to feel insulted" (G). Financial incentives misrecognize the qualitative and altruistic satisfactions of doing good work—satisfactions that draw many people to health care in the first place. By treating people as if they work merely for pay, financial incentives threaten to make them do just that:

The problem with pay-for-performance is not that it doesn't mold behavior. The problem is that it does mold behavior. You get exactly what you're paying for, which might not, in the end, when you're finally on your deathbed, be exactly what you wish you'd gotten. (G)

REINVENTING PROCESSES, ONE STEP AT A TIME: KAIZEN

Since most people in health care want to improve the quality of their work in the first place, Berwick argues, the real task for quality-of-care managers is to give them ways to do so: "The average hospital, the average doctor, cannot improve what they do, because they don't know how" (G). Berwick has often referred to health care's failure to solve this problem as a "learning disability" ingrained in the sector's structures and culture.

The manager's task of overcoming that disability exceeds merely measuring progress and setting goals, a point Berwick drives home in one of his speeches with a story about coaching his daughter's soccer team. With the team struggling at mid-season, Berwick found his managerial authority called into question by an unimpressed fourth-grader when he couldn't explain to her how to win. "You mean," she asked him, "you're the coach and you don't know how to play the game?"

"Sure I do," I said. "I point out the scoreboard, I motivate, I make guidelines, I tell you pass-pass-pass-shoot. That's my job."

"You don't get it," said Lizzie. "It doesn't help me when you yell, 'pass-pass-pass-shoot.' You have to tell me how. How do you play soccer?"[7]

Learning how to provide better health care requires, first and foremost, a detailed understanding of the multiple processes by which care is delivered. As Lizzie might point out, this means that managers will have to listen to the people in the field—and in effect, revising a process according to Berwick's theory of continuous improvement cannot happen entirely from the top down. One example that he has learned from is, in fact, the Toyota Production System, which established world-class quality control and improvement standards in part by encouraging suggestions from employees on the floor.

Berwick quotes the systems theorist George Box to explain the basic principle of continuous improvement: "Every process produces information on the basis of which the process can be improved" (CI). This model of continuous improvement is often referred to as *kaizen* (改善), which literally means "improvement" in Japanese; the term originated from the post-World War II collaboration of Japanese industrialists with American theorists like Deming. Since the *kaizen* process occurs one step at a time, it is often translated as "continuous improvement." The goals and tactics of kaizen include the elimination of waste, just-in-time delivery, production load leveling, standardized work, paced moving lines, and right-sized equipment. Measurements of error are not discarded, but are focused narrowly on the aspect of a process targeted for improvement, providing direct and immediate feedback on how each small change affects the overall process.

Berwick's writings and speeches have continually exhorted health care managers and workers to think creatively about the improvement of processes. A quite basic example, with clear parallels in the redundancy and mutual interference that can plague workers in health care, is the command he used to stop his daughter's soccer team from clumping around the ball. "Girls in such circumstances," he says wryly, "get kicked more often than the ball does," and he solved the problem with three words:

"Run to Space." That means, whether you think it is rational at the time or not, try not to run to where the ball is. Run to where it isn't. Run to where nobody is. If you do that, a surprisingly large number of times, the ball will pop out to you, all alone, and you will get a chance to pass or shoot. (EF)

In another speech, "Escape Fire," he uses the example of an "occupied" sign on the bathroom door at IHI to illustrate the virtue of a production solution known as a "forcing function" (*EF*). Unlike the signs we have all seen on the doors of airplane restrooms, Berwick explains, the one at IHI worked independently of the door's lock. Anyone wishing to open the door thus had not only to read the sign, but also to second-guess whether someone might just have forgotten to flip it. This created a lot of unnecessary guesswork—and embarrassment. After recounting his comic effort to make the process work by drawing attention to it—making signs for the sign—Berwick explains that what was really needed was a new process, one including a "forcing function" connecting the sign to the lock, and thus eliminating choice in a situation where choice could only produce error.

Another important production technique emphasized in Berwick's work is continuous flow, sometimes referred to as *kanban*. *Kanban* (看板), like *kaizen*, originated in post-WWII Japan. Kanban is often thought of as just-in-time (JIT) production, although the Japanese word simply refers to the "sign" or "card" used by a production unit to signal the need for an item. The idea is that waste and inefficiency are reduced by having everything when you need it, but only when you need it. In a health care setting, this would translate into improved scheduling systems for physician offices or hospital diagnostics, both of which often leave patients—the "inventory"—in long delays in cold examining rooms and hospital hallways.

While Berwick has excelled at imagining how production techniques originating in business and industry might revitalize processes of health care delivery, he has never confused a clinic with an assembly line, and is acutely aware of the cultural differences between the two sectors. He recognizes that these differences are particularly and legitimately challenging for physicians, who—like Berwick's own father—have traditionally seen themselves as independent decision-makers: "Physicians...seem to have difficulty seeing themselves as participants in processes, rather than as lone agents of success or failure" (CI). They have often resisted the application of models derived from business and management theory to medicine, and the reasons for this are many and complex: medicine has historically celebrated individual rather than group achievement; physicians are uncomfortable when patients and profits stand in conflict; and physicians have often stood to lose both freedoms and financial rewards when the business world, whether in the form of hospital management or HMO executives, has encroached upon their work.

Yet Berwick argues that any real change in the health care system will require not only the assent but also the leadership of practicing physicians. His argument to enlist them is not that they should sacrifice freedoms for the good of the system, but that they in fact stand to gain as much as anyone:

Physicians and health care managers who study and apply the principles of continuous improvement daily will probably come to know better efficiency, greater effectiveness, lower cost, and the gratitude and loyalty of more satisfied patients. They will be able to make better decisions and carry them out more faithfully. (CI)

CHANGING SYSTEMS, NOT PEOPLE

Berwick's thinking about how to change health care processes depends on his intimate knowledge of those processes, but at its core is the basic insight that to improve a system, you have to change it. Berwick credits Paul Batalden with first explaining this to him, and he calls it "the central law of improvement":

> [E]very system is perfectly designed to achieve the results it achieves. This aphorism encodes an understanding of systems that lies at the root of current approaches to making systems function better. The central law reframes performance from a matter of effort to a matter of design. (CI)

Berwick admits that working harder within a given system can lead to improvement, and is far from discouraging such efforts. But, he argues, "such improvement is not fundamental; it does not often represent a new level of capability" (CI). The engine of fundamental change, he explains, is not effort but "scientifically based redesign," which can produce "extraordinary" results:

> Five years ago I would have thought that you could get lower mortality and shorter waits and lower cost with changes. I would have suspected it. Now, I absolutely know it, and its dramatic, dramatic potential. (G)

Changing a system requires finding a standpoint outside of it. The NDP was an attempt to do just that, and IHI has its origins in the NDP's effort to apply quality improvement methods drawn from other industries to health care. To this day, IHI continues to reap the benefits of this basic strategy, articulated by Berwick in his article on "Continuous Improvement":

> Modern technical, theoretically grounded tools for improving processes must be put to use in health care settings. The pioneers of quality improvement... have left a rich heritage of theory and technique by which to analyze and improve complex production processes, yet until recently these techniques have had little use in our health care system. (CI)

Berwick firmly believes that knowledge from outside of health care is a powerful means to improve quality of care; almost every one of his speeches brings in some major lesson from another industry. In a 1995 speech, he retells how the American automobile industry managed to move from 1980, when the three major auto makers were hugely unprofitable and approaching bankruptcy, to 1995, when all three had record profits (although, Berwick points out, they did not stay at that level). The lesson, as he explains it, is that they "figured out a better way to make a car" (*EF*).

Yet it does not follow from all this that the best solutions for health care will be market solutions. Berwick's views on the drawbacks of pay-for-performance are one example of his reservations about such solutions, and he is no less skeptical of them on a larger and more systemic level. Responding to an economic analysis by Joseph Newhouse that he finds generally admirable, Berwick insists that it provides a good picture, but not the whole one:

> Economists predict, perhaps, that in the right market context things might fix themselves. I think not. The core issue is fragmentation, and the solution lies in forms of assembly and cooperation that the prevailing structures in health care cannot achieve. Disciplines divide from disciplines, organizations from organizations, events from events. Patients cross over these boundaries time and again, and their needs get lost in the disorder. To meet their needs requires huge reorganization, a reinvention of care that few organizations can tackle now, even if the market made them want to.[8]

For Berwick, the bottom line in health care is patient care rather than profit, and some kinds of competition encouraged by the market take place to the detriment of both. After criticizing how different hospitals in a market will continue to compete when it would be in their own and their communities' best interests to cooperate, he characteristically condemns the activity while making the point not that the leaders involved are incompetent or apathetic, but that they need to re-envision their roles:

> It is stupid. It is stupid activity led by very smart people… It is rather a matter of some missing skill, some capacity that our leaders, despite their genius, and despite their shared good intentions overall, do not have

THE TOXIC ASSUMPTION THAT MORE IS BETTER, AND THE NOBILITY OF COST-CONTAINMENT

While unnecessary competition is one source of waste in health care, Berwick's involvement with the issue of waste dates back to his experience with geriatrics as an intern, and his sense that health care was being over-delivered to elderly patients—it was, he felt, just "not what they needed." The same belief—that appropriate and coordinated care could be both higher quality and lower cost—was an underlying tenet of the early HMO movement, and helped Berwick decide to join HCHP.

These early experiences came full circle when Berwick's aging father underwent rehabilitation after a hip fracture, as Berwick discusses in his 1994

IHI speech "Quality Comes Home." The speech tells a story of unnecessary and untimely health care: the strong sedation his father clearly did not need, the discontinuance of the Parkinson's medication he desperately did need, and the unavailability of a wheelchair early in his stay, leading to a debilitating pressure ulcer:

> Two weeks after he got home—almost entirely bedridden and almost certainly never to walk again—a wheelchair finally came: the latest model, with postural supports, custom back rests, and hand controls he can never use. We never asked for it; the home care company simply ordered it. It's beautiful. The price: $6,000. It sits proudly and nearly unused in the corner of his bedroom. (*EF*)

To Berwick, this is emblematic of the severe mismatch between supply and demand in health care: too many and too expensive things provided when they are not needed, and simple and inexpensive things not provided when they are. The answer, to Berwick, lies not in spending more money, but in spending money more intelligently: "We have not developed sound ways to help our patients seek their own self-interest, and we have allowed the public to proceed on the dangerous, toxic, and expensive assumption that more is better."

This assumption is toxic because it unthinkingly associates high expenditure with high quality. Conversely, cost-containment—the effort to make health care efficient—becomes associated with health care managers pitting a financial bottom line against the best interests of patients. Neither of these equations holds, Berwick argues. "There is," he writes emphatically, "no difference between quality and efficiency. It's the same thing looked at with the same crystal, through a different facet":

> Right from the start, it has been one of the great illusions in the reign of quality that quality and cost go in opposite directions. There remains very little evidence of that. There may be some innovations that raise cost while raising quality, but many, many improvements reduce costs. (G)

As his father's case showed, high expenditure often correlates with mismanaged care, not with health benefits we cannot afford. Unclear thinking about the correlation of expenditure and quality is, he argues, a particularly acute problem when it comes to investing in new technologies: "We have a learning disability in this country with respect to the difference between technologies that really do help and technologies that are only adding money to the margins of the companies that make them, without essentially paying their way in value" (G).

Yet if some players in the health care sector seek to profit at the expense of quality, Berwick believes that many of those concerned with cost-containment also understand that decreasing quality in order to cut costs would be no solution at all—the very opposite of efficiency. He gives the example of employers:

> The employers on the whole are of course interested in cost-containment—the costs are insane—but they also want good care for their employees, because it helps their labor-management relationships, and many of them are ethical.

Berwick would like the struggle to contain costs to be re-imagined with such motives at its heart. The real motive to strive for efficiency in health care, for the wise and timely use of medical resources, is not profit but patient health:

> The search for cost-containment is not just a necessary one—it is a noble one—the idea that we're wasteful, and that we are hurting people by doing things that can't help them. We're spending 40 percent more than the next most expensive country on earth. It is inconsistent and expensive care.

To see cost-containment in this way would mean recasting the health care debate on its broadest level. It has become commonplace to pronounce the U.S. health care system (like all health care systems, for that matter) to be badly broken. Usually, this is understood as a statement about the complex issues involved in financing the system—concerns over rising health care costs, the uninsured, and the long-term solvency of Medicare. Berwick argues against this emphasis, going so far as to say that there may even be too much money in the system: "The waste level in American medicine approaches 50 percent. It's certainly in double digits, and this has to be absolutely pasted onto the quality agenda."

Integrating Medicine and Social Science

The story of Berwick's career is one of integration, at many different levels. The most important of these has been Berwick's triumph over the tension between his two greatest lifelong interests: the interest in medicine that he inherited from his father, and the interest in the social and management sciences—including public policy, economics, statistics and operations—that dates back to high school.

The relationship between them changes distinctly over the course of his career. At first, during college and medical school, they compete with one another for Berwick's time and attention. He leaves medical school for a year to attend KSG, and then later finds himself so immersed in clinical work that he has no time for research. This tension takes a new turn after residency, when Berwick begins working at HCHP: his job, explicitly, is to do both—to practice as a pediatrician and to oversee research as well. This seminal period in Berwick's career, when his interests at least coexist peacefully, lays the philosophical foundations for IHI. With the founding of IHI begins the third stage, beyond mere coexistence, in which Berwick begins using the social and management sciences to change the way medicine is practiced.

This integration was due not to luck as much as to persistence—as Berwick explains, he consistently refused to let go of either interest:

> I constantly tried to have my cake and eat it too. My tactic was to try to find how to have both. Like the Kennedy School and medical school, or clinical work and policy work. It's that unwillingness to give up one for the other that probably also played a large role…perhaps a longer-standing personality trait of optimism, or stubbornness, or a reluctance to choose.

Berwick credits three key experiences in particular with enabling him to bring together social science and medicine in the way that he has. The first of these was his pivotal experience at KSG:

> What the Kennedy School did was take vague ideas I had had about evaluating practices and gave them a sharp intellectual edge, because the subject matter—economics, decision theory, operations research, statistics—all provided really strong methodological frameworks for doing what I intuitively was trying to think about, which was being critical of care, from a policy perspective. I could see the social sciences interest giving me a lens with which to view health care. By giving me the tools, it made it possible for me to have my cake and eat it too.

The second key experience was the example set by Berwick's mentor, Howard Hiatt, the dean of the Harvard School of Public Health. As Berwick explains: "He didn't take it for granted that health care was what it needed to be, he was arguing that it needed to be different, so he was a great leader." Finally, Berwick credits his experience working as a physician for making him want to use his social science training to change the health care system:

> I remember nights on call at the hospital when I would watch patients go through tremendous amounts of anguish and invasiveness and in the back of my mind I would be saying, "Why are we doing this, what's going on?"

Berwick's long struggle to answer these questions has not been easy: "You have to get off the beaten path slightly, and that can be a little bit uncomfortable." He again credits Hiatt for reassuring him, at an early stage and when he needed it most, that a productively critical attitude towards the status quo would be worth whatever discomfort it caused. Berwick tries to return the favor, urging his own students to be similarly uncompromising:

> When I have mentees, I try to tell them to figure out how to have everything they want, especially in medicine, because it is such an extraordinarily plastic field. Believe me, the Venn diagram overlaps somewhere.

Integration Manifested:
The Quality Movement and Patient-Centered Care

Berwick has integrated not only the methods but also the styles and cultures of his two major fields of interest. His emphasis, for example, on "improvement" at all costs, is characteristic of thinking in business and policy, as is his focus on addressing problems at a systemic level; clinicians and health care managers have more often tried to solve a problem from within the constraints of existing systems. Perhaps unintentionally, he has also embraced a charismatic style of leadership more typical of government than of clinical medicine. He relies on his considerable skill as a public speaker to convey his program for change, which in turn feels as much like a quasi-political movement within health care as a managerial strategy. Berwick believes that to instruct, he must also inspire.

It is this interpersonal aspect of his work that fundamentally motivates Berwick. For Berwick, studying for the sake of studying—just like measuring for the sake of measuring at HCHP—is never the point. The point is to fix things. If his emphasis on systemic change can seem abstract, at its heart is an acute sense of how bad systems can impinge upon good people, both patients and health care workers, and a desire not so much to remedy the problem as to enable others to do so. This explains why IHI is more like a consulting firm than a health services think tank. What makes IHI unique is its ability to implement change by providing tools, knowledge, and inspiration.

The fact that Berwick is more motivated by outcome than by sheer intellectual challenge also underlies his patient-centered approach to improving care. While medical research may focus on the cancer, Berwick believes it is equally necessary for medical care to focus on the cancer patient, even and perhaps especially when what is best for the patient is a less aggressive approach to fighting the disease. Berwick is more impressed by the artful and appropriate allocation of the tools of medicine than by its sheer power alone. His early experience with geriatric care was crucial in shaping this view; it is part of why pediatrics appeals to him, and why he believes so strongly in physicians playing a greater role in preventive medicine.[9]

Bringing it Home: Making Health Care Personal

One of the greatest ways in which Berwick inspires change is by making health care—which often seems so huge and impersonal, both to patients and practitioners alike—intensely personal. His personal experience has shaped his thinking about the health care system, and he integrates this into the way he communicates his ideas, whether this means an anecdote about his daughter's soccer team or the more serious matter of the care received by his father.

In 1998, Berwick's wife Ann, a powerful environmental lawyer, developed a rare disease that led to a hospital stay of over 60 days. Her experience dramatically underscored Berwick's convictions about the flawed state of the health care system. He devoted much of his 1999 speech at IHI, "Escape Fire," to recounting the details of the experience. He begins the speech by explaining what led him to overcome his reluctance to make such personal matters part of a public debate:

> My dilemma is this: Our ordeal has been enormously painful and intensely private, and it is by no means over yet. To use it for any public purpose, even to speak about it, risks crossing a boundary of propriety and confidentiality that ought not to be crossed. Yet this has been the formative experience for me overall in the past year—the experience of the decade—and it resonates so thoroughly with the mission of improving health care that not to learn from it also seems wrong. (*EF*)

Throughout his account, he maintains his belief that what needs to be changed is the system itself, not the people in it. Ann's experience left him more impressed than ever with the "goodwill, kindness, generosity, commitment, and dignity of the people who work in health care—almost all of them" (*EF*).

But in many ways the system failed: "The errors were not rare; they were the norm" (*EF*). Physicians would say that Ann should not get a certain drug—and she would get it the same afternoon; a drug needed immediately took three days to get. Ann's knowledge of which sleeping medications were working was ignored; tests were delayed, leaving her at times on gurneys in the hallway. As caregivers changed, their failure to communicate with each other forced her to explain her lengthy story again and again.

Her care to date, Berwick notes, had cost upwards of $150,000, and he estimates that at most half of this had any chance of helping her. He emerged from the experience more impressed than ever with the urgent need for change—for the kind of change that would create a health care system worthy of the people involved in it:

> Put very, very simply: the people work well, by and large, but the system often does not. Every hour of our care reminded me, and alerted Ann, about the enormous, costly, and painful gaps between what we got in our days of need and what we needed. The experience did not actually surprise me, but it did shock me. Put in other terms, as a friend of mine said, before this I was concerned; now, I am radicalized. (*EF*)

Notes

1   "Continuous Improvement as an Ideal in Health Care," *New England Journal of Medicine* 320 (5 January 1989): 53-6. Cited internally hereafter as "CI."

2   The impact of the early years of the joint M.D.-M.P.P. program at Harvard is also discussed by two of its other early participants, David Blumenthal (page 72) and Harvey Fineberg (page 186).

3   Donald Berwick, Shan Cretin, Emmett Keeler, *Cholesterol, Children, and Heart Disease: An Analysis of Alternatives* (New York: Oxford Unieversity Press, 1990).

4   Donald Berwick, A. Blanton Godfrey, Jane Roessner, *Curing Health Care: New Strategies for Quality Improvement* (San Francisco: Jossey-Bass, 1990), xvi.

5   *Ibid.*

6   "Interview: 'A Deficiency of Will and Ambition': A Conversation With Donald Berwick," *Health Affairs* Web Exclusive, January 12, 2005. Interviewed by Robert Galvin. Cited internally hereafter as "G."

7   From the speech "Run to Space," as reprinted in *Escape Fire: Designs for the Future of Health Care* (San Francisco: Jossey-Bass, 2004). This book will be cited internally hereafter as "EF."

8   Letter to the Editor, *Health Affairs* 21, no. 5 (2002). To learn more about Newhouse, see page 374 of this book.

9   For more on Berwick's vision of patient-centered care, see his article "A Primer on the Improvement of Systems," *Boston Medical Journal* 312 (9 March 1996): 619–22.

J. Michael Bishop

Chancellor Emeritus, University of California at San Francisco
1989 Nobel Laureate in Physiology or Medicine

Michael Bishop, along with his colleague Harold Varmus, won the 1989 Nobel Prize in Physiology or Medicine for their groundbreaking research in oncology. In this profile, Bishop discusses how his interest in teaching and basic science led him to medical school, and then eventually to a career in academic research rather than clinical practice. He also reflects on the importance of following one's true interests over prestige or strict adherence to established pathways.

EDUCATION & TRAINING

1953–1957	A.B., Gettysburg College
1957–1962	M.D., Harvard Medical School (HMS)
1959–1960	Research Fellow, Pathology, Massachusetts General Hospital (MGH)
1961–1962	Research Fellow, Bacteriology and Immunology, HMS
1962–1964	Intern and Resident, Internal Medicine, MGH

CAREER PATH

1963–1967	United States Public Health Service
1964–1967	Research Associate (Cell Biology), National Institute of Allergy and Infectious Diseases, National Institutes of Health
1967–1968	Visiting Scientist, Heinrich-Pette Institute, Hamburg, Germany
1968–1970	Assistant Professor, Microbiology and Immunology, University of California-San Francisco (UCSF)
1970–1972	Associate Professor, Microbiology and Immunology, UCSF
1973–	Professor, Microbiology and Immunology, UCSF
1981–	Director, The George Williams Hooper Research Foundation, UCSF
1982–	Professor, Biochemistry and Biophysics, UCSF
1994–	University Professor, UCSF
1998–2009	Chancellor, UCSF

SELECTED PUBLICATIONS

How to Win the Nobel Prize: Notes from an Unexpected Life in Science. Cambridge, MA: Harvard University Press, 2003.

Scientific American Molecular Oncology. New York: Scientific American, 1996.

To take a chance on the unknown—to dismiss the importance of prestige on my decision, to not hook up with one or another premier institution, but to go to the place where the opportunities were greatest, and where the need for me was greatest—was the boldest career decision of my life.[1]

—J. Michael Bishop

Over the course of his academic career, J. Michael Bishop has catapulted himself from a rural two-room schoolhouse (with just one teacher for multiple grades) through Gettysburg College and Harvard Medical School to the University of California at San Francisco (UCSF), where he has worked as a researcher and professor for more than three decades. While his early work focused on animal virology, his research eventually gravitated towards oncology, earning him and Harold Varmus the 1989 Nobel Prize in Physiology or Medicine for their discovery of proto-oncogenes. Bishop continues to supervise his own lab, and until 2009 served as the eighth chancellor of UCSF. He is the author of numerous articles and books, including an autobiography, *How to Win the Nobel Prize: Notes from an Unexpected Life in Science.*

FROM THE PARISH TO MEDICAL SCHOOL

J. Michael Bishop grew up in rural Pennsylvania as the son of a Lutheran minister, and spent much of his childhood in and around his father's two parishes. He had his first glimpses of medical practice and research as a teenager, when he became friendly with a local physician, Robert Kough, who tended to members of Bishop's family. As he explored the field through his new mentor, Bishop found that he was less captivated by the medical profession and medical practice than by the scientific study of the human body. From that point on he realized that his path lay in the sciences, although exactly what his focus would be remained unclear.

Bishop attended Gettysburg College, where he majored in chemistry, and graduated knowing that he would attend medical school but "still knowing nothing of original research in science." He did have, however, "a vague interest" in being an educator—something instilled in him by his college professors who had inspired him to pursue "a career where I would use my head a lot, and where creativity would be important." Accordingly, it was Bishop's desire to teach that initially drew him into the academic world.

Despite his distinct preference for research rather than clinical practice, Bishop did not choose to pursue a Ph.D. He explains that, particularly at that time, it was quite common for biomedical researchers to have medical degrees and not Ph.D.s. An ardent reader and writer, he was also attracted to the "deeply humane element in medicine that involves not only caring for people, but the sort of instincts that give rise to poetry and drama." Furthermore, he felt that the medical degree would preserve more career options:

> There was no obvious career track in front of me in a Ph.D., and I realized that medical school, if nothing else, was an extremely broad preparation; I appreciated that. I could see that you could go in many different directions out of medical school.

An associate dean at the University of Pennsylvania, upon learning of Bishop's interest in teaching, encouraged him to attend Harvard Medical School instead of Penn, and so at the age of 22 he left his home state of Pennsylvania for Boston.

Harvard Medical School

Harvard presented Bishop with a new set of challenges. He had gone to medical school aiming at an academic career that he understood to be centered around teaching. At HMS, he quickly came to realize the importance of research in academic careers—and he found that he was less prepared for such a career than many of his classmates:

> That was a rude awakening for me. It wasn't unpleasant, because I discovered how exciting research can be... I was awakened to research by newfound friends among my classmates, particularly John Menninger (now at the University of Iowa) and Howard Berg (now at Harvard University). I sought summer work in a neurobiology laboratory at Harvard but was rebuffed because of my inexperience. My interest in practicing medicine declined. I became ambivalent about continuing in medical school, yet was at a loss for an alternative.

Nevertheless, he continued his medical training, meanwhile planning to pursue academic research and not medical practice. "I wanted to become a scientist, an investigator, a scholar. I wanted a career that was rooted in the life of the mind." He enjoyed interacting with patients in a clinical setting, but he found the shortage of effective treatments for heart disease and cancer deeply frustrating—a frustration that drove him in his work at the lab bench. Another frustration of practicing medicine was the lack of continuous challenge:

The early months or years of really being on the front lines of medicine are a tremendous intellectual challenge. But then, there develops an element of routine. Congestive heart failure is congestive heart failure—it's still treated the same way.

Academic research, however, seemed like it would never get routine—as soon as one challenge was met, one's mind could be redirected toward the next. He saw it as a chance to "participate in the life of the mind in a way that was more open-ended than the practice of medicine."

Midway through medical school, Bishop's nascent research career got a significant boost when he was offered the opportunity to spend a year working with two pathologists, Benjamin Castleman and Edgar Taft, in the department of pathology at Massachusetts General Hospital (MGH). This gave him his first significant research experience, the platform on which he would build a research career in the remaining years of medical school. It also led to a passion for molecular biology, which would later become his chosen field of study.

He returned to HMS aware, however, that the "inner sanctum of molecular biology" was not accessible to someone like him—someone with medical training rather than advanced study in the underlying science. In his third year at HMS he discovered that animal virology, which he elected to study that year in a course taught by Elmer Pfefferkorn, was a field that was ripe for increasing laboratory-based research but was also accessible to someone with medical training. He spent increasing numbers of hours working with Pfefferkorn, and was granted permission to continue this work in lieu of several of his fourth-year requirements by "an enlightened dean" at HMS.

A Last Foray into Clinical Medicine

Bishop continued with his traditional medical training, becoming an intern and resident at Massachusetts General Hospital. "That magnificent hospital admitted me to its prestigious training despite my woeful inexperience at the bedside, and despite my admission to the chief of service that I had no intention of ever practicing medicine."

Upon completion of his residency, Bishop had sufficient credentials to begin his true research career. He began this with a post-doctoral fellowship at the National Institutes of Health designed to "train mere physicians like myself in fundamental research." Bishop's career as a research scientist solidified during the fellowship, both in his resolve and accomplishment. He published his first papers (focusing on the replication of poliovirus), and he developed close relationships with research mentors, most notably his advisor Leon Levintow. When Levintow left for the University of California at San Francisco (UCSF) midway through this fellowship, Bishop began working with Gebhard Koch, and soon thereafter elected to follow Koch to Hamburg, Germany, where he continued his post-doctoral training.

CHOOSING AN INSTITUTION

In 1968, after finishing an additional year of post-doctural training, Bishop received two faculty position offers: one from Johns Hopkins, and the other with his former mentor Levintow at UCSF. He chose the latter, which he considers to be among his wisest career decisions. While UCSF is now one of the preeminent research universities in the life sciences, at the time it was still a relatively unknown institution. As difficult as it was to turn down a position at Hopkins, Bishop saw that UCSF really needed him, and would thus offer him the best opportunities; at a more established institution, where he was not as needed, he feared he would not be given the same types of opportunities.

Taking this chance proved an excellent move for Bishop and began a long and successful career at UCSF, culminating in his appointment as chancellor in 1998. He has had, in effect, a symbiotic relationship with the school: they gave him some wonderful opportunities in the early part of his career, and he, in turn, has significantly contributed to the school's rising and now world-class status as a research institution. Bishop's decision to go to UCSF—which was in many ways risky—forms the basis for one central piece of advice he has for his students:

> I think it's wrong to have too rigid an agenda. Try what you want to try... If you want to do a career that's never going to make you famous, but that's what you want to do, do it. If you want to be a practicing physician in a small town, do it. While you may never become famous, you will probably become a small icon.

At UCSF, Bishop continued his work on the poliovirus with Warren Levinson in a search for the replication mechanism of retroviruses, one of the great puzzles in animal virology at the time. Disappointingly, two other scientists working on the same problem beat Bishop and Levinson to the breakthrough discovery of reverse transcriptase, the enzyme enabling retrovirus replication. Bishop describes this as a sobering moment, noting that a "momentous secret of nature had eluded me." He recovered from the disappointment, however, and built on his competitors' discovery in his own continuing research.

In the early 1970s, Harold Varmus, who later became head of the Sloan-Kettering Cancer Institute in New York City, joined Bishop as a post-doctoral fellow, and soon became his closest research partner. Their focus extended from retroviral replication to the mechanism by which normal cells become cancerous. This research led to their discovery of proto-oncogenes, normal cellular genes that become cancer genes through a process of retroviral transduction and mutation. Bishop and Varmus were awarded the 1989 Nobel Prize for Medicine or Physiology for this work.

A Passion for Teaching and the Thrill of Scientific Discoveries

Across his career, Bishop has found teaching—which is what originally drew him towards academia—just as compelling as his research: "I find the two vocations equally gratifying." Bishop admits that many American professors, especially in the sciences, find teaching undergraduates something of a distraction, taking away precious time from their laboratory research. Bishop, however, has found that it is quite possible to effectively integrate these two activities so that they complement one another.

The desire to solve specific problems, however, has always driven Bishop in his research career. By focusing on grandiose scientific pursuits like finding a cure for cancer or for AIDS, he believes the media has glamorized what motivates most scientists. Instead, he claims, "Most scientists desire to find out something that nobody knew before, no matter how humble."

Belonging to the vibrant international scientific community means being intellectually stimulated all the time:

> It's really like a drug, and I'm not the first person to say that. The conventional way for scientists to greet each other is to say, "Hi Mike, what's new?" And "what's new" doesn't mean "what car are you driving these days?" It means "have you found or learned anything new?"

The thrill of scientific discovery has provided Bishop with the constant challenge he was seeking, and has been the driving force behind his entire career:

> Week in and week out, you find something you didn't know about before. And the opportunity to make a major discovery—which in all honesty I realized without ever expecting it—is of spectacular promise. Although, if you let that drive you, you're setting yourself up for horrible disappointment.... You just have to accept the fact that you are going to fail most of the time, and you have to learn to live with that. You have to get your kicks out of the little steps you take.

Note

1   "Retroviruses and Oncogenes II," Nobel Lecture of J. Michael Bishop, December 8, 1989. *Les Prix Nobel.*

David Blumenthal

President, The Commonwealth Fund
Former National Coordinator for Health Information Technology, U.S. Department of Health and Human Services
Former Director, Institute for Health Policy, MGH/Partners HealthCare

David Blumenthal's career has been shaped by his desire to combine two interests into one coherent career path. In this profile, he discusses his struggle to integrate public policy and clinical medicine into his career. A nationally respected health policy expert whose career has taken him from government to academic work and back, he also reflects on the complicated, multifactorial nature of many career decisions, and the trade-offs that they require.

EDUCATION & TRAINING

1966–1970	A.B., Harvard University (Government)
1970–1975	M.D., Harvard Medical School (HMS)
1972–1975	M.P.P., Kennedy School of Government (KSG), Harvard University
1975–1976	Intern and Resident, Medicine, Massachusetts General Hospital (MGH)
1979–1980	Resident, Medicine, MGH

CAREER PATH

1977–1979	Subcommittee Staff Member, United States Senate
1980–	Instructor, Assistant Professor, Associate Professor and Samuel O. Thier Professor of Medicine and Health Policy, HMS
1980–1981	Josiah Macy Fellow in Health Policy, KSG
1981–1987	Executive Director, Center for Health Policy and Management, KSG
1987–1991	Senior Vice President, Brigham and Women's Hospital
1987–1988	Chief Health Advisor for the Dukakis for President Campaign
1998–2009	Director, Institute for Health Policy, MGH/Partners HealthCare
2001–2009	Director, Harvard Interfaculty Program for Health Systems Improvement
2008	Senior Health Advisor to the Obama campaign
2009–2011	National Coordinator for Health and Information Technology, U. S. Department of Health and Human Services
2011–2012	Chief Health Information and Innovation Officer, Partners Healthcare System
2012–	President, The Commonwealth Fund

SELECTED PUBLICATIONS

David Blumenthal and James A. Morone. *Heart of Power: Health and Politics in the Oval Office*. Berkeley: University of California Press, 2009.

Everyone's career is a kind of organic expression of who they are and what they've been. So it's very hard to disentangle what you've been from what you are. I've had diverse experiences, and that's created who I am.... Every decision was multi-factorial; it's hard to reduce them to the calculus of a career.

—David Blumenthal

David Blumenthal was fifteen years old when President John F. Kennedy was assassinated. A lifelong Democrat, Blumenthal recalls Kennedy's death as an emotional event that not only shaped his generation, but also directly influenced his career path. The Kennedy era instilled in him the desire to choose a profession that helped people, and initiated a lifelong interest in policy and its impact on people's lives. Blumenthal's strong and enduring desire to ask "big questions" and to think about issues in terms of their larger significance has also shaped his career: "Being at a place where big questions matter is important to me." This combination of factors has drawn Blumenthal to four main areas of work—clinical medicine, health care policy and politics, health care management, and academic health services research. He has served as a congressional staffer, hospital executive, campaign advisor, senior official in the Department of Health and Human Services, and practicing physician.

CHOOSING MEDICINE

Blumenthal's competing interests were manifest as early as college: at Harvard, he chose to major in government. He continued to explore his interest in public policy as an avid editorial writer for the *Harvard Crimson.* After graduating, he considered pursuing a career as a journalist, but ultimately decided against it: his real interest was in writing editorials, and he knew that he would have to spend years on a daily beat before he would be allowed on the op-ed page. In addition, journalism seemed to him "a young person's field" and did not appear to offer anything in the way of stability. He considered pursuing a Ph.D. in political science and becoming an academic, but he rejected immersing himself in the academic world, which he had come to view as unattractively conservative. It was the 1960s, and much of the nation's youth, Blumenthal included, had turned away from the "establishment."

As Blumenthal's graduation rapidly approached, the reality of the war in Vietnam loomed: "I realized I had three options for avoiding combat: Canada, divinity school, and medical school." Neither Canada nor divinity school were viable alternatives, so Blumenthal focused on his interest in medicine. He took the MCAT and applied to Harvard Medical School, which accepted him for the fall of 1970.

Medical school was challenging, but it did not offer the intellectual stimulation that government and public policy had provided him during his undergraduate years. He remained committed to completing his course work, however. An opportunity to enroll in the fledgling joint M.D.-M.P.P. program at the Kennedy School of Government (KSG) made this perseverance easier. Blumenthal found himself "enthralled" with the subjects and the dynamic instructors he encountered in the program, including Richard Neustadt, Tom Schelling, Graham Allison, and Richard Zeckhauser.

Blumenthal's passion for the policy sphere led him to debate whether to complete a residency after graduating; he ultimately decided that his training was of limited value without it. He interviewed and was accepted at the Massachusetts General Hospital (MGH) internal medicine program. While working at MGH, however, a position opened up with the staff of Senator Edward Kennedy, then chairman of the Senate Subcommittee on Health and Scientific Research. Kennedy went to Neustadt, one of the founders of KSG, for suggestions, and Neustadt recommended Blumenthal. Having missed involvement in policy during his residency, Blumenthal was eager to accept the offer. He left for Washington, D.C. six months into his junior residency.

POLICY ON CAPITOL HILL

Blumenthal spent almost three years on Capitol Hill, deeply immersed in the policymaking process and taking a large role in developing several major pieces of legislation. He reveled in the role: "During that time, I was reconciled to the idea of giving up clinical medicine."

After several years working in Congress, however, Blumenthal realized that there "wasn't all that much you could actually do" as a legislative staffer. He thought that serving in a senior management role in government, possibly in the executive branch, might provide him with more opportunity. Two positions that struck him as promising were assistant secretary for health in the Department of Health and Human Services, and administrator of the Health Care Financing Administration (HCFA).[1] Candidates for these positions were typically hired from outside of government, so he he decided to resume his non-governmental career in preparation for future opportunities to work in one of those governmental roles.

Shortly thereafter, Edward Kennedy announced his candidacy for the 1980 presidential election. Many of Blumenthal's friends thought he was crazy to leave, thinking that he would be offered a senior position in the administration if Kennedy were to win. The decision was difficult at the time, but Blumenthal concluded that it would be difficult for Kennedy to unseat a democratic incumbent (Jimmy Carter). He was also deeply concerned that Kennedy would be assassinated, as his two brothers had been when they had obtained or sought the presidency. As it turned out, Kennedy lost his bid for the Democratic presidential nomination and the Democrats lost the Senate that year. Had Blumenthal stayed, he would either have been forced to work on the minority side—a frustrating position after working for the majority leader—or, even worse, been laid off when Kennedy's staff was forced to downsize.

Blumenthal's decision to leave government reflected a major change of course in his career:

> I had to make a decision between a Washington career and a non-Washington career, and I decided that a non-Washington career made sense in the long term. The calculation was that I would become an academic, or base myself in an academic career, and go in and out of government over time. I think that as time progressed the world changed, and people who served in government came from many other different careers—that had been less true prior to that. At a certain point, I decided that this was the significance of the decision—that I was really going to be an academic, and that's where I was going to base my career.

Another factor in his decision to leave D.C. was his unfinished clinical training. It was clear that if he continued with a political career in Washington, he would not complete his residency. Since he had already begun his training at MGH, returning to Boston seemed to make the most sense:

> Coming back to Boston was about calculating where to live, where I could have a satisfying career. There were a lot of options in addition to medicine here—academic, state government, excellent medical institutions. It seemed like there were more options to do what I wanted to do in Boston.

A HARD LANDING IN BOSTON

Blumenthal's return to Boston was difficult. It turned out that he had not been given credit for his second year of residency, so he had to return as a junior resident. The work was intense: "I had no time to follow policy or even have a cup of coffee with Richard Neustadt."

Then, during November of that year, the Blumenthals had their first child, and Blumenthal's wife, a practicing psychiatrist, decided to leave her previous position with a large medical institution and to begin a part-time private practice at their home. The consequent drop in in his wife's income, together with that in his own upon returning to residency, was so steep that the IRS, incredulous, promptly audited them. The young family spent thousands of dollars proving themselves innocent of tax fraud. "The IRS came in to measure my wife's home office, to make sure that she was writing off the correct amount on her returns."

Things improved for the Blumenthals, however. His wife began building up a fulfilling private practice in psychoanalysis, and the young couple took pleasure in the newfound joys of parenting. As Blumenthal became more senior in his residency, he found his clinical work increasingly satisfying:

> I enjoyed it more because I was starting to put the pieces together. I still found medicine to be not, essentially, intellectual: it's a trade, and you learn to do mechanical things. But as I became more senior, rather than having eighteen things to do and just doing them because I was supposed to, I could think about these tasks as part of the larger process of solving a problem: if the patient came in with a cough, I would start with the lungs.

LAYING THE FOUNDATION OF AN ACADEMIC CAREER

By the time he completed his residency, Blumenthal was better able to balance his clinical work with health policy. In 1980, he accepted a fellowship from the Macy Foundation in Health Policy at the Kennedy School. After the fellowship year, he joined the faculty of the KSG as a Lecturer in Public Policy, started to do research, and taught courses on health policy and on the legislative process. During this time, one of his most important research interests came into focus—the relationship between academic medical centers and their communities. He conducted studies of the relationships between universities and industries in the life sciences. He was to continue this line of inquiry for much of his subsequent academic career.

In 1986, Blumenthal took a year off from his other duties and reduced his teaching load by half in order to devote himself to writing and research. He published six articles over the course of the year. It was clear to him, however, that he was not likely to find a long-term home at KSG. He had never pursued a Ph.D., and the types of research articles he published—which mostly ran in clinical journals like the *New England Journal of Medicine* and the *Journal of the American Medical Association*—were not widely appreciated at KSG. It was clear that he would be more at home in the medical world, where the field of health services research was beginning to take root.

At the same time, Blumenthal was increasingly interested in gaining management experience, and he was soon offered a position as senior vice president at Brigham and Women's Hospital (BWH).

AN UNEXPECTED OFFER

Just after he accepted the offer at BWH, Blumenthal received a phone call from Senator Kennedy, who wanted him to return to Washington as staff director for his subcommittee on health. Surprisingly, Blumenthal decided to reject the offer with little hesitation. The White House was under Republican control, so it would be difficult to push through significant Democratic legislation. More importantly, Washington did not offer as much opportunity for professional growth:

> I turned the position on Kennedy's staff down because it seemed to me that going back to the Hill was taking a step back to something I had done already, rather than going on to something more challenging. I decided to go to the Brigham primarily because I thought that would expand my experience. It was also about working in the private versus public sectors—one involved a lot of business, whereas the other was just policy. I was anxious to understand what it meant to be a manager. It was not really a hard decision. It was a matter of moving forward or moving back.

Blumenthal's decision did not mean an end to his political involvement, however. During his first year and a half at BWH, Blumenthal served as the chief health advisor for former Massachusetts Governor Michael Dukakis's 1988 presidential campaign. This commitment took a significant amount of Blumenthal's time, but the hospital was quite tolerant of his involvement—not only had Dukakis been a patient at BWH, but Blumenthal's service to the campaign was beneficial to the hospital's image: "It was the best of both worlds. I was gaining management experience, and was involved in health care policy at the national level."

Accordingly, Blumenthal did not settle into his position at the hospital until eighteen months after he was hired. When the Dukakis campaign came to an end, Blumenthal applied his undivided attention to BWH, but he found himself struggling with the operational nature of the position.

He decided to leave BWH in 1991, a difficult choice that involved many factors. He recognized, first of all, that a career in management would likely require him to change jobs at some point and thus to leave Boston. This would have been extremely disruptive to his wife's career as a psychoanalyst: she had spent years building up a practice that revolved around long-term care for her patients. On a personal and intellectual level, Blumenthal had also begun to doubt that a management role was best for him. Passionate about what he calls the "big picture" questions of health policy, he found that his administrative work was overwhelmingly devoted to administrative matters—"making sure that the pills were distributed correctly to each patient every morning"—and to delicate interpersonal negotiations:

> Managing an institution is not really health policy...it is mostly about people: getting people to work together, nurturing them, organizing them, stimulating them, and helping them think through their problems. It's a lot of coaching. You have to be a real people person to be good as a manager. Much of it is managing yourself in relation to other people—knowing what to say, when to say it.

Blumenthal understood how crucial both these administrative and interpersonal matters were to the success of an organization, and while he enjoyed them to a point, ultimately decided that he wanted to focus his time and energy primarily on other things:

> The main reason why I left was that I enjoy writing and I enjoy thinking about these issues—and that part of me wasn't going to be satisfied as a manager. I wasn't getting the opportunity to write or to be creative in thinking about the most pressing health care issues I cared about.

LAUNCHING THE INSTITUTE FOR HEALTH CARE POLICY

After leaving BWH, Blumenthal focused on his academic research and clinical practice, and began to lay the groundwork for what would become the Institute for Health Care Policy at MGH/Partners HealthCare: "It was a very challenging period—probably the riskiest thing I did, since I had to earn my own salary." He began by conducting research within the division of general internal medicine at MGH. Six years later, in 1997, the group became a funded institute whose mission is to "conduct world class research on the central health care issues of our time." It focuses on academic health centers, academic-industrial relationships, and issues of access to care, managed care, primary care, program evaluation, quality of care, and risk adjustment.

The program, which has grown by roughly 30 percent each year since its founding, owes its existence to Blumenthal's efforts. Perhaps most importantly for Blumenthal, his work at the institute has also demanded reflection on big questions: "My role was to bring ideas together, and to build on the resulting foundation. If I was to pick one word to describe myself it would be bridge-builder, translator, or facilitator."

Blumenthal's time as director of the institute came to an end in March, 2009, when he was appointed by President Obama to the position of national coordinator for health information technology in the Department of Health and Human Services. A senior advisor on health care policy during

Obama's campaign, Blumenthal spoke with particular force about the need for, and long-term benefits of, electronic record keeping in modern health care, a subject on which his clinical experience and academic research had made him an expert. In this role at HHS, Blumenthal was charged with putting in place the plans to build an interoperable, private, and secure nationwide health information system and to support the widespread, meaningful use of health IT. After nearly two years in the Obama administration, in 2011 he returned to Partners HealthCare where he served as their chief information and innovation officer during a time of significant change in their health care IT infrastructure. Then, at the end of 2012, he assumed his new role as president of The Commonwealth Fund, taking over from Karen Davis (page 152). The Commonwealth Fund, based in New York, is one of the nation's most prominent health care and social policy philanthropies and think tanks, and an organization with which he had often collaborated over the course of his career.

COMPLEXITY AND COMPROMISE

Blumenthal is introspective and honest about the decisions he has made in his career. These decisions have been complex, involving difficult trade-offs and sacrifices, and he is hesitant to gloss over the inherent uncertainty that was present at each step. At times he has had to choose between clinical practice and policy and make compromises between his own career needs and those of his wife:

> It's hard to classify almost anything as a mistake. If there are decisions that I've second-guessed, one would be the decision to come back to Boston after working on the Hill—I might have been happier staying in Washington. I find the work of government very compelling. If I could have made a career in and around government, I think I might have been able to do some important things there. But I ended up, in any case, having a very fulfilling opportunity in the Obama administration, so I really have few regrets in retrospect.

REFLECTIONS ON CLINICAL PRACTICE AND ACADEMIC RESEARCH

Blumenthal's feelings toward clinical practice have evolved across his career. Practicing medicine provides him with some of his deepest satisfactions: he has treated some patients for thirty years, in some cases seeing three generations in a single family, and he considers the longevity of his patient relationships to be a great privilege.

At the same time, Blumenthal has found himself drawn away from clinical practice by his deep passion for the world of public policy. In his research on health policy, however, he has had to set aside his own political views: "If researchers are seen as biased, they will lose credibility. You have to advocate separately from your research work." To develop this point, he compares the role of a researcher to that of a clinician: just as a clinician must advise the patient about treatment options, but must refrain from making discretionary decisions on the patient's behalf, the researcher must serve as an advisor without allowing his personal opinions to intervene. "In both cases," Blumenthal emphasizes, "you have to leave your politics at the door."

The time commitment required by medical practice, especially during training, gave Blumenthal little outlet for his creative drive and failed to satisfy his desire to ask important and fundamental questions. He was able to integrate medical practice and health care policy research more seamlessly across later stages of his career, continuing to see patients up until his appointment in 2009 in the Obama administration.

Blumenthal believes that the most difficult aspects of his academic career have been learning to ask the right questions and to be patient:

> To give you an idea of the kind of patience you need to have, it's sometimes five or six years from the time I write a grant until the work is published. I've been doing work in some areas for twenty years, just building one study on top of another, extending the work. You get so far with one piece of research and then you say, "Oh, that leaves this unanswered." There's always another question.

By this process, Blumenthal has produced more than 250 manuscripts to date, an average of almost a publication a month since he completed his residency.

The immediate rewards of medical practice have provided a counterweight to the constant deferral of gratification required by research:

> With medical practice, you have the sense of contributing on a daily basis. In business, at the end of the year either you've made some money or you haven't, and if you're an investment banker, either you've done some deals or you haven't. That might give you a different feeling than what I do.

He has found his profession at times emotionally grueling:

> You have to be able to withstand the stress involved in submitting your work for the judgment of others. Academic work—at least any work of any worth—involves risk, and egos can be bruised. In the academic world it takes the form of grants being rejected, and searing critiques that make you feel rotten—you have to have a certain amount of ego strength.

But it also provides unique and satisfying rewards. Among the deepest of these, for Blumenthal, has been the opportunity to mentor younger colleagues:

One thing that happens as you get older and more senior is that you begin to have younger people who work for you, and you get a lot of gratification out of their careers maturing. It provides a bookmark seeing them grow, mature, writing their own articles, and getting their own grants funded. As you get older, you have the opportunity to "parent" more broadly. I think you will find that as people get older they talk more about the people who work for them. When you are young, it's hard to understand why they do this, because you are so focused on moving yourself along. You may be only vaguely conscious of the fact that there are people older than you who are trying to make it happen for you. And if it does, they feel very good about it.

Note

1   The Health Care Financing Administration (HCFA) was renamed the Centers for Medicare & Medicaid Services (CMS) in 2001.

THOMAS R. CECH

Former President, Howard Hughes Medical Institute
Professor, Chemistry, University of Colorado-Boulder
1989 Nobel Laureate in Chemistry

A Nobel Prize winning scientist himself, Thomas Cech, in his nine years as president of the Howard Hughes Medical Insitute, influenced virtually every field of biomedical research. In this profile, he discusses the path that led him from an early interest in physical chemistry to the biochemical research that has been at the center of his career ever since. He also discusses his views on the relationship between biomedical research and medicine, on the importance of teachers in the sciences, and on the need to see basic scientific research as a long-term endeavor.

EDUCATION & TRAINING

1966–1970	B.A., Grinnell College (Chemistry)
1970–1975	Ph.D., University of California-Berkeley (Chemistry)

CAREER PATH

1975–1977	National Cancer Institute Fellow, Massachusetts Institute of Technology, Department of Biology
1978–	Assistant, then Associate Professor (1978–1982), Professor (1983–1989), Distinguished Professor of Chemistry and Biochemistry (1990–), University of Colorado-Boulder
1988–	Investigator, Howard Hughes Medical Institute
2000–2009	President, Howard Hughes Medical Institute
2009–	Director, University of Colorado BioFrontiers Institute

SELECTED PUBLICATIONS

Kruger K, Grabowski PJ, Zaug AJ, Sands J, Gottschling DE, Cech TR. "Self-splicing RNA: Autoexcision and autocyclization of the ribosomal RNA intervening sequence of tetrahymena." *Cell.* 1981 Nov; 31(1): 147–57.

"Rebalancing Teaching and Research." *Science.* 2003 Jan 10; 299(5604): 165.

"Fostering innovation and discovery in biomedical research." *Journal of the American Medical Association.* 2005 Sep 21; 294(11): 1390–3.

FURTHER INFORMATION

Howard Hughes Medical Institute: www.hhmi.org
Cech Lab: cechlab.colorado.edu

Photo credit: Paul Fetters for HHMI.

One of the great ironies of medicine is that you have to know a lot of science to get into medical school, you have to know a lot of science to get through medical school—and then for most physicians, within ten years they have forgotten the science they knew.

—*Thomas Cech*

Whether he is discussing how to seek out an inspiring mentor or how to conduct basic scientific research, Thomas Cech emphasizes the importance of both determination and receptivity to the opportunities that present themselves. These qualities underlie his own success as both a researcher and an educator; he admits this latter skill was slower in developing, though he has come to value it tremendously. Probably best known for winning, along with Sidney Altman, the 1989 Nobel Prize in chemistry for groundbreaking discoveries about the function of RNA (ribonucleic acid) in cellular chemistry, Cech is a professor at the University of Colorado at Boulder and director of the University of Colorado BioFrontiers Institute. From 2000 to 2009, he was also president of the Howard Hughes Medical Institute, the nation's largest private financer of biomedical research and education. As president at HHMI, Cech was able to draw on his years of experience in biomedical science to guide the institute's tremendously influential funding, which supports activities ranging from the research projects of an elite group of about three hundred lead investigators in the U.S. to educational initiatives impacting science students at all levels.

A CLEAR-CUT PATH

Cech grew up with a physician father who enjoyed science more than he enjoyed medicine, and seized every opportunity to infuse daily family life with scientific conversation. It was almost inevitable, then, that Cech himself would come to relish science. Beginning in elementary school, he never once deviated from his determination to become a scientist.

Cech highlights the roles that key teachers played in his life. Decades after his fourth-grade science teacher first exposed him to the wonders of geology, he can still remember her name. While his desire to be a scientist never faltered, his specific academic interests varied considerably. In college he began to tire of his original specialty, physical chemistry, because the tedious laboratory work was too different from the classroom learning he enjoyed. Fortunately, at the height of his discomfort and uncertainty as a first-year graduate student at the University of California at Berkeley, he met John Hearst, a physical chemist who directed his attention to DNA research. This foray into biological chemistry piqued Cech's interest: "As luck would have it, it turned out that it fit my temperament and my style of working much better, so I enjoyed that. That was an important point." Since this crucial experience with Hearst, Cech has always been deeply involved in biomedical research.

Cech believes that finding such teachers is a matter not so much of luck as of the patient attentiveness that comes from enduring interest in a subject:

> There are always opportunities out there and you just have to keep your eyes open. The chances that you'll come across an inspirational teacher in any given year might be small. But the chances that you'll come across an inspirational teacher if you're receptive over several years is very high.

Students who channel their dissatisfaction with their teachers into persistence rather than complacency are much more likely to succeed, according to Cech: "People have to not be satisfied with an uninspiring situation and just look around until they find someone who inspires them."

Becoming a Teacher

Despite his admiration for and debt to his own teachers, Cech himself was initially unenthused about classroom teaching. He entered academia at the University of Colorado in order to pursue the molecular research that had fascinated him in graduate school; teaching was simply an adjunct responsibility. In time, however, he grew to appreciate and even embrace the challenges of the classroom:

> I went into being a professor thinking it would just be a way of being able to do biomedical research without having to worry about commercial applications or having someone else direct your research—I wanted the freedom. What I didn't realize, and what I should have realized, and what I think most young people going into universities don't realize, is that the definition of professor is that you're a teacher. It's not a good idea to go into a university job without feeling a commitment to and enjoying teaching.

Yet that commitment came slowly to Cech himself, as he readily admits. He explains that this was in part because of the challenges unique to teaching at a large institution where enrollments in basic science courses could be dauntingly large. In the process of adjusting to this situation, the drudgery of grading and other paperwork sometimes seemed to outweigh the interpersonal rewards of teaching:

> It took me quite a while to develop that interest, especially when you're at a university where there are a lot of large classes and huge numbers of students and it's difficult to even get the exams written and graded and it becomes sort of mechanical—which of course is not the best kind of teaching, either.

During his decade as president of the Howard Hughes Medical Institute, Cech's responsibilities kept him away from the teaching role that he had come to value. Hoping to make the initial experience of science students at his university a more rewarding one, Cech volunteered to teach freshman chemistry upon his return to the classroom at Boulder in 2009.

One of the things that Cech values most in teaching undergraduate and graduate students is the contrast between the frequent, human satisfactions of teaching and, on the other hand, the longer-term challenges of scientific research. He compares teaching to the practice of medicine:

> If you're a practicing physician, and you spend eight or ten hours at work, some good things happen. There are some people who are helped and who feel better at the end of this. Research isn't that way at all. In research often, at the end of any given week, you feel like you know less than you did the week before. Teaching is more like being a practicing physician. If you spend time preparing your lecture and are devoted to interacting with your students, and put in the hours, good things happen.

Once professors realize that both they and their students can benefit from strong teaching, he suggests, then teaching is no longer a burden. Yet arriving at such a perspective on teaching can prove challenging, especially for science faculty hired for and evaluated primarily on their research.

THE MOTIVATION OF BIOMEDICAL RESEARCH

Cech believes that what draws himself and his colleagues back to the laboratory day after day is the fundamental intellectual quest to understand how life functions. While that quest derives much of its excitement and value from its potential to generate real-world applications, Cech explains, such applications are often not an immediate concern for scientists engaged in the process of basic research:

> The medical applications are things that sometimes come along, and you keep your eyes open for them, and you try to exploit them when they come along, but for most basic molecular, cell, and structural biologists, especially for someone like me who has more of a chemical training, the real excitement day-to-day is just understanding how molecular assemblies are assembled

and how they function. This provides the groundwork for others to come along and apply it to health care.

Reflecting on the recent past of medical technology, Cech reasons that just as current products evolved out of basic research conducted a few decades ago, the basic research of today will fuel the products of future generations. Of course, since not every line of research today will prove useful tomorrow, Cech emphasizes that delays and frustrations are a normal and necessary part of the scientific process. A passionate advocate for basic research, he argues that advances in applied science depend on understanding the unforeseeable potential of such work, and thus on funding projects that advance knowledge but may not have immediately apparent uses:

> The attitude you should have is that you do not know right now which of these discoveries will be clinically important in twenty years, but you have great confidence that, if you get a group of people together working individually on different aspects of basic cellular biology and neurobiology, some reasonable fraction of these discoveries are going to facilitate the medical advances of the future.

Cech believes that the payoff from this "reasonable fraction," not just for scientists but also for the population as a whole, can be staggering, and is well worth the wait.

MEDICINE VERSUS BIOMEDICAL RESEARCH

Unlike many other professionals involved in the biomedical field, Cech never considered attending medical school or becoming a physician. For him, medicine is "too far removed from science," for while medical training is clearly steeped in all areas of science, routine medical practice is not. "It's the old 'use or lose' dictum," he argues. "If science isn't useful in your everyday responsibilities, you don't have much incentive to keep up to date with it."

As an example, he relates a story of a visit by his wife to her doctor. Having heard that her husband had recently won the Nobel Prize, her physician inquired about the nature of his research. She mentioned that he studied biological catalysis by RNA (ribonucleic acid), at which her doctor's face lit up: "'Oh, yeah!' he exclaimed. 'That's usually done by DNA, isn't it?'" The physician, Cech points out, "didn't even know that most enzymes are proteins!" But Cech adds that this is by no means to be held against him: "This is not an unintelligent person, but it shows you how important it was for him to know molecular biology in order to do his job: roughly zero." Cech himself has remained in daily contact with the biology and chemistry that he learned during his undergraduate and graduate studies.

THE NOBEL PRIZE

The research that eventually won Cech the Nobel Prize is an example of how this daily contact with scientific practice enabled a basic research project to proceed flexibly enough to produce major and unforeseen results. In the course of studying the genetic structure and functioning of a single-celled pond organism, Cech and his research team happened upon something unexpected: it appeared that certain biochemical reactions were taking place in the organism in the absence of any protein. The established theory up to this point had been that only proteins were able to catalyze biochemical reactions. Cech adapted his research to investigate this anomaly. What he and his team discovered revolutionized the field of biological chemistry and fueled a new generation of research: they established the self-splicing capability of RNA. They discovered that RNA, in other words, was not simply a passive carrier of genetic information, as had previously been thought; it could also, like protein, catalyze biochemical reactions.

The findings of Cech's group were immediately seen to have significant implications for the understanding of evolution and the origins of life on earth. An early review article on their research in *Science* explained how it had the potential to solve the vexing "chicken and egg problem of early evolution: proteins are required for making nucleic acids, and vice versa; worse, proteins are required for protein manufacture."[1] The discovery that RNA could catalyze reactions on its own, in the absence of proteins, eliminated the need for such circular reasoning, allowing for a different and more plausible picture of the earliest biochemical processes to emerge.

Cech's discovery has important applications not only for evolutionary science but perhaps also for medicine, as it demonstrates that RNA enzymes could be used to destroy viral or cellular RNAs in humans. Medications based on these enzymes may well be developed in the future.

For this work carried out in the early 1980s, Cech shared the 1989 Nobel Prize in chemistry with Sidney Altman, whose research had independently arrived at similar conclusions almost simultaneously with Cech. He has received many other awards for this and other research, including the Albert Lasker Award for basic medical research (1988), the National Academy of Sciences Award in molecular biology (1987), and the National Medal of Science (1995).

NEW HORIZONS: THE HOWARD HUGHES MEDICAL INSTITUTE

In 1988, Cech received a prestigious appointment as one of the approximately three hundred lead scientific investigators funded by the Howard Hughes Medical Institute (HHMI). With an endowment valued at $17.5 billion as of 2008, HHMI is the largest private financer of biomedical research in the United States and one of the world's largest philanthropic organizations. It grants over three quarters of a billion dollars each year for scientific research and education.

Cech's ongoing success both as a research chemist and an educator made him an attractive candidate when HHMI found itself in need of a new president: in 2000, Cech was successfully recruited for the position. Cech's role at HHMI gave him the opportunity to turn insights gained as a researcher into principles guiding the institute's extensive program of grants and research funding. Under Cech's leadership, the institute continued to play a leading role in medical science; its researchers made advances in the understanding of heart disease, cancer, and asthma, among many other illnesses. Staying true to Cech's belief in the importance of basic research, the institute also continued to fund research with immense long-term potential but less immediate payoff. One of Cech's hopes for the research he helped to sponsor as president of HHMI is that it will form the basis for medicines and technologies to be developed 30 years and more in the future.

While proud of HHMI's ability to fund research on its own, Cech also used his position there as a platform to advocate for change in the national and global research community on a larger scale than HHMI could effect on its own. Particularly concerned about increasingly conservative funding practices at the National Institutes of Health, whose $30 billion annual budget dwarfs that of HHMI, Cech has argued for the need to support younger researchers, more interdisciplinary research, and more "innovative, high risk / high reward research."[2] Most importantly, perhaps, he has made a case for a broader application of HHMI's core principle of funding not projects but people, giving ambitious scientists the flexibility to follow through on the unforeseen consequences of their own work.

Notes

1   Roger Lewin, "RNA Can be a Catalyst," *Science*, New Series, 218 (November 1982): 872–4.

2   "Fostering innovation and discovery in biomedical research," *JAMA* 294 (September 2005): 1393.

David C. Chin

Distinguished Scholar, Johns Hopkins Bloomberg School of Public Health; Former Senior National Partner, U.S. Healthcare Industries Advisory Practice, PricewaterhouseCoopers LLP

A leading health care consultant and a physician by training, David Chin has drawn on his medical background and experience in a wide range of managerial roles to serve clients in all sectors of the health care industry. In this profile, Chin describes the experiences that made clear to him why physicians with business expertise can benefit both other providers and patients as well. He also discusses the challenges and satisfactions of combining these disciplines, as well as the difficult balance between work and personal life and a career strategy that he calls "repotting."

EDUCATION & TRAINING

1967–1971	A.B., Harvard College
1971–1975	M.D., Harvard Medical School
1975–1978	Resident, Internal Medicine, Beth Israel Medical Center
1978–1980	M.B.A, Graduate School of Business, Stanford University (Robert Wood Johnson Clinical Scholar)
1980–1981	Post-Doctoral Fellow, Department of Internal Medicine, Stanford University Medical School

CAREER PATH

1981–1983	Assistant to the Associate Medical Director, Harvard Community Health Plan (HCHP)
1983–1985	Director, Health Centers Division, HCHP
1984–1985	Associate Medical Director, HCHP
1985–1987	Deputy Medical Director for Operations, HCHP
1987–1992	President and Medical Director, Health Centers Division, HCHP
1991–1994	Member, Board of Directors, Baxter International Corporation
1992–1994	President, Novalis Corporation
1994–2010	Partner, Healthcare Advisory Practice, Coopers & Lybrand (1994–1998), PricewaterhouseCoopers LLP (1998– 2010)
2006–2010	Leader, Health Research Institute, PricewaterhouseCoopers LLP
2011–	Distinguished Scholar, Johns Hopkins Bloomberg School of Public Health

ADDITIONAL INFORMATION

PwC Health Industries: www.pwc.com/us/en/health-industries/index.jhtml

Because I have both an M.D. and an M.B.A., I function as a translator. I can relate to a doctor in terms of how he or she thinks and I can relate to a manager in terms of how he or she thinks—then I act as the bridge.

— *David Chin*

David Chin's career has been shaped by a desire to apply business management skills to health care delivery systems, and by an ongoing desire to broaden the scope of his impact. His management roles within the health care industry have included practicing physician, health insurance executive for a large and established HMO, and president of a small and successful HMO service provider. As a partner and senior consultant in the health industries advisory practice at PricewaterhouseCoopers, he drew on this range of experiences to analyze the health care industry and identify trends within it, helping PwC's clients adapt their business strategies accordingly and thrive in this constantly changing sector. At PwC, Chin focused on key topics for the future of health care such as strategic planning, profitability, information technology, and changes in governmental policy.

FROM MEDICINE TO MANAGEMENT

Chin's interest in integrating disciplines dates back to his high school education at the Browne & Nichols School in Cambridge, Massachusetts, where he was exposed to and intrigued by both the humanities and social sciences. Chin's parents encouraged him to go to MIT and study engineering, a highly respected field within their Chinese immigrant community, but he "disappointed" them by choosing Harvard. Starting school as a biology major, Chin switched to government after he became certain he wanted to attend medical school:

I figured that I would get my full dose of science in medical school, so I might as well take advantage of a full liberal arts education at Harvard. And I have always been glad that I did. I got a much broader exposure than I would have if I had stayed hardcore pre-med.

Though Chin learned much about economics and organizational structures in his undergraduate courses, he never seriously considered a career in business. It was Chin's experience at Harvard Medical School, where he enrolled in 1971, that convinced him of the importance of applying management skills to health care delivery. During medical school, Chin served on the board of the South Cove Community Health Center in the heart of Boston's Chinatown. Among the challenges faced by the clinic in the early 1970s was the recruitment of chiefs for its services, which Chin realized was part of a larger problem in the health care system:

> I made the observation even back then that there was not really a shortage of clinicians. There was a shortage of medical professionals who knew how to manage. We needed physicians who understood both the clinical issues and the management issues, and they were not that easy to find.

This realization solidified Chin's interest in bridging the gap between medicine and management. He considered pursuing degrees like the M.P.H. or the Masters in Public Policy (M.P.P.), which he could have pursued at Harvard's Kennedy School of Government. Ultimately, he decided that a different kind of program would better suit his interests:

> The focus of the M.P.P. was on public policy. I wasn't interested in a career in government or in making policy—I was interested in taking the management sciences and trying to solve problems in the operations and delivery of medical care. My experience at South Cove was seminal. How you organize a delivery system, how you fund a delivery system, how you operate it, how you establish controls—all of that seemed less about policy or public health, and more about management.

Likewise, Chin says, "the modern M.P.H. programs give you management skills, but not the full-dose bonus effect of the M.B.A."

Chin therefore postponed management training until after his residency, which he completed in medicine at Beth Israel Hospital in Boston. At the end of his junior residency, Chin asked the chief of the primary care program, Tom Delbanco, about entering an M.B.A. program. Delbanco initially suggested Harvard Business School, but Chin had already spent eleven years at Harvard and wanted to broaden his experience. Delbanco arranged for Chin to meet with Alain Enthoven from the Stanford Graduate School of Business. Chin was excited by the Stanford program, and his concerns about the financial burden of the two additional years of training were relieved when he was selected to be a Robert Wood Johnson Clinical Scholar.

During their two years of funding, RWJ Clinical Scholars are expected to be, as the name suggests, both clinicians and scholars. In addition to their graduate work, they are required to continue with clinical practice and to conduct research on a topic of benefit to the larger health care system. While at Stanford, Chin researched the finances of academic departments of medicine, and had his own panel of patients at the VA Hospital. "It was a prelude to what I have been doing for the rest of my career—management, clinical care, etc."

Juggling these multiple commitments did not prove as challenging as residency, however: "An M.B.A., after medical school and residency, seems like a piece of cake. As an intern you are doing one hundred hours a week, but in an M.B.A. program, you have no night call." The one sacrifice he recalls was missing the weekly "LPFs": "Friday afternoon at Stanford Business School we had what we called the LPF, the liquidity preference function—which meant that we drank." These sessions conflicted with the weekly meeting of all of the Stanford RWJ Clinical Scholars, during which they taught each other about their research.

After completing the M.B.A., Chin spent a year as a fellow completing his research with Stanford professor and health care systems expert Halsted Holman; this research was later published in the *New England Journal of Medicine*.[1]

INTEGRATING MEDICINE AND MANAGEMENT

Chin returned to Boston in 1981. His family was there, and he had the chance to work at the Harvard Community Health Plan (HCHP), which was at that time a rapidly expanding pioneer in the field of staff-model HMOs. Fascinated by HCHP's business model, Chin accepted a position as assistant to the associate medical director that allowed him to combine both medical practice and management:

> The typical dilemma that an M.B.A. student faces upon graduation is whether to go into a staff position (e.g., in strategy, finance, etc.) or into line operations, where you actually manage a piece of the firm's production. The way it played out at HCHP was that I had the opportunity to see patients, and I had line operational responsibilities for some departments. It seemed like an ideal job out of business school—I did not have to make any trade-offs, and I was working for what was at the time an avant-garde health care organization.

The "avant-garde" nature of HCHP provided Chin and many of his colleagues with a particular sense of meaning in their work:

> HCHP was on the vanguard. It appealed to me in a systemic sense, in that organized health care seemed a better way of caring for a population of people than the fragmented fee-for-service system. It was formed by Bob Ebert, the dean at HMS. I knew him and he was a very special leader, and everyone there felt that we were part of a very special organization.

By 1987, Chin was president and medical director of the health centers division of HCHP, giving him line management responsibility for the entire staff model, including five hundred physicians and more than three thousand nurses and other staff members.

A Smaller Company, and a Broader Impact

Throughout his tenure at HCHP, Chin had become increasingly fascinated by different models for health care delivery and by broad trends affecting the industry. Chin left HCHP in 1992, and shortly thereafter became president of the Novalis Corporation. During the early 1990s, anticipation of heightened levels of managed care had led many provider organizations (hospitals and group practices) to extend their business into the payer side of health care, either by starting full HMOs or by integrating their services to become more competitive in winning managed care contracts. This interest in vertical integration characterized many of the changes in health care during this period. The Novalis Corporation provided HMOs and health systems extending into managed care with software and infrastructure to manage patients, physician networks, and global risk contracts.

Novalis was a significant change for Chin in several ways. While HCHP was a large organization of several thousand employees, Novalis was a small start-up with fewer than fifty. Accustomed to working *in* the health care industry with HCHP, Chin was now providing services to the industry with Novalis. On the one hand, this meant that Chin was one step further removed from patients; on the other, he could now have an impact on a much larger number of organizations. Finally, and perhaps most importantly, Chin was now in an essentially entrepreneurial position. This meant taking on a host of new responsibilities, such as marketing, finance, business development, and strategy.

Chin was intrigued by the work Novalis was doing. Expansion at HCHP was very capital-intensive and necessarily gradual, since it required building clinics and other medical facilities. With an independent practice association (IPA)-model organization like Novalis, however, rapid expansion was much more feasible, since the company was in essence leveraging the capital that already existed in the physician practices before they joined. Chin also had the opportunity to franchise the concept of an IPA-model HMO for academic medical centers that were interested in getting into the HMO business. This new kind of model was a direct response to the sorts of constraints that Chin had perceived at HCHP.

INTELLECTUAL DIVERSITY AND CUTTING-EDGE RESEARCH: THE TRANSITION TO HEALTH CARE CONSULTING

In 1994, a headhunter contacted Chin to let him know that Coopers & Lybrand, a predecessor to PricewaterhouseCoopers and at the time one of the big six professional services firms, was looking for a direct-admit partner. After two years at Novalis, Chin felt ready for a role that would give him experience with a wider array of companies within the health care sector:

> The opportunity that Coopers & Lybrand presented to me was the ability to do consulting not only for insurance companies, which I had worked for, but also for hospitals, academic medical centers, and even employers.

At the same time, he felt like consulting would give him a chance to apply the skills he had learned in his previous positions in a way that would allow him to have a greater impact:

> As a primary care physician, you solve problems for patients; as a manager, you solve problems for organizations; and as a consultant, you hopefully solve problems across multiple organizations. But it's all the same thing—it's all about solving problems.

Chin believes that his already extensive experience in health care led the headhunter to believe he would be a suitable candidate for the position at Coopers & Lybrand. Ultimately, however, it was the ability to generate business demonstrated at Novalis that convinced Coopers & Lybrand to offer him a partnership:

> When I talk to physicians interested in consulting, I give them this analogy: In medicine, the skill that is valued the most is your technical skill. Second are your people skills, and third is your ability to bring in business. In consulting, it is the exact reverse: number one is business development, two is personal skills, and three are your technical skills. In consulting, the people who make it to the top are those who can sell.

Chin enjoys and excels at sales and business development, but he also finds the content-side of consulting compelling. The emphasis, he explains, is always on bringing in new knowledge, which means that there is always something new to learn:

> What people are interested in from consulting firms is thought leadership: what's ahead, what's coming around the bend. We survey CEOs and try to figure out what's coming next—clients value that, and it gives us visibility in the marketplace. It lets us approach clients and say, "Look, if you believe our projections of what's going on in the future, then here are some actions that you might consider taking to prepare for that kind of future." And this opens up opportunities for us to help them.

The move to Novalis had put Chin in a position to serve the needs of multiple organizations. Joining Coopers & Lybrand, which merged with Price Waterhouse to become PricewaterhouseCoopers in 1998, was a further step in the same direction, allowing him to serve a still broader spectrum of companies and individuals in the health care sector:

> Some years we do more work with employers helping them select health plans. Other years we do more work with academic medical centers, helping them restructure their operations. Some years we end up working for insurance companies helping them with their operations, medical management, improving provider relations, or reimbursement. Intellectually it is just very diverse.

The close interrelationships among the providers, payers, and employers that a consultant serves create considerable opportunity for accumulating expertise: "The knowledge you gain from each type of client benefits the others. For instance, the payers are asking 'How do we forge better relationships with providers?'" As a result, PwC and other consulting firms typically group providers, payers and employers together in their health care practice. (Producers like pharmaceuticals, biotechnology firms, and medical device companies have a very different set of questions—"How do you get a drug through clinical trials faster?" is one example offered by Chin—and are therefore grouped together in a different consulting practice.)

Chin compares the intellectual excitement of his job to that experienced in academia: "Academics conduct cutting-edge research that allows them to get grant money to do more cutting-edge research, which is similar to what we do in consulting." Consultants search for intellectual breakthroughs that will help organizations operate more efficiently, and thus better serve their patients.

Crossing Bridges—and Paying Tolls

"Consulting is intellectually extremely fulfilling—more so than my previous jobs. The cost," says Chin, "is the travel." Partnerships like PwC typically have fairly flat organizational structures, and therefore all of the partners remain involved in client services, shuffling between multiple teams involved in a range of projects. This keeps consultants, particularly the firm's senior leaders, on intense travel schedules—they often spend up to 80 percent of their time away from their home office. As Chin explains, this is an unavoidable consequence of the consulting business, and a key part of what makes its services so valuable:

> Consulting is rewarded very well. The reason that people are willing to pay those dollars is in part because you travel: by going across sectors in the industry, you have access to information that people working within a particu-

lar segment of the industry can't get access to…it's the role of being a translator. You can translate not only across the geography of a particular segment, but across segments.

The constant travel that is required affects Chin's home life. Having initially returned to the Boston area to be closer to his parents and other relatives, Chin continues to think very carefully about the impact that his decisions have on his family. While his daughter was in middle and high school, he limited his consulting travel to "east of the Mississippi and north of the Mason-Dixon line, so that I could get back and forth—fly out in the morning and come back that evening." While he candidly acknowledges that his wife did most of the child-rearing while he was traveling, he points out that frequent travel also offers its advantages: his daughter Lesley has traveled all over the world with the help of his frequent flier miles.

CONTINUING CLINICAL PRACTICE

Chin has continued practicing medicine on a part-time basis throughout his career. When he realized he would likely spend much of his career in management positions, he approached Tom Delbanco, his former department chair, and arranged to serve as a clinical instructor in medicine at Harvard Medical School. This position involves precepting residents in ambulatory medicine twice a month at Beth Israel Deaconess Medical Center on a pro bono basis. This involvement in clinical care not only keeps him abreast of changes in medicine—he makes a point of trying to learn something new in each session—but also adds to his credibility as a consultant:

> I can truthfully say that I stay in touch with clinical medicine. It relates to the translator role. I can get up and say, "I stay in contact with clinical medicine—I haven't become a suit." It helps me when I consult with academic medical centers.

Proving his commitment to hands-on medicine is not the only reason Chin has continued to practice:

> Most importantly, I really enjoy it. It's fun to keep up with the residents, you keep learning something, you stay in touch with clinical medicine. You invest all these years to gain clinical skills—it seems like a shame to give it up.

Chin believes that flexibility and openness to opportunity are necessary for anyone who wants to have a varied and productive working life in health care. His conviction that transitions are vital to any career dates back to his time in business school:

> The dean of Stanford Business School was retiring as we were graduating. He used to be president of Ford Motor Company and one of the original "whiz

kids" before coming to Stanford. His advice to all of us at graduation was to consider changing careers every ten years. He said, "All of you will be successful in whatever you do, but consider 'repotting' every ten years."

In light of this advice, Chin anticipates a change in his own path sometime in the future. Ideally, he hopes for the opportunity to teach a new generation of health care professionals about the intersection of business and medicine:

It may make sense to anticipate that we, as physicians, will be practicing more in groups and less as lone eagles. Adding to the medical school curriculum courses on how to work in teams and how medical organizations work might make sense. Contributing to that effort could be an interesting challenge for my next repotting.

AFTERWORD

Many partnership-based consulting firms such as PricewaterhouseCoopers have a relatively early mandatory retirement age, intended to allow partners to pursue a second career through which they can give back to their professional and other communities. Therefore, in 2010, Chin retired from PwC as a full-time partner, choosing to serve the health care community by educating its future executives. In 2011, he joined the Bloomberg School of Public Health at Johns Hopkins as a Distinguished Scholar. In that role, Chin has developed and implemented a new executive education program for teaching health care executives how to transition health systems from a fee-for-service model towards an "accountable care" model. A health system following this model, known as an accountable care organization (ACO), is paid for delivering coordinated, high-quality and cost-effective care, rather than simply being paid by volume. While Chin is optimistic about the potential of the ACO model to improve health care delivery, he is also aware that the transition will be a difficult one for many physicians, and so his teaching to executives emphasizes communicating and partnering with providers. "You can have a great idea," says Chin in an interview about the program, "but if you can't get the people, the docs, the managers and the nurses to buy it, it's not going to happen."[2]

Note

1   David Chin et al., "The relation of faculty academic activity to financing sources in a department of medicine," *NEJM* 312 (1985): 1029–1034.

2   David Chin, interview with Brian W. Simpson, "Transformer Man," *Johns Hopkins Public Health*, Spring 2013.

JORDAN J. COHEN

Chairman, The Arnold P. Gold Foundation;
President Emeritus, Association of American Medical Colleges

As president of the Association of American Medical Colleges from 1994 to 2006, Jordan Cohen served as the spokesperson for American academic medicine. In this profile, Cohen discusses how his involvement in the young and rapidly growing field of nephrology contributed to his initial success in academic medicine, and how he gradually transitioned to take on leadership and administrative positions as the emphasis in renal research shifted. Finally, he also discusses the level of commitment he believes the next generation of leaders will require in order to effect positive change in health care.

EDUCATION & TRAINING

1952–1956	B.A., Yale University
1956–1960	M.D., Harvard Medical School
1960–1962	Intern and Assistant Resident, Boston City Hospital
1962–1964	Research Fellow, Renal Medicine, New England Medical Center Hospital
1964–1965	Senior Resident, Boston City Hospital

CAREER PATH

1965–1971	Director, Division of Renal Disease, Rhode Island Hospital
1965–1971	Assistant then Associate Professor, Medical Sciences, Brown University
1969–1971	Lt. Col., U.S. Army Medical Corps, Walter Reed Army Institute of Research
1971–1982	Chief, Renal Service, New England Medical Center Hospital
1975–1976	President, Medical Staff, New England Medical Center Hospital
1976–1982	Professor of Medicine, Tufts University School of Medicine
1982–1988	Physician-in-Chief & Chairman, Department of Medicine, Michael Reese Hospital
1982–1988	Vice Chairman, Department of Medicine, University of Chicago School of Medicine
1988–1994	Dean, Schools of Medicine, State University of New York at Stony Brook
1988–1994	President, Medical Staff, University Hospital-Stony Brook
1994–2006	President, Association of American Medical Colleges
1995–2007	Clinical Professor, Department of Medicine, Georgetown University School of Medicine
2006–	Chairman, The Arnold P. Gold Foundation
2007–	Professor of Medicine and Public Health, George Washington University

I don't think there is a set pathway. What matters is a personal commitment and a willingness to get involved. No matter what one does in medicine, it's always in a context of some sort of organized setting. Whether it's in a multidisciplinary practice or in an academic setting in a division or department, there are always opportunities to take on administrative roles and leadership roles.

—Jordan Cohen

Jordan Cohen began his medical career in the relatively young field of nephrology, leading the way in the development of new clinical techniques like dialysis and kidney transplantation. As nephrology shifted away from the physiological techniques in which Cohen had been trained and toward a focus on the cellular and molecular level, however, he found himself with fewer opportunities for research. Channeling his energy into education and administration, Cohen began a second chapter in his career that would prove every bit as successful as the first. After serving in leadership positions at Brown, Tufts, the University of Chicago, and the State University of New York at Stony Brook, as well as in a number of professional societies, Cohen became president of the Association of American Medical Colleges in 1994, a position he would serve in for twelve years. In that role, a culmination of decades of service to the medical profession, Cohen addressed issues of policy, quality improvement, education, and standard setting in the network of professional societies that constitute organized medicine.

CHOOSING MEDICINE

A significant portion of Cohen's college education was funded by an ROTC scholarship that specified that he could not pursue a pre-med track. But Cohen's strong desire to channel his interests in physics and math into a discipline that would also provide "people content" led him to give up the scholarship in order to prepare for medical school. However, Cohen had little understanding of the medical profession. His only exposure to the field had been his childhood pediatrician, whom he saw once every few years. For this reason he found that he was fascinated by every course and specialty at Harvard Medical School. Influenced largely by his mother's struggle with clinical depression, he had originally considered a career in psychiatry, and later considered surgery, but he finally settled on internal medicine after a rotation in that field at Massachusetts General Hospital during his fourth year. Cohen describes this decision as "quixotic," since he was drawn to such a wide variety of medical disciplines. If he had completed his rotations in internal medicine earlier during medical school and his rotations in surgery later, he says, he might just as well have decided to do his residency in surgery. As it was, he had already applied to residency programs in surgery when he decided that he wanted to pursue medicine, and had to send out a second round of applications.

Cohen continued his training as a medical resident at Boston City Hospital. His mentors there encouraged him to pursue a fellowship that would let him discover whether clinical research appealed to him as part of a career. He had enjoyed a project in physiology that he had worked on in medical school, and decided to incorporate that focus. He gravitated toward renal medicine, a specialty he considered arcane:

> What I liked about it was that it was very physiologic and, in some sense, predictable. You could reason from first principles some of the clinical things that were going on, and that's how it appealed to my physics and math interests, if you will.

Renal medicine was a new field that was attracting a lot of talent, and Cohen wanted to be part of that up-and-coming group. He did a fellowship with one of the pioneers in the field, Bill Schwartz, at Tufts University's New England Medical Center: "It was a very, very formative period...I learned how to do science, to communicate science; I learned how one could combine a career in research with clinical activities." The experience inspired him to pursue a career in academic medicine.

Finding Opportunities with Growth Potential

Around the time that Cohen was finishing his fellowship, Brown University was staffing its newly founded medical school. Thrilled at the opportunity to be on the ground floor of a new school with a potentially new approach to medical education, he accepted a position as director of its Division of Renal Disease. The position also allowed him to acquire experience in research administration, as he had to set up his own lab. Cohen found the experience exhilarating.

Within a year Cohen was chairing the curriculum committee. He also practiced clinically, taught students, and helped to develop the hospital's services. He stayed at Brown for four years, and claims that he would have probably stayed forever had it not been for the Vietnam War:

> The Berry Plan was a plan during the Vietnam unpleasantness that allowed

physicians to defer their service in the military until they finished their residency by saying that they would agree to go in afterwards. For reasons I can no longer remember, I elected not to join. So here I was at age 34 and a half, my draft board was in Kansas City where I had grown up and I was in Providence, Rhode Island. The Kansas City board had a doctors' quota, and I was absolutely first on their list of potential people to fill it.

Cohen was drafted, and relocated to the Walter Reed Army Institute of Research in Washington, D.C. He was disheartened by what he thought would be a disruptive move, but eventually he was able to take advantage of his time in the army by conducting research and writing chapters for medical textbooks. At the end of his service, he was fully planning to return to Brown.

Instead, however, Bill Schwartz invited Cohen back to Tufts and the New England Medical Center. Schwartz had just been appointed chairman of medicine at Tufts, leaving the division chief position vacant, and he asked Cohen to fill it. "It was a wonderful opportunity to return to the institution where I had my training," Cohen recalls. He remained in that position for eleven years.

Cohen's time at Tufts coincided with, in his opinion, the heyday of renal medicine: "We had a chance to establish both dialysis and transplantation services at the New England Medical Center (NEMC) during my time at Tufts." These two therapies fundamentally changed the field, and Cohen acknowledges that one of his major motivations during this time was developing and implementing new clinical knowledge. He thrived professionally, earning the rank of full professor within five years; he participated in the house selection committee and the admissions committee, and became president of the medical staff in 1975.

MANAGING MEDICINE

It was during this period of time that Cohen had his first experience participating in a medical professional organization. The American College of Physicians (ACP) was putting together a council in order to communicate with sub-specialty groups, which were becoming increasingly more common in internal medicine. Cohen offered to represent nephrologists at the council, and ended up chairing it. He also became a regent of the ACP and chaired its educational policy committee.

Cohen's career focus was shifting. He was becoming more involved in administrative and policy issues, and he had fewer research opportunities:

The research that I was involved in was physiologic research; it was whole-body research. By that time, the field had really begun to shift to the more cellular and basic level with a lot of molecular biology and cell biology, which

I was not trained in and didn't have, certainly, the opportunity to get retooled in some of those areas. I felt in terms of research opportunities that I would have, it was probably not going to be as productive and as exciting as it had been in the past. So I was thinking about other areas that I wanted to continue to be involved in: it was education and administration, which I was doing a lot of and found rewarding. So I decided it was time to think about trying to do something at the departmental level.

Cohen left Tufts and NEMC and took a position as vice chairman of medicine at the University of Chicago and physician-in-chief at Michael Reese Hospital and Medical Center, which gave him the chance to develop a community academic medical center affiliated with the university: "It really broadened my experience enormously in terms of getting an insight into what the real practice of medicine was like," he says. It also exposed him to one of the earliest managed care organizations in the country.

Cohen wanted to strengthen the connection between the hospital and the university. He supported a proposal to merge the two institutions, citing important advantages in terms of academic relationships and the university's hospital network. When the merger failed to occur, he saw it as a signal that the environment was not conducive to the initiatives he supported. Seeing little potential for growth, he moved on.

The State University of New York at Stony Brook was a relatively new medical school looking for a dean, and Cohen leapt at the opportunity to build its clinical program. It was a chance to nurture their already strong basic science departments while also developing research and clinical programs. He gave up practicing medicine at this point, in order to devote himself fully to administrative leadership. He recruited new people to head 21 of the school's 24 departments, and rewrote the curriculum in a day and a half when he was stuck in a hotel in Seattle between flights:

> It was a good opportunity to think through how an academic medicine center could have an impact on a region, in terms of the quality of its health care and the access to various services. That was an interesting part of my responsibilities, to try to conceptualize that and develop those relationships that were working in that direction.

SHAPING THE FUTURE OF MEDICAL EDUCATION

Cohen joined the Council of Deans at the Association of American Medical Colleges when he became dean at Stony Brook. Soon after, AAMC asked him to chair a taskforce. The combination of his taskforce experience, his activity with other organized medical societies, his positions as dean at Stony Brook and president of its medical staff, and his administrative leadership made him a prime candidate to lead the AAMC. He became president of the organization in 1994, and continued in the position until 2006. His principal goals were to improve the quality of medical education throughout the country, to foster integrity in medical research, and to promote professionalism in the care of patients, and Cohen launched successful new initiatives in each of these areas during his twelve-year tenure.

After stepping down from his role as president of the AAMC in 2006 Cohen was elected to serve as the new chairman of The Arnold P. Gold Foundation. The mission of the Arnold P. Gold Foundation is "to perpetuate the tradition of the caring doctor by emphasizing the importance of the relationship between the practitioner and the patient." Their focus is to reach future physicians while still in training and help them "combine the high tech skills of cutting edge medicine with the high touch skills of effective communication, empathy and compassion." More than 90 percent of all medical students in the U.S. participate in at least one of the foundation's projects.

A CAUSE WORTH WORKING FOR

Throughout Cohen's career, he has kept his eyes open for opportunities to make a difference to his profession: "I felt as if I wanted to see if I could have a larger influence on [medicine] generally, and I think the challenge that that has provided was something I was always attracted to."

Cohen realizes that he has been successful in part because of his enthusiasm for the work he has done, so he advises students to get involved in organized activities in order to identify their passions. He believes that, especially today, with so many challenges facing the medical profession, there are great opportunities to have a meaningful impact:

> I think we're entering a phase in medicine where we're going to need many, many people who are willing to participate in standard setting and value maintaining activities. I think the profession is beleaguered at the moment with lots of things that are threatening professionalism and threatening the commitment that medicine has historically had—and should have as a service profession in the context of a social contract. I've felt that that's been one of the most rewarding opportunities, to be able to nurture that aspect of the profession. There's going to be a greater and greater need for people to do that, and I think it's going to be very satisfying as a career. It's worth working for; it's worth struggling to maintain when the struggles are in the direction of improvement and are something of value. I think that is about all one can ask of a career.

Robert "Robin" B. Cook

Author

Robin Cook has written more than twenty bestselling medical fiction novels and has sold over one hundred million books. His writings, targeted at the general public, are intended to shed light on biomedical ethical issues. In this profile, Cook discusses the important role his medical training plays in his writing, and how the popular novel came to be the medium he uses to effect change both within and outside of the medical community.

EDUCATION & TRAINING
1958–1962	B.S., Wesleyan University
1962–1966	M.D., Columbia College of Physicians and Surgeons
1966–1969	Resident, Surgery, Harvard Medical School (HMS)
1969–1971	U.S. Navy, USS Kamehameha, later Sea-Lab
1971–1975	Fellow, Ophthalmology, HMS (Massachusetts Eye and Ear Infirmary)
1975–	Kennedy School of Government (still on leave of absence)

CLINICAL POSITIONS
1975–1980	Private Ophthalmology Practice, Marblehead, MA
1975–1980	Clinical Instructor, HMS (Massachusetts Eye and Ear Infirmary)

SELECTED WORKS OF FICTION

Nano. New York: Putnam, 2013.

Death Benefit. New York: Putnam, 2011.

Cure. New York: Putnam, 2010.

Intervention. New York: Putnam, 2009.

Foreign Body. New York: Putnam, 2008.

Critical. New York: Putnam, 2007.

Crisis. New York: Putnam, 2006.

Marker. New York: Putnam, 2005

ADDITIONAL INFORMATION
www.robincook.com

When I got to medical school, almost immediately I realized that it was very different from the romantic image I had prior to matriculation. I felt like I had been somehow mistaken about the kind of profession I was going into. The process of getting there was not going to be what I hoped from watching the Marcus Welby M.D.'s and the Dr. Kildares and the Dr. Ben Caseys. It was during my first year that I said, "Someday I'm going to write a book about medicine. And it's not going to be based on the romantic image of medicine, but will be much more realistic."

—Robin Cook

When the door to Robin Cook's Beacon Hill brownstone swings open, one is immediately struck by his interest in classical art. A collection of Grecian urns, Athenian imagery, and a commissioned mural of Roman ships battling off Carthage distinguish his front room, though the art collection gives way to paint-splattered tarps and other signs of construction as one approaches the front stairs; the combination of art and debris almost makes the room look like an oddly displaced archaeological dig. Cook himself just might pass for the room's archaeologist: tall and slim with graying hair, his silver-rimmed glasses reflect the soft light spilling through a large picture window. Only his warm, wry apology for the construction dispels the temptation to mythologize the writer at work. "I expected it to be done by now," he sighs, "but I really can't blame anyone but myself, since I'm the contractor." With those words, the romance of archaeology gives way to the reality of home improvement.

Cook's career as a physician and novelist has sprung from this tension between romance and reality. Attracted to medicine in part by the glamorized version of it he saw on television, Cook chose to make his own early, grittier fictions out of his disappointment with the reality of the system—and out of his desire to improve it. In his many novels, he has brought to life the potentially dry dilemmas of health care policy for readers both in and outside of the medical profession, and has sought to create stories that would encourage serious reflection on the possibilities for medicine and health care as they actually exist.

"Born a Hundred Years Too Late": Early Aspirations

As the décor of his house suggests, Cook really does have a fascination with archaeology, and has had it since childhood. In fact, long before he considered medicine, he had other aspirations:

> I wanted to be an archaeologist; I was fascinated with Egypt when I was younger. Reality set in around freshman year in high school and I realized that what I liked about archaeology didn't exist anymore—the idea of finding buried treasure and lost cities. Nowadays, archaeology is plodding and slow—you spend a lot of time with broken pots. I realized I'd been born about a hundred years too late to go into the field.

While Cook recognized that his archaeological ambitions were impractical, medicine still was not a clear second choice for him. He recalls wishing he had the desire to be a doctor, especially as he observed the "secondary gain that students that wanted to go into medicine received, even very early on in their lives." Still, unsure about the difficulties of spending most of his time with the very ill, Cook did not consider medical school until later in his high school career.

An amalgam of events in his sophomore and junior years of high school pushed Cook towards medical school: "It wasn't an epiphany, but rather a number of different encouragements." These influences came from both school and home: Cook's mother took courses in first aid so she could participate in a local volunteer ambulance service, and she worked for an obstetrician who encouraged Cook to come in and watch a cesarean section, an event Cook recalls being very powerful. A dedicated high school biology teacher later encouraged him to enter the science fair with a project in comparative anatomy, which won him first prize.

Excelling in the sciences was a great impetus for him, but after his first year at Wesleyan University, Cook realized that there was something more fundamental motivating him:

> When I got to college, I realized how many other people wanted to go into medicine, and how competitive it was to get into medical school, not to mention a top-tier program. And I happen to be a very competitive person. That was a real encouragement—if everyone else wanted to go into medicine, I thought, it must be the right decision.

With acceptance into a good medical school as his paramount concern, Cook drove himself to work hard and take the courses in which he would have the most success: the sciences. A chemistry major, he remembers being afraid to take any course where he might receive the B that would ultimately mar his transcript. He therefore found himself in his senior year without much exposure to the liberal arts or to writing. Because he had done so well in his major courses, Cook was able to become a member of Wesleyan's Honors College and write a senior thesis. This would prove to be his first exposure to the thrill of independent writing and a glimpse into his future:

> I thought that writing a thesis was mainly attractive because it wasn't something that I had to worry about whether I got an A or a B. It was either accepted or not accepted, and I didn't need the credits to graduate. I selected to do an undergraduate thesis on a subject that I'd never taken a course on, African nationalism, which of course caused quite a stir. Wesleyan asked a visiting Harvard professor to be my tutor, and he was very enthusiastic about it. When I went to see him he piled me up with an enormous number of books and—even though this was the first time I met with him—he kind of outlined exactly how I would write this and that. I remember leaving his office and thinking, "I thought I would do an independent study, but it feels like I am more of a research assistant." I never went to see him again until the day the thesis was due, and I walked in and put it on his desk. For someone who was afraid to write anything because I was afraid to get a bad grade, it was very rewarding to suddenly take it upon myself to write a 120-page paper and do it all by myself.

With this first experience of authorship in the back of his mind, Cook moved on to his first year of medical school at Columbia University.

A DECONSTRUCTION OF MEDICINE

Cook's idea of what the medical world would be like had been formed by images absorbed during childhood from novels, movies, and television:

> All of these images were skewed towards the metaphysically romantic: the young doctor in white, rushing down the hall in the middle of the night, saving a life. Also, there seemed to be in the portrayals of medicine this wonderful collegiality, like medicine was this intellectual club where people spent a lot of time discussing things.

Cook found himself frustrated by the gap between his experiences and this ideal. He found the competitiveness that had spurred him on in his undergraduate years was amplified in medical school, and the atmosphere felt almost anti-intellectual:

> I had the mistaken idea that once you got to medical school all the negative aspects of competition would stop, that you're all there to become the best doctor you can and to help each other. Instead, the competition actually gets fiercer. We had an introductory address the first day we were there—in our new white coats and we were all very proud—and one of the professors got up and talked about our time at Columbia. He said that about five percent of us might be invited to stay on as house staff, meaning, "You better do well." But what it really meant was not necessarily to do well, but to do better than the person sitting next to you. It put us immediately in competition with each other.

Cook resolved then that he would someday write a book exposing the perils of a medical education built on competition; stubborn, century-old teaching methodology; and over-worked students and residents. But he was forced to put off the inception of the actual writing as he worked his way through the next four years. When he did finally have time to write his first book, it would ironically come about through a new and pressing set of obligations.

Choosing a Residency

As Cook finished the first leg of his medical education, the Vietnam War was looming. Fearful of being drafted into the army, Cook felt rushed to choose a residency in order to obtain a deferral through the Berry Plan:

> You had to choose what you were going to specialize in to get the exemption. I thought I'd want to do surgery. I again saw this in a competitive light, but medical students don't get a good idea of what surgery is really like. I observed that the surgeons had strong personalities—they would get mad at incompetence, and throw hemostats around the room if something wasn't right—and for some reason that was impressive. The people in surgery that seemed to be having the most fun were the orthopedics guys, so that appealed to me. I was able to get a commitment from Columbia to do orthopedics there.

During his residency, Cook realized that surgery, much like medical school, was different from what he had imagined it would be:

> Before you go into surgery you think it's going to be very exact. You look in the textbooks and this layer is green and this layer is purple and you can see it all very clearly, but actually doing it you can't see anything. It's very inexact, and orthopedics is probably the most inexact in terms of surgery. The other extreme is eye surgery, the most exact.

The precision of ophthalmology attracted Cook, but even more appealing was the possibility of another Berry Plan deferral to do a second residency in the discipline. Although he applied, he was unable to avoid the draft a second time. Cook entered the navy in 1969.

The Navy and *The Year of the Intern*

Once drafted, Cook's medical school experience proved useful: he had worked in a blood/gas lab at Columbia and had been asked to set up a similar lab for the Jacques Cousteau Oceanographic Institute in Monaco. On the institute's research vessel, Calypso, Cook had a chance conversation with the U.S. naval commander of the famed Sea-Lab Project, Captain Bond, who offered to help Cook should he ever need it. When Cook received his draft notice, he called Captain Bond, who remembered him even though it was half a decade later. Bond said he would try to get him assigned to the Sea-Lab, but to do that, Cook would have to volunteer for Submarine School and Deep-Sea Diving School. Cook did so, and he was rewarded with an assignment to the Deep Submergence Systems Project, the new name for the Sea-Lab.

Prior to joining the diving research organization, Cook asked to take a tour of duty on a nuclear submarine, the USS Kamehameha. While he dealt with medical issues that arose on the sub, Cook found himself with free time. He realized that the USS Kamehameha would afford him a good opportunity to write the novel he had been considering since his first year of medical school.

In 1972, *The Year of the Intern* was published. Cook intended it to be an exposé of medical training:

> I thought that if the general public knew what it was really like to go through medical training, they would find it fascinating and cry out for change. That, unfortunately, didn't happen. Mainly because my first book didn't sell many copies or cause the stir that I had expected. After getting over the dismay of how badly it did, I decided to read it myself again. I realized that it wasn't entertaining or fun. It was interesting, but not engrossing. I had to recognize that if you want to get a message out to the general public it can't be in a boring format. If you get millions of people to read something and you're capable of convincing them that their view counts because the issue is something that directly affects them, you can effect change.

With this goal in mind, and his military service out of the way, Cook recommenced his residency training. He had been accepted into the Harvard ophthalmology residency program at the Massachusetts Eye and Ear Infirmary prior to his military service.

EFFECTING CHANGE THROUGH FICTION

During Cook's second residency, it became clear to him that the field of medicine was undergoing radical changes. He was concerned with "the progressive removal of doctors' freedoms," singling out the economic and care-giving restrictions placed upon physicians by the health management organizations that were rising in popularity at the time:

> I couldn't convince my fellow residents that medicine was changing—I was probably more sensitive to those issues because I'd written that first book, and I was looking at medicine as a profession rather than with the narrow vision which is encouraged by the way medicine is taught. The better you do, the more encouraged you are to specialize. And the more specialized you are, the more you have blinders on; not only do you see just your particular area rather than the whole body, but the less you think about the profession of medicine in general.

As Cook became certain of the importance of these issues, he became increasingly convinced that few lay people were even aware of them, much less debating them in the political or social arena:

> If those of us in the profession weren't thinking about these issues, how was the public going to? There seemed to be a tremendous difference in knowledge about the field from the point of view of a physician and the point of view of a non-physician. I'd become convinced that bestseller fiction was the way to fill that void.

After finishing up his residency, Cook felt that one way to advocate for the biomedical issues he championed was to go into politics. He decided to enroll at the Kennedy School of Government: "I thought that I could help in terms of policy, being on the inside of medicine." But Cook's experience at the Kennedy School quickly convinced him that politics was not for him:

> In politics today you practically have to fundraise continuously. The other part of politics that I personally would have had trouble with is the art of compromise. In politics, what they mean by "compromise" is that you actually agree to something that you can't stand in order to get something else.... I did not want to be a politician, but it did give me the tools that would enable me to combine my knowledge about medicine and my sense of where change was taking the field. And I thought that maybe I could help change medicine in a way that would be more positive.

Concurrent with his time at the Kennedy School in 1976, Cook was working at his ophthalmology practice two and a half days a week, teaching at the Massachusetts Eye and Ear Infirmary, and preparing to promote his second novel, *Coma*, which he had written at night and on weekends during his last year of ophthalmology residency. He used *Coma*'s story-line to approach the many issues that he saw in his daily practice of medicine:

> The major issue in *Coma* is the disparity between the supply and demand for organ transplantation. It brings to light the fact that medicine is not the homogenous profession people think it is—there are good doctors and bad doctors; good hospitals and bad hospitals. The public was shocked to find out that the doctor was the bad guy in the book. But the curious thing was that no doctors were surprised.

Part way into his first year at the Kennedy School the film version of *Coma* went into production in Los Angeles, requiring Cook to fly cross-country frequently. The increasing demands on his time led him to withdraw from the Kennedy School, though he notes that he has remained on a leave of absence ever since, and does not entirely rule out the possibility of returning.

During the 1980s, Cook wrote novels at the rate of almost one a year.

At first he continued to practice a few days a week and to teach at the Massachusetts Eye and Ear Infirmary, but as his writing took up more and more of his time, he began to decrease his practicing hours. Eventually, Cook sold his practice.

An Insider Looking Out

Although Cook has not had a clinical practice for twenty years, he still considers himself primarily a physician who happens to write popular fiction. It is this vantage point that he believes gives him access to the topics for his novels and allows him to write in a realistic and compelling way:

> Let's say I was trained as a journalist, and I was trying to look into and write about the medical profession. Well, medicine tends to be very leery of outsiders. And there are certain things about medicine that, unless you've actually been there, you can't understand. A surgeon, for instance, will experience an awful panic if something goes wrong. Part of the experience is learning to control that panic, and look for the next logical step. A journalist would never know that, but having gone through it, you know the feeling that whatever it is you're working on is essentially in your hands. I had to be on the inside looking out, rather than the outside looking in.

When Cook chooses a topic to write about, he uses this position inside the profession to research it thoroughly by spending time with practitioners in the field and, when necessary, continuing to take courses. For instance, he took a course in forensic pathology to prepare for the several books he has written about medical examiners. He also, of course, does his fair share of reading, but with an eye to the medical profession as a whole rather than to his own medical specialty: "I cancelled my subscription to the ophthalmology journal and subscribed to the *New England Journal of Medicine*. I go to medical conventions and read widely."

With the topics of his novels ranging from virulent contagions to xenotransplantation to HMO advertising, Cook prides himself on predicting the next medical debate and in making many seemingly difficult issues accessible to the public. With many medical topics, he says, "the scientific research is esoteric, but anyone can grasp the basic concepts." Cook is also confident that he has caught people's attention with the issues he has chosen:

> I have gotten a lot of feedback from people. In *Toxin*, I wrote about the e-coli problem in processed hamburgers. Many people wrote to me or told me that they have stopped eating hamburgers since that book. Now that wasn't necessarily the message, but it was indicative of the fact that their attention was taken, and that they understand that the problem affects them.

The front covers of Cook's novels do not mention his medical degree. He uses his authority as a physician sparingly, in part because he feels that the impact of his books comes not from his training but from his ability to explain the significance of key issues in the world of bioethics and health care. In some of his books that address issues on which he feels physicians have a particular authority, though, he does includes a note at the end, signed "Robin Cook, M.D.," discussing the topic from his perspective as a doctor. For example, in *Vector* (1999), a novel about bioterrorism, he included an essay explaining that he believed a bioterrorist attack in the United States in the near future to be likely. Such an attack would be homegrown, the essay said, and would start out through the mail. As it turned out, in fall 2001, Cook's predictions came true when several letters containing anthrax were received by offices in the government and media.

Cook is proud of the impact of his work, but he is aware that his method of delivery—medical mystery thrillers rather than *New York Times* editorials—allows different readers to take away different messages. For instance, his stated motivation for writing *Coma* was to "dramatize the looming shortage of organs for transplantation." His dream was that "an entertaining novel and a subsequent movie could influence public policy to nip the developing problem in the bud." In a letter to his fans on the 25th anniversary of *Coma* he explained: "Although I succeeded in scaring people away from operating room 8, which certainly wasn't my goal, the larger issue was not solved."

IMPACTING NATIONAL POLITICS

Though reluctant to label himself politically, Cook admits that in his younger years he was very much a Democrat. In the years since, he has become much more enamored with aspects of the Republican Party, especially the idea that the "government is not the solution for everything." At the same time, he is bothered by what he describes as "the strong influence of the far right on the Republican Party."

A few of Cook's novels have tackled particularly heated political topics and played a role in subsequent debates. In 1993 he wrote *Fatal Cure*, his response to the Clinton Health Care Plan. The book tells the story of two physicians working at a hospital within an "enlightened system of 'Managed Care.'" Their lives and patients are destroyed by the ramifications of the system. Senator Bob Dole (R-KS) cited the book in a public speech while debating the plan.

Another such novel was *Seizure*, released in 2003, which focused on the issue of the U.S.'s regulation of stem cell research and therapeutic cloning. The book made a strong case for the use of stem cells in research, a practice many conservatives have opposed because of the cells' origins in aborted fetuses. Senator Orrin Hatch (R-UT), a traditionally conservative Republican opposed to the research, discussed the subject at length with Cook. Hatch was eventually convinced by Cook's arguments for the importance of the research. To help persuade and inform his fellow members of Congress, he asked Cook to personally sign six hundred copies of *Seizure*, which Hatch then distributed to every member of the House and Senate.

CLOSING THOUGHTS

Cook's decision to stop practicing clinical medicine was based on clinical reality and not on a lack of interest. "I couldn't in good conscience operate on someone and then run off to L.A. to work on a movie version of one of my books." The decision was not made without regret: "I miss clinical practice. If I had to do it all over again, I would still go to medical school. I feel lucky I was able to practice for quite a while."

At the same time, Cook feels that he has in some ways been able to have a broader impact through his writing—something that he credits simply to good timing. He may have been born one hundred years too late for archaeology, but he was right on schedule to write about biotechnological and biomedical ethical issues:

> Fifty years ago, I wouldn't have had all these things to write about. Today, every day there is some issue about the relationship between medicine and society that the public should know about. People need to have this information so that they can play the role they are supposed to play in a democratic society.

RICHARD F. CORLIN

Past President, American Medical Association
Practicing Gastroenterologist

As past president of the American Medical Association (AMA), Richard Corlin considers himself a medical politician who remains a clinician at heart. His experiences as a practicing gastroenterologist, a policy advocate for medical associations, and president of the AMA exposed him to the relationship between politics and health care reform. The profile examines his motivations for getting involved in the health policy debate, and he articulates his strong feelings about the need for physicians to be actively engaged in policy development.

EDUCATION & TRAINING

1957–1961	B.A., Rutgers University
1961–1965	M.D., Hahnemann Medical College
1965–1968	Intern and Resident, Hahnemann Hospital, Philadelphia, PA
1968–1970	Lt. Commander, Heart Disease and Stroke Control Program, U.S. Public Health Service
1970–1972	Fellow, Gastroenterology, UCLA

CAREER PATH

1972–	Private Practice Physician, Gastroenterology
1978–1979	President, Los Angeles County Medical Association (LACMA)
1992–1996	Member, Advisory Committee, National Institutes of Health+
1976–1991	Member, House of Delegates, California Medical Association (CMA)
1992–1993	President, California Medical Association
1977–2000	Member, House of Delegates, American Medical Association (AMA)
1995–2000	Speaker, House of Delegates, AMA
2000–2001	President-elect, AMA
2001–2002	President, American Medical Association

ADDITIONAL INFORMATION

AMA Website: www.ama-assn.org

You hear people say, "Oh you know, the golden age of medicine is past, I wouldn't want my sons to be doctors, or our daughters to be doctors," and my attitude is that I almost get angry when I hear that because it's still the best thing you can do. I mean, it's wonderful. I've been at it thirty-some-odd years, and it's still exciting.

—Richard Corlin

While Richard Corlin knew from the age of three that he wanted to be a doctor, he ascribes his ascent through the world of health care policy mostly to "happenstance." "Life," says Corlin "is what happens to you while you're making other plans. Something will come along…and you'll say, 'Hey, I want to get involved with this.'" This has been the pattern of Corlin's career: while he has remained first and foremost a practicing clinician, he has repeatedly found himself in the right place at the right time—in California when the malpractice insurance crisis struck, or in a clinic where two colleagues were affected by gun violence—to make a difference in matters of policy. A sense of obligation to society and to his profession has led him repeatedly to do just that.

ORIGINS IN MEDICINE AND MEDICAL POLITICS

While Corlin cannot recall a specific event that led him into medicine, he also cannot recall a time when it was not his plan: at the age of fourteen, one of his first summer jobs was as a morgue orderly at a hospital. He attended Rutgers University, where he was an "acceptable" student, and then applied to medical school in his senior year. "I got into medical school because I had unbelievably high MCAT scores and they took a chance on me," he explains. He was accepted to Hahnemann Medical College in Philadelphia, where he finally felt motivated to study:

> I studied by the clock from 7 to 11 every night, four hours Saturday afternoon and eight hours on Sunday. I lived in a room at the YMCA in Philadelphia a block from the medical school. It was $6.25 a week. And I was determined that this was what I wanted to do and I was going to study—I graduated second in my class.

After an internship and residency in Philadelphia, Corlin went into the navy and was soon transferred into the Public Health Service. On the verge of a two-year assignment as physician for the federal penitentiary in El Reno, Oklahoma, he was contacted about an unexpected opening in the heart disease and stroke research unit in San Francisco. After two years of research there, he went to UCLA for a fellowship in gastroenterology. After completing his fellowship, Corlin set up a private practice in gastroenterology.

Five months after Corlin started his practice, the California malpractice insurance crisis hit. He went to a meeting and found his call to action:

> Everybody was yelling and screaming: "We have to do this, we have to do that, we should strike, we should not strike." And I simply said: "I don't know what the issues are, really, but if we're going to do something, for God's sake, let's all do the same thing at the same time."

Corlin feels that physicians tend to be independent-minded, and trying to convince a group of doctors to form a cohesive group is something akin to "herding cats running off in a zillion different directions," but his ideas struck a chord. Based on what he sarcastically calls his "magnificent policy statement," he was drawn into action with this group, and eventually helped to lead the passage of California's landmark Medical Injury Compensation Reform Act (MICRA) of 1975.

The desire to help fix the California malpractice insurance crisis launched Corlin on an extended career through the ranks of the county, state and national medical associations. In 1978, he became president of the Los Angeles County Medical Association; then, after serving in the House of Delegates of the California Medical Association, he assumed its presidency in 1992. At that time he was also a member of the House of Delegates for the American Medical Association, and became its speaker in 1995. In 2001, Corlin became president of the AMA.

THE CLINTON PLAN

As Corlin was taking his position as speaker in the AMA's House of Delegates, the Clinton administration introduced their plan for universal health care insurance. Because of his involvement in the AMA, Corlin was invited to Washington, D.C. to participate in a one-day panel where the Clinton Plan—which had been developed largely in secret—would be revealed to a select group of experts for their reaction. He recalls that he "knew there was trouble" when he got a call the night before leaving for Washington, telling him: "Don't go into the White House. Go into the Old Executive Office Building, and we'll take you through a tunnel. That way nobody will see you going in." Corlin, of course, agreed to this request, but wondered two things aloud in response: "First, if anybody saw me, who would recognize me? And second, even if they did, so what? You know, we weren't talking about the Manhattan Project."

Ultimately, the Clinton plan died in Congress after failing to gain significant popular support. Corlin believes that the crux of the problem lay in poor planning and unrealistic expectations of how the population would react to the country's first national health care plan:

> It wasn't Harry and Louise and those commercials that the insurance companies paid for that killed it—that was just the icing on the cake. The Clinton administration didn't realize that the biggest problem we had in this country was 40 million people without health insurance. Instead of trying to deal with that, they wound up with a circumstance where the 240 million people in this country who have health insurance—with problems, to be sure, but for whom it's working reasonably well—ended up having to say, "Now let me see, I'm going to give up the health insurance I currently have, and instead get some central government coordinated program that's brand new. I don't think so."

Corlin believes this reaction could have been avoided if physicians had been adequately involved in the plan's development:

> If you had people there that had true clinical experience, they would have known how patients react enough to say, "You can't do it this way." Instead of turning to medical associations or practitioners and saying, "Advise us, help us, participate," everybody who was a part of the leadership of the profession was excluded. And you can't do that and expect to get good results.

Corlin believes that the Clinton Plan was well-intentioned and reasonable in theory. He sees its failure as particularly distressing because of the otherwise opportune moment when it took place: "It was a tragic loss, because that happened at a time when we had all the money in the world to do anything we wanted to do."

Corlin points to the Evaluation and Management codes developed by the Health Care Financing Administration (HCFA, now the Center for Medicare and Medicaid Services) as another example of an important idea that failed due to the exclusion of physician input. HCFA, he explains, alienated and angered many physicians by not including them in the development of these codes:

> They developed a system that was so arcane that they had to scrap the whole system...and we still have nothing. But they have thoroughly angered the medical profession, when what they should have done, instead of turning the AMA and all the other specialty societies into their enemies, is to say, "Take a year, develop a committee that represents the appropriate medical associations, with the right input. Develop a system that clinically will work. Give it to us to see if we think administratively it will work, and if so, we'll put it in place." They would have had us as their allies doing their work for them.

GUN-RELATED DEATHS

One of Corlin's major initiatives while president of the AMA was to take an active stance on reducing gun-related deaths in the U.S. Corlin is proud of his efforts to depoliticize this issue. By taking an epidemiological approach to gun violence, he changed a political debate about the Second Amendment into a debate about a public health problem that the medical establishment could play a special role in addressing.

Corlin first realized the significance of the issue when it struck two people he knew. First, one of the assistants at Corlin's office was killed in a drive-by shooting after a Memorial Day barbeque. The next incident involved a colleague's young son, who was playing with some friends at home when they discovered a handgun under the bed. Knowing he was not allowed to play with the gun, the colleague's son threw it on the floor. When it hit the ground it went off and shot and killed his friend. To Corlin, this tragic accident had little to do with the Second Amendment:

> It is not a gun control issue; it is a product safety issue. If you take a Smith & Wesson that's fully loaded, you can drop it on the floor a hundred times, it's not going to go off. You don't have to be a rocket scientist to figure that one out. A gun that goes off when it's dropped is a gun that should not be on the market.

These accidental deaths only represent about 700 of the 30,000 annual gun-related deaths in the U.S., but—despite the resistance of the National Rifle Association—Corlin felt the AMA needed to concern itself with the larger issue of gun-related death:

> The NRA says the only things that are to be dealt with are the accidental deaths. My approach is to say, "Doctors have never concerned ourselves just with accidental deaths. We concern ourselves with avoidable deaths." And of the 30,000, even though only 700 are accidental deaths, at least 19,000 of them are avoidable deaths. And we deal with avoidable deaths.

Corlin recalls that across three summers in his youth spent working in hospitals in Newark and Elizabeth, New Jersey—as a morgue orderly, an ER orderly, and driving an ambulance—he never saw a gunshot wound, whereas today, urban ERs deal with them nightly.

CAREER REFLECTIONS

Accounting for his energetic entrance into policy work, Corlin observes, "I'm a fairly quick study on issues. I'm a pretty good public speaker. And I love history." His concern with history—with understanding the successes, mistakes, and limitations of past health care reforms—inspired him to expand the public policy dimensions of his career. Still, he explains that the origins of his political involvement were somewhat left to chance:

> If I had been in training, and had finished one year later, and the malprac-
> tice crisis issues had occurred during the time I was in training, rather than
> during the time when I was out in practice in the community, I probably
> wouldn't have been involved in it at all. And my life and career would prob-
> ably have been very different.

Despite his role as a "medical politician," Corlin characterizes himself as "somebody who's concerned about health policy development, and clearly a clinician first and foremost." Corlin is thus careful to emphasize that his turn to policy was not a turn away from practice: "I've always loved clinical stuff. But I just found that the policy issues and the political issues were something that I perhaps could do some good in."

For Corlin, the major downside to his involvement in policy is the degree to which it limited his time and energy as a practitioner. During his tenure as president of the AMA, his partners essentially took over his practice: his patient volume at the end of his term was one third what it had been before. While he expects to build his practice back to 90 percent of its initial volume, he speaks wistfully of lost opportunities to perform procedures and interact with patients.

THOUGHTS ON MEDICAL PRACTICE TODAY

Corlin cannot conceive of a career path more rewarding than that of a clinical physician. Because of his passion for clinical practice, he finds himself somewhat frustrated with practitioners who complain about the state of the profession:

> So we get sniped at around the edges from the government and HMOs. You
> know what a lot of guys forget is that Medicare, for all its problems now,
> is what made doctors rich. Before Medicare, people over 65 didn't have the
> money to pay. Being a doctor was never a license to be the richest person in
> town. We do very well financially; most of the time we're very well respected
> members of our community. As far as the golden age of medicine is con-
> cerned, it doesn't relate to how much doctors make, it relates to how much we
> can do for patients.

Consequently, he thinks it a shame that physicians seem increasingly to advise individuals, including their children, against going to medical school:
"When people say that to me, I frankly say, 'Tell me again what it is you'd
rather be doing, and why aren't you doing it?' I really have no tolerance for
that. I think the profession is still wonderful." Corlin notes that one of the
largest sources of satisfaction about medicine for him is the never-ending
nature of medical progress. Physicians are continually able to do more for
their patients than they were in the past:

I compare now to when I graduated medical school: organ transplants were in their infancy, and those sorts of things are routine now. Hypertension was treated with diuretics then. Leukemia was almost one hundred percent fatal. The list goes on and on. And it's like peeling an onion: every time you peel back one layer there's something below it. We cure certain diseases—we uncover them—and then people live long enough to get new diseases. We cure them, they live long enough to get more diseases.

Impacting Health Care Policy

For individuals considering combining medicine and health care policy, Corlin emphasizes the variety of career paths and different options available—both with and without the medical degree: "There's a tremendous amount to be done in health policy development that does not require the medical background." Another alternative is to approach health care from the writing and research sector of the medical establishment. "People in those fields," says Corlin, "are not often willing to devote the time to public policy issues, which is regrettable because they have a distinct contribution to make—a perspective that is often not well thought of."

For physicians hoping to extend an arm into the policy world, Corlin emphasizes the importance of a stellar clinical reputation—which he believes to be an essential foundation for physicians in policy. He does not see it as crucial to add a master's degree to a medical education (e.g., an M.D.-M.B.A.), but thinks that combining a medical degree with an additional master's is beneficial to those who "truly want to use their second degree based on their particular knowledge of the M.D." He encourages medical students and young medical professionals to take advantage of both education-related and extracurricular opportunities:

> The difficulty is at times, you get people saying, "Well, if I'm not going to get paid for it, I'm not going to do it." And that's unfortunate. I think what has to happen is people have to be willing to take the bends in the road, or the forks in the road as they come, and in many cases as they come unexpectedly.

Corlin also emphasizes the importance of remaining flexible with oneself and one's decisions, even after a path is chosen. He illustrates this with an analogy to dating and relationships:

> The best analogy I can give is you start dating somebody and you really think you're interested and involved with them, and all of a sudden you begin to get doubts and concerns. You're going to act on those doubts and concerns and change the direction of that relationship. You're not going to say, "Well, you know, four dates ago, because I was heading in this direction,

I'm going to keep going that way." It's not likely to lead to a good result. Just be responsive and malleable to changes in your attitude about your professional life.

David M. Cutler

Otto Eckstein Professor of Applied Economics, Harvard University

One of the most influential health care economists of his generation, David Cutler has served two presidents and helped to shape the Affordable Care Act. In this profile, he discusses how his work as a policy-maker and his academic studies of health care economics have informed each other. Emphasizing the importance of health care's distinctiveness as an industry, and of attending to the views of the many different people who contribute to it—doctors, nurses, patients, insurers, IT specialists—he articulates a compelling vision of health care's future based on the wisdom acquired from three decades as a leading scholar and reformer.

EDUCATION

1983–1987	A.B., Harvard University (Economics)
1987–1991	Ph.D., Massachusetts Institute of Technology (Economics)

CAREER PATH

1991–1995	Assistant Professor of Economics, Harvard University
1993	Senior Staff Economist, Council of Economic Advisors; Director, National Economic Council
1995–1997	John L. Loeb Associate Professor of Social Sciences, Harvard University
1997–2005	Professor of Economics, Department of Economics and Kennedy School of Government, Harvard University
2003–2008	Dean of the Faculty of Arts and Sciences for Social Science, Harvard University
2005–	Otto Eckstein Professor of Applied Economics, Department of Economics and Kennedy School of Government, Harvard University

SELECTED PUBLICATIONS

"Is Technological Change in Medicine Worth It?" *Health Affairs* 20(5), Sept./Oct. 2001, 11–29 (with Mark McClellan).

"Why Have Americans Become More Obese?" *Journal of Economic Perspectives* 17(3), Summer 2003, 93–118 (with Edward Glaser and Jesse Shapiro).

"Value of Medical Innovation in the United States: 1960–2000," *NEJM* 355, 2006, 920–927 (with Allison B. Rosen and Sandeep Vijan).

Your Money or Your Life: Strong Medicine for America's Health Care System. Oxford: Oxford University Press, 2004.

The Quality Cure: How Focusing on Health Care Quality Can Save Your Life and Lower Spending Too. Berkeley: University of California Press, 2014.

A very important lesson in health care about anything in policy is that you have to be able to talk
to people at multiple levels—you have to be able to
talk to experts and have it make sense, and you need
to be able to talk to individuals and have it make
sense.... If you screw up either audience, you're
dead, so you have to get both of them right. And
it's not that one is better than the other; they're just
thinking about different things.

—*David Cutler*

Over the last two decades David Cutler has emerged as one of the nation's foremost health care economists, directly influencing several of the
most important developments in health care policy. A leading thinker about
innovation in quality of care, health care information technology, and health
care financing, he has served as a senior advisor to Presidents Bill Clinton
and Barack Obama. His 2004 book, *Your Money or Your Life*, summed up
over a decade of intense study of the value obtained by increased spending
on health care. For Cutler, value has never been simply a question of dollars,
but rather a question of the well-being and longevity that a dollar spent on
health care can buy. He served for five years as the dean for social sciences in
Harvard's Faculty of Arts and Sciences. He currently serves as the Otto Eck-
stein Professor of Applied Economics at Harvard University and the Kennedy School of Government.

DISCOVERING HEALTH CARE

Cutler landed as a freshman at Harvard College in 1983 with the intention of studying physics. He had a long-standing interest in public policy,
however, and during his freshman year his interests evolved towards economics. Despite having two siblings who were physicians, he says, he never
seriously considered becoming one himself, but health care as a field did
attract him: "There was some implicit encouragement that health care was a
good profession to go into, although I don't know why it so captivated me."
He attributes his specialization in health care economics, in particular, to the
encouragement of Larry Summers, who at the time was one of Cutler's professors in economics at Harvard. Summers, Cutler explains, "was one of the
people who convinced me to learn about health care, because there weren't
many economists who knew a whole lot about it, and that seemed a bit of

a shame." The political climate in the United States during these years also shaped his sense of health care's importance as a public policy issue. "This was the '80s," Cutler recalls, "so health care was a big deal."

After graduating from Harvard, Cutler enrolled in graduate school in economics at MIT, where his focus on health care economics intensified. For his Ph.D. dissertation he studied how the financial incentives of the Medicare program impacted patient care.

After completing his doctoral work in 1991, Cutler returned to Harvard's economics department as an assistant professor. Meanwhile, the importance of health care in national politics had continued to grow. Bill Clinton campaigned on the issue in his 1991 run for the presidency, and his victory led to Cutler's first transition from the university into government. At the young age of 28, Cutler found himself in Washington, D.C., helping to shape the new administration's ambitious plan for reform.

THE HOPE AND DISAPPOINTMENT OF THE CLINTON ADMINISTRATION

The Clinton administration was not Cutler's first foray into politics. Through his mentor, Larry Summers, he had worked while in graduate school on the 1988 presidential campaign of Governor Michael Dukakis. Early on in the Clinton campaign, several of the same people who had advised Dukakis were assembled to advise Governor Clinton, and Cutler was invited to join them: "It struck me as a fun thing to do," he recalls, "and a way to contribute to the world." Cutler went to Washington in 1993 with a joint appointment to the Council of Economic Advisors and the National Economic Council, hoping to contribute to the most sweeping health care reform since Medicare.

His hopes were, unfortunately, disappointed, as the Clinton health care plan ultimately failed to gain adequate support to become law. "It was a very difficult year," he recalls, but also, for better and for worse, an invaluable learning experience. During his year in the Clinton administration, Cutler gained a new appreciation of the depth and complexity of health care, an appreciation driven in large part by the exposure his position gave him to people representing a wide range of professions and perspectives in the field. "I got to know a lot of people in the industry and in Washington, who one then just talks with and interacts with regularly," he recalls.

The high value Cutler places on these conversations, in retrospect, mirrors his sense of what was failing to happen as the Clinton administration was rolling out its proposal. Cutler recalls that within the administration, "there was an aura that health care reform was going to happen…and that presumption was not right, but that presumption colored everything." This overconfidence led to a broad failure to communicate:

In the end I think [the plan] was not very good because there wasn't an underlying theme to it that made sense—you couldn't tell people exactly what you wanted to achieve. You could tell them in some broad sense, but you couldn't tell them at a level that actually made sense to them. ... So in the end it didn't really stand up, and the whole thing just fell apart.

LESSONS LEARNED FROM THE CLINTON EXPERIENCE

Cutler walked away from this experience having learned what he feels was one of the most important lessons in his career: "You have to be able to talk to people at multiple levels." This difficult lesson—on the importance of seeing issues from different people's perspectives—became a central theme of his career.

Shortly after the failure of the Clinton plan, Cutler wrote an article in *Health Affairs* in which he articulated his optimism, now that systematic reform had been stalled, about taking an "incremental" approach to health care reform, and he emphasized the urgency of cutting costs. "Rising health care costs," he argued, "have contributed to fiscal imbalance in the public sector and to labor market and insurance market problems in the private sector. If we do nothing else, it is essential to address the health care cost problem."[1] Adapting his policy recommendations to the political possibilities of the moment, Cutler recommended a set of reforms to existing programs, such as Medicare and the insurance pool available to federal employees, that would increase market efficiency and thus stem the rise of health care spending.

FROM "HEALTH CARE ECONOMICS" TO "HEALTH CARE (WITH AN ECONOMICS BACKGROUND)"

Despite its difficulties, and in many ways because of them, Cutler's time in the Clinton administration was pivotal in changing his sense of the context for his work. In the years that followed, he explains, "my work kept drifting from health economics into health care with an economics background." He came to see himself increasingly, in other words, not as someone analyzing the health care industry from his own perch within the academic discipline of economics, but rather as having a primary involvement in the field of health care policy itself. His relationships with people from across the health care industry increasingly started to shape his work: "I've benefited enormously from interacting with people who are not just economists," he says.

During the second half of the 1990s, Cutler's work began to tackle a wider range of questions about health care policy. It was during these years that, often in collaboration with colleagues from other disciplines, Cutler began publishing papers dealing with clinical practice and with technological change in the health care industry.[2]

Dealing with this wider range of issues prepared Cutler for a renewed study of the health care system as a whole. He credits this change in his thinking, in part, to the 2001 Institute of Medicine (IOM) Study *Crossing the Quality Chasm*, which—building upon the 1998 IOM report *To Err is Human*—sought to examine the complexity of the system and the challenges of improving its safety and quality of care:

> I remember reading *Crossing the Quality Chasm,* and it crystallized in my mind a lot of things about how the organization of this health care system was really screwed up. And I've spent most of the time since then thinking about and working on these systems issues: What does it *mean* to have a poorly functioning health care system? How do you get to have a better system, and what are the attributes of that?

THE PLEASURES AND PAINS OF POLITICS: HEALTH CARE REFORM IN THE OBAMA ADMINISTRATION

In the mid-2000s, Cutler's innovative approach to improving health care quality drew the attention of Barack Obama, at the time a U.S. senator from Illinois and a rising star in the Democratic Party. When Obama decided to run for president, he invited Cutler to serve as a senior health care advisor to the campaign. He helped to draft the campaign's platform on health care, and also spoke about the issue on its behalf across the country. While Cutler's role in the Clinton administration had included recruiting support for the plan on a national level, his advocacy role for the Obama campaign had a different intensity.

Cutler now identifies his time with the Obama campaign as the biggest turning point in his career. His role for the campaign, which lasted two years, involved both formulating policy and trying to communicate with the public about that policy: "It was helping to figure out what makes a coherent health care plan, talking with people about it, writing about it, talking to reporters about what's going on in health care in the world. It was involvement with health care at a public level."

Obama's health care team had absorbed the lessons of the Clinton experience, and so they worked with the necessity of clear and persuasive communication about reform in the forefront of their minds: "The presumption was that you had to *convince* people to support you or it wasn't going to work. It was a very different starting point than in the Clinton administration."

He speaks enthusiastically about this aspect of his work, and admiringly about the president's own skills as a communicator:

> It was satisfying in an absolute sense, in part because I think the president

articulated some very important things very well. And I think people in the public learned a lot. The press and [policy] professionals had a very good discussion of it.

"Not," he adds with some chagrin, "that the public *always* had a great discussion of it." As a public speaker, Cutler prefers explaining the issues to drumming up partisan enthusiasm. He has no taste for what he calls the "raw, brass-knuckled" aspects of political work, and regrets the effect that they have often had on the public conversation about the Obama administration's health care plan: "Whenever push comes to shove, it's always easier to claim that the other party is going to kill grandmother." This is tragic not just because it misrepresents the other side's policies, Cutler believes, but also because such claims mask what he sees as a broad, bipartisan consensus about the need and the possibility for change: "What everyone believes, at a technical level, is that you *can* make the system work better, and be cheaper and higher quality."

BALANCING ACTS: POLITICS, TEACHING, AND SCHOLARSHIP

While Cutler has played significant roles in formulating both the Clinton and the Obama health care reform plans, his primary role during these years has been that of a scholar and teacher. He teaches both graduate and undergraduate students at Harvard University, and also has an appointment at Harvard's Kennedy School of Government. At the undergraduate level, Cutler designed a course in health care economics at a time when the subject was still a rarity in economics departments; the course has been consistently popular for over twenty years, usually drawing around 150 students.

Cutler is keenly aware that his political activity has at least the potential to affect the perception of his academic work, but he says that on the whole this has not been a problem. He is particularly forthright about his views with students:

> I tell my classes, "Look, you deserve to know where your professor is coming from, so I'm going to tell you, and periodically over the course of the semester I'll tell you why, but if at any point over the course of the semester you feel like I'm trying to brainwash you, then I haven't done my job right. So you've got to tell me that, and I can tell you why I said what I said, and how to interpret what I said." And my classes seem fine with it.

He has worried more, he says, that journalists in the field might perceive him as unreasonably biased, although he has been "pleasantly surprised" so far that this has not been a major issue. Reporters have for the most part treated him as "someone who has views, but whose views flow from the way I look at the world, from the way I interpret evidence about the world. They've been willing to talk to me, willing to listen to me."

Among his peers in the academy, particularly economists, Cutler says, a shared scholarly ethos, and mutual respect among those who adhere to it even when they disagree, tends to predominate over suspicions of partisan bias:

> Economists believe that they can read any paper and understand it and decide whether it's correct or not. And so as long you're forthcoming about exactly what you did, and they trust you enough not to have distorted things willfully, you're fine... People will say, well, tell me *why* you're thinking what you're thinking? You know, does it make sense economically? And you talk to people and they agree or disagree, but they understand that you've got some economic basis for what you're saying.

Cutler is reluctant to say which of his many professional roles has been most important to him over the years. "Economics is all about balancing different things," he says, and so he tends not to think about his career in terms of sacrificing one activity for another. What he values most about any of his roles, he says, is the chance to make a positive difference in the world, and he has a rich awareness of how his work in any one role can have an unanticipated impact over the long term. He recalls his satisfaction and surprise, for example, upon reading a 2011 profile of one of his former students in *The Atlantic*: Todd Park, who had become CIO for the Department of Health and Human Services, credited Cutler's undergraduate course at Harvard as the experience that first sparked his interest in health care.[3]

PRINCIPLES OF DAVID CUTLER'S CAREER

"All good work is collaborative" is an axiomatic statement for Cutler, a thread that runs through his way of talking about all of the major themes of his work in recent years. These themes include the importance of measuring the value obtained for the money spent on health care, as opposed to merely cutting spending; the continuous improvement of quality in health care; an increasingly acute awareness of the industry's complexity; and the irreducible dependence of any attempt to influence policy on effective communication at multiple levels. The following sections will focus on each of these themes in turn.

FROM CUTTING COST TO MEASURING VALUE

Following his service to the Clinton administration, Cutler's widening range of interests led to a crucial change of emphasis in his economic analyses. Instead of focusing on the question of *how* to cut wasteful spending—a concern often dominant in public discussions about health care during these years—Cutler increasingly questioned the underlying belief that higher spending signaled inefficiency. In a 2005 interview, Cutler recalls an encounter with a fellow economist who quite bluntly asked him: "Why is it you think I get too much health care?"[4] These words stayed with him. In subsequent years, Cutler's work asked increasingly nuanced questions about the *value* that individuals were getting in return for their health care spending. Cutler would later explain the reasoning behind this line of inquiry in his 2004 book, *Your Money or Your Life*:

> Start with a basic observation: The goal of medical care is to improve our health. The system works well if it improves health sufficiently to justify its cost, and poorly if it does not. That seems obvious, but it has deep implications. Most significantly, it implies that controlling medical costs is not an important goal in itself. Lowering costs is good if we are overspending, but bad if we are getting valuable care.[5]

This shift in his focus, from cost-cutting to the measurement of value, as well as his move towards thinking about the larger system, came together in a widely acclaimed 2006 article in the *New England Journal of Medicine* entitled "The Value of Medical Spending in the United States, 1960–2000." Noting that annual health care spending per capita, adjusted for inflation, had risen from $700 in 1960 to $6,000 in 2006, Cutler and his colleagues sought to analyze the value in increased life-expectancy realized for that increase in spending. Some of their findings confirmed the common-sense view that health care had grown extraordinarily expensive in recent years: from 1990–2000, for a person 65 years of age, the cost in health care spending for each additional year of life was a staggering $145,000. Yet taken altogether, their findings challenged the view that most of the increased health care spending had been wasteful or excessive. For the 1960-2000 period as a whole, they found, life expectancy had risen by an average of nearly seven years, and the inflation-adjusted cost for each additional year of life was $19,900. They therefore concluded that "on average, the increases in medical spending since 1960 have provided reasonable value. ... The national focus on the rise in medical spending should be balanced by attention to the health benefits of this increased spending."[6]

QUALITY OF CARE: "MEDICINE AND CAR SALES ARE VERY DIFFERENT"

Cutler has often argued for the potential of free markets to improve efficiency and lower costs in health care, but he has consistently resisted what he views as oversimplified models of the market for health care. This resistance stems from his appreciation of the special positions of those who consume and provide health care—caregivers and patients, Cutler believes, are very distinctive sorts of sellers and buyers, motivated by factors that extend well beyond price and profit.

While Cutler has been an impassioned advocate for expanding access to health insurance in the United States, he does believe firmly that competition can improve care: "When markets get competitive, you really figure out who's providing the valuable service and who's not." In some ways, he insists, competition in health care can spur innovation in the way that it does within any other industry:

> We know that we're going to iterate our way through the next decade. ... Every firm is iterating its way—it's not that health care is any different. Back when we used to admire Toyota, the thing about Toyota was that it had productivity growth *every* year; it didn't just get to be good and stay good, because it was always experimenting, always learning to do something a little better. The same is true of Walmart—it's always learning to do something better. That's going to have to be a feature of health care—always learning to do something better.

Yet Cutler also cautions that the kind of innovation that works for Walmart or Toyta won't necessarily work in health care. This is because health care is a uniquely personalized service, not a commodity for which a low price will be the most important factor in shaping the market:

> What do people really want in health care? It turns out it's really two things. One is that they want the organization to work for them; they want it to be focused on them and getting them better. ... And the other thing they want is that when something is really wrong, they want very specialized brainpower to deal with them. That's what a doctor is: a doctor has immense amounts of training designed to help in very complicated situations.

Cutler has therefore been sharply critical of those who press too far the analogy between health care and other industries:

> For those interested in economics, medicine and car sales are very different. Medicine has always been very special because health is so fundamental to the good life, because doctors have such immense influence over our health, and because medicine is more technically complex than nonspecialists can handle. For these reasons, medicine has always been viewed as a noble profession.[7]

For Cutler, the nobility of health care has to be taken just as seriously by economists as by ethicists. It would be foolish to ignore the importance of the profit-motive in health care, but no less foolish to ignore the economic significance of other motives.

Those special motives are as important for providers as for patients. The people working in health care at all levels, Cutler says, "are the most dedicated people in the economy." While his economic analyses have attuned him to the power of financial incentives for both good and ill in the industry, he is far from seeing this power as absolute, and believes that even economic analysis has to take account of motives apart from profit. Fundamentally, health care professionals "have a very idealistic notion" about what they do, he insists. They also often feel "intensely frustrated because they're in a system they can't adjust. ... They feel incredibly trapped. And that's a very bad situation for them to be in, and it helps you to think about, 'Well, what's the environment that's putting them in that [situation], and how could you change that feeling?'"

Though Cutler never wanted to be a clinician, his work articulates a deep understanding of and sympathy for the clinician practicing in today's increasingly bureaucratic system:

> We cannot continue to have a system ... that turns off doctors left and right, gets them not to go into primary care, makes them be embittered about the profession, tell their children they do not want to become doctors, and runs itself over and over again.[8]

Cutler's appreciation for individuals and their motives is balanced by his attention to the systems and organizations in which they function, and he emphasizes the common ground between health care organizations and other businesses: "If you look at any good business," Cutler says with a note of excitement in his voice, "it basically does three things":

> It has a very good IT system; it has a very good compensation system, so it says, "whatever it is we value, we're going to incentivize"; and it frees up workers to make that happen. So it doesn't specify "you will do exactly this," it says, "your job is to make this happen, figure out *how* to make it happen." And health care has none of those at the moment, but it's moving in all those directions.

These three themes— information technology, incentivization, and coordinated but decentralized management—organize Cutler's most recent and most comprehensive discussion of quality in health care in *The Quality Cure* (2014).

Cutler is optimistic that better technologies can help to improve quality of care, in part by enabling physicians to spend more of their time exercising their highest-level skills. The high value that patients place upon medical expertise, he hopes, will concentrate physicians' use of their time increasingly on tasks for which their training uniquely prepares them:

> When you look at how a primary care physician spends his or her day, probably 80 percent of what they do is in fact doing something that a less well trained person could do just as well. Probably about 20 percent of what they do is doing things for which you need a doctor. So what the system will almost certainly do is move that 80 percent down. ... So doctors will spend their time doing what consultants do, which is analyzing really hard situa-

tions, using all their intellectual firepower, and then making sure that things are going well.

In the case of diabetic patients, for example, Cutler predicts that as they test their insulin levels each day, their data will be wirelessly transmitted and put in an electronic medical record. Their physicians would be signaled when something is amiss, and would monitor statistics for their diabetic patients regularly:

> And so they'll get regular reports: "92 percent of your patients with diabetes are fine ... but there are 8 percent which are quite problematic, and maybe we should spend some time on those."

The flow of information in the current system, Cutler explains, is far from seamless, and this is in part because the money to implement new technologies simply has not been available. Thanks to the Obama administration's stimulus funds, however, he believes that innovation in IT is happening faster than for many other aspects of health care. He cautions, however, that the benefits of this technology will not materialize instantly, but gradually over the course of the next decade: "It takes a while to learn how to use an entirely new system and reconfigure practices to benefit from it."[9]

Managing Complexity: "Anything Can Work in the Right Organization"

Health care, Cutler believes, is not only a distinctive but a uniquely complex part of the economy. A third recurring theme in Cutler's work, therefore, concerns the importance of finding managers able to appreciate and control this complexity. His initial first-hand experience with this came during his time in the Clinton administration: "I learned a fair amount about how to run an organization, because I saw both really good people and really bad people running organizations."

Management is one of the aspects of health care that Cutler describes himself as currently "most worried about." So too, he notes, are many health care managers: Cutler mentions an article in the *Harvard Business Review* by [health care manager] Tom Lee that begins with the sentence, "The problem with health care is people like me."[10] The article, explains Cutler, says that many managers in health care, while perhaps well versed in clinical medicine or public health, have little formal training in managing complex organizations. This is a problem, says Cutler, because a health care organization "is about the most complicated organization in the world":

> If you think about the health care production process as a production process, you are customizing a product for each specific customer that's entirely different and completely ungradeable. And it is the most complicated pro-

duction process of anything. Compare it to making cars, making iPhones, whatever. And yet we think that it's ok to have people in charge of it who actually don't know anything about how to run something.

Cutler is optimistic about the prospect of change, but cautions that the way in which it gets implemented will make all the difference:

> If it's seen as, "Here's the person who laid off 3,000 workers in St. Louis coming to save health care," it'll be a failure. If it's seen as, "Hey, we need to change, and this is a guy who actually knows how to make complicated organizations work and can help us out, and is working with the clinicians," then it could be successful.

As he puts it in *The Quality Cure*, "it would be a big mistake to run a hospital the way outsourcing firms run manufacturing plants."[11] Again, Cutler's sensitivity to the distinctiveness of the health care industry is central to his thinking about the management practices best suited to it. For example, he discusses with nuance the reasons why a pay-for-performance scheme is inappropriate for individual physicians, but optimal for health care organizations as wholes.[12]

The success of change in any industry, Cutler says, depends on "organizational culture," on the relationships and expectations that have been established among the diverse actors in the organization. This means that there are no cookie-cutter, one-size-fits-all solutions in health care. Everything depends on sensitivity to local circumstances and to diverse human concerns: "Anything can work in the right organization," Cutler says, "but anything can fail in the wrong organization."

UNDERSTANDING WHAT'S ON PEOPLE'S MINDS

Cutler's distinctive approach to health care economics may have its roots in this eagerness to attend to what's on people's minds. Even as he strives to articulate solutions to system-wide problems, he never forgets that the successful implementation of any solution requires thinking about what needs to be communicated at this moment, to some particular audience.

> It's helpful both to understand what our theories say and also to know what the people involved say, and to be able to walk back and forth between them. Just as an example, if you talk to hospital CEO's now, what most of them will tell you is, they're scared about the future, because of the Affordable Care Act, what's happening in health care and so on. They're trying to figure out which way to go, which way to turn, what to do with their institutions. Well, that's very helpful as you try to think about policies.

This kind of attention to the concerns of different groups is at once an obligation and a pleasure for Cutler: "I like to talk to lots of folks—I just enjoy getting together and hearing from them, exchanging ideas with them." As he talks through different issues, his rich sense of the importance of addressing multiple audiences with regard to every aspect of health care policy becomes apparent. The example of evaluating bypass surgeons readily comes to mind for him, and leads to a fluent and detailed consideration of the legitimate needs of different groups:

> The bypass surgeons are not going to believe [in a ratings system] unless it's very very sensitively risk-adjusted, and there are twenty-seven metrics and you've got to have all those metrics or they're just not going to believe it— which is perfectly fine, absolutely, totally right. If you try to explain to the public what those twenty-seven metrics are and why it's important to do all that, and here's the risk-adjusted rating, they'll throw up their hands. So for the public, what you want to communicate is three stars, two stars, one star. But for the clinicians, you'd better have given them the backup behind that.

Cutler's sensitivity to different perspectives within health care has also helped him to identify areas in need of further study by economists. In this regard, he gives the example of the costs entailed by malpractice laws:

> There's a huge difference between what economists think about the impact of malpractice fears on what's done in medicine and what doctors will tell you. … The entire economics literature says there's a very small amount of money, and every clinician you talk to says there's a huge amount of money in stuff that they do solely because they're afraid of being sued. And I have no idea who is right.

Instead of siding with the economists and dismissing what clinicians say as self-interested exaggeration, Cutler takes the stark difference between the two accounts as a reason to consider a more rigorous and sensitive analysis. "It may be," he concedes, that the costs resulting from liability fears are actually "a very big deal, but none of the things economists have looked at have actually captured any significant variation in it."

While there is a clear set of trends articulated throughout Cutler's research, he has continued to collaborate with colleagues on a much broader range of research as well. For instance, among his most popular and widely read articles was an article that appeared in the *New England Journal of Medicine* in 2009 which looked at the long-term effects of obesity and smoking on life expectancy in the U.S.—a topic many would argue is firmly within the field of public health.[13] Cutler's skill in crossing academic boundaries is evidenced not just by his ability to collaborate with academics from a wide range of fields but also by his ability to actually have his work published in some of the most prestigious journals of multiple different specialties.

LOOKING BACK, AND FORWARD

When asked what he would consider having done differently, Cutler turns again to the fundamental importance of understanding different perspectives within the health care system:

> I think it would have helped if earlier in my career I had spent more time in government. Or I might have spent some time working in an insurance company, or a large provider system, or a state government. Something with more exposure to what's on people's minds. That turns out to be so important.

His advice to those interested in health care economics is to seek out just this kind of experience. An advanced degree in economics is essential, he says, but "if you want to really get into anything about health, you need to know something about the world beyond just economics." He encourages his graduate students to spend significant time reading journals like *Health Affairs* and the *New England Journal of Medicine* rather than just journals dedicated to the economic dimensions of health care. Health care economists interested in policy, he believes, have to approach the field with a genuinely interdisciplinary curiosity:

> You see plenty of economists who don't know anything about health care trying to write things about health care. And it is just silly. And you see plenty of health care people who don't know any economics who say things that are just silly. I think you need both.

Cutler expresses a great deal of satisfaction with his job and the variety of roles it allows him to play. That said, he does not rule out the possibility of working outside the realm of academia if the right opportunity presents itself. Rather than aggressively seeking out such opportunities, Cutler has a rather Zen approach to career planning. He remembers one of his graduate advisors, the Nobel Prize-winning economist Peter Diamond, talking happily about the unexpected discoveries of day-to-day intellectual life:

> "When I wake up," [Diamond said], "I think about things, and sometimes they work out, and sometimes they don't. And if they work out, I work on them more. And if they don't work out, I don't work on them more. So it's sort of that pinball feeling, if it goes this way it goes this way, if it goes that way it goes that way."

In this spirit, Cutler has an ethical compass rather than a detailed map for his future career:

> I hope at the end, when the ball finally settles down, I can feel proud of myself for having done whatever I could to help the country be better, or the world be better. And as I go along, I just think about what will help to do that.

Notes

1   David M. Cutler, "Cutting Costs and Improving Health: Making Reform Work," *Health Affairs* 14, no.1 (1995): 161–172, quotation at 161.

2   See for example "What is Technological Change?" in *Inquiries in the Economics of Aging*, ed. David Wise (Chicago: University of Chicago Press, 1998), 51–81, and "The Costs and Benefits of Intensive Treatment for Cardiovascular Disease," in *Measuring the Prices of Medical Treatments*, ed. Jack Triplett (Washington, D.C.: Brookings, 1999), 34–71.

3   Simon Owens, "Can Todd Park Revolutionize the Health Care Industry?" *The Atlantic*, June 2, 2011.

4   Roger Lowenstein, "The Quality Cure?" *New York Times Magazine*, March 13, 2005.

5   Cutler, *Your Money or Your Life*, p. xii.

6   David M. Cutler, Allison B. Rosen, and Sandeep Vijan, "The Value of Medical Spending in the United States, 1960–2000," *New England Journal of Medicine* 355 (2006): 920–27, quotation at 920.

7   David M. Cutler, "Mitt Romney: Physicians Should Be Like Car Salesmen," *JAMA*, June 20, 2012.

8   David M. Cutler and Gail R. Wilensky, "Perspective Roundtable: Health Care in the Next Administration," *NEJM* 359, no. 15 (2008): e17 (www.nejm.org/doi/full/10.1056NEJMp080756).

9   David M. Cutler, *The Quality Cure*, 90.

10 Thomas H. Lee, "Turning Doctors into Leaders," *Harvard Business Review*, April 2010.

11 Cutler, *The Quality Cure*, 141.

12 Cutler, *The Quality Cure*, 144–148.

13 S.T. Stewart, D.M. Cutler, A.M. Rosen, "Forecasting the Effects of Obesity and Smoking on U.S. Life Expectancy," *New England Journal of Medicine* 361 (2009): 2252–60.

Karen Davis

Professor, Health Policy and Management, Johns Hopkins Bloomberg School of Public Health
Former President, The Commonwealth Fund

Trained in economics, Karen Davis has spent her career at the intersection of academia, philanthropy, think tanks and government. From 1994–2012 she led The Commonwealth Fund, one of the leading philanthropic health policy research funds. In this profile Davis discusses how she has merged her interest in social issues with her quantitative background to focus on the issue of care for the underserved. She also reflects on the different types of impact one has across the academic, government and philanthropic worlds.

EDUCATION & TRAINING

1961–1965	B.A., Rice University (Mathematics and Economics)
1965–1969	Ph.D., Rice University (Economics)

CAREER PATH

1968–1970	Assistant Professor of Economics, Rice University
1970–1974	Research Associate, The Brookings Institution
1974–1977	Senior Fellow, The Brookings Institution
1977–1980	Deputy Assistant Secretary for Planning and Evaluation/Health, U.S. Department of Health and Human Services (HHS)
1980–1981	Administrator, Health Resources Administration, Public Health Service, HHS
1981–1992	Chairman, Department of Health Policy and Management, School of Hygiene and Public Health, The Johns Hopkins University
1992–1994	Executive Vice President, The Commonwealth Fund
1994–2012	President, The Commonwealth Fund
2012–	Eugene and Mildred Lipitz Professor in the Department of Health Policy and Management and Director of the Roger C. Lipitz Center for Integrated Health Care, Johns Hopkins University

ADDITIONAL INFORMATION

Johns Hopkins Bloomberg School of Public Health: http://www.jhsph.edu

The Commonwealth Fund: http://www.commonwealthfund.org/

From the very beginning what I was interested in was seeing that people who need health care get it. If there's something we have a cure for and we don't help people, I just think that's outrageous. That people die from a condition that's not controlled is outrageous, and disproportionately, the people who don't get help are low-income, uninsured, minority populations—all of the barriers stand in their way.

—*Karen Davis*

As an undergraduate math major at Rice University, Davis was initially certain that she wanted a career in the computing industry. It was the early 1960s, however, and the civil rights movement was was in full swing. Her increasing awareness of the movement caused her to question whether limiting her studies to mathematics would equip her to deal with the social issues she increasingly felt were most important. Hoping to bring her education into closer contact with these issues and the people behind them, she added a second major in economics: "Economics at that time focused on eliminating poverty. I thought that if I went into economics I could make more of a difference," she says. "I was very much influenced by the social revolution." After graduating in 1965 she decided to continue on in her economics department as a graduate student. She earned a Ph.D. in 1969 and then continued on for an additional two years as an assistant professor.

Davis's core skills involved quantitative research and analysis, but she was motivated by the impact that quantitative decisions could have at a personal level, on individual people's lives. She recalls in particular her involvement in a study on rural health care in the South, which she conducted shortly after receiving her doctoral degree:

We visited eighty clinics from Texas to West Virginia, and really pushed to expand coverage for nurse practitioners and physician assistants in rural clinics; we actually got it enacted into law. That was a different experience for me, because up until then I had done a lot of analysis, computer runs on what black Medicare beneficiaries got in the way of services versus white. But it was really eye-opening going and visiting these clinics and seeing what it really took to provide care in a way that is responsive to patients. It made me think of it in human terms, not just in number terms. In 1974, there were physicians who wouldn't use their stethoscopes on black patients—they thought they would get them dirty. There was a hospital with a cafeteria where they painted the tables white and black so that people would know where to sit—ten years after the Civil Rights Act.

As a result of this experience and others like it, Davis resolved to focus her career on pushing for changes that would alleviate inequalities in the availability and quality of health care: "My motivating drive is to see that people who need medical care get it."

EARLY CAREER PATH: GOVERNMENT AND ACADEMIC WORK

In 1970 Davis felt it was time to leave academia and take her work closer to where policy was actually being made. She did this by moving to the Brookings Institution, a prestigious independent left-leaning think tank in Washington. While there she was able to both immerse herself in public health research and also to become an advocate for the changes in policy that the conclusions of her research were supporting. "I got to testify before committees—Medicare, Medicaid. We put out a book every year," Davis recalls. "I felt like all this research I was doing would inform policy."

She took her move away from academia and towards actual policy one step further when in 1977 she was asked by President Jimmy Carter to serve as deputy assistant secretary of planning and evaluation/health at the U.S. Department of Health, Education and Welfare (which became the U.S. Department of Health and Human Services in 1980). Davis immediately felt at home in a government role: "Once I got into government, I felt that was why I had done the research."

Davis was a political appointee, however, so her term ended in January 1981 with the beginning of the Reagan administration. Despite the rewards of her direct role in government, Davis missed the opportunity to conduct intensive research that she had enjoyed at the Brookings Institution. With the experience she had gained in health policy both there and in government, she received many prestigious academic job offers:

> I had an offer for a tenured professorship with Hopkins. It was the Department of Health Policy and Management. At Duke I had an offer to be chairman of Health Administration at the medical school. I also was offered a vice presidency...I was in exile with the Democrats, but it seemed natural to me: research and writing is what I do.

Ultimately Davis decided to join the faculty at Johns Hopkins University. While at Hopkins, she remained involved in government affairs, testifying eight to ten times per year, and she was instrumental in the outcome of some key policy decisions. Of these, the decision in which she is most proud to have played a part was the approval of Medicaid coverage for low-income children and pregnant women. Davis also devoted much of her energy at Hopkins to completing several books on health care policy and financing, including *Health and the War on Poverty: A Ten Year Appraisal* (1978) and *National Health Insurance: Benefits, Costs, and Consequences* (1975), which were both published by the Brookings Institution, and *Health Care Cost Containment* (1990), published by the Johns Hopkins University Press.

THE COMMONWEALTH FUND

In 1992, after twelve years at Hopkins, Davis received another enticing offer. A contact at the Commonwealth Fund in New York recruited Davis to join the Fund as executive vice president, and promised she would be groomed to become president within a few years. The offer seemed like a fantastic opportunity, so she decided to relocate from Baltimore to New York. She began as an executive vice president and two years later became the Fund's president.

A private foundation that supports independent research on health and social issues, the Commonwealth Fund makes grants to fund research aimed at improving health care practice and policy. The Fund is dedicated to helping people become more informed about their health care, and to improving care for vulnerable populations such as children, elderly people, low-income families, minority Americans, and the uninsured. Its two national program areas are improving health insurance coverage and access to care, and improving the quality of health care services.

Davis's core responsibilities as the Fund's president revolve primarily around setting the policy direction for the Fund's philanthropic investments and communicating the results of the Fund's work to the people who have the power to use them. She describes the first task as "figuring out what the opportunities are where we can make a difference with the $25 million or so that we invest every year." Achieving this goal depends upon both a thorough understanding of the present and a visionary sense for the future:

> Part of my work is figuring out what the issues are. Not just today, but two years from now, because the work is going to take one to two years to do, so we've got to start the right projects now so that we will have the answers to questions that people will be asking in the future.

Such a forward-thinking role has its drawbacks, however. Davis notes that one of the most challenging parts of her job is the lack of immediate results and the uncertainty about what her work is accomplishing while projects are underway:

> When you're in the non-profit world and you're trying to inform public policy issues or provide information to patients, it takes time to make that hap-

pen. Then you can never be sure of the difference made by your own work. We spent $25 million: what was the value that came out of that? We want to get as much mileage as we can out of the money we spend, but how do you assess that?

While closely intertwined, the roles that academia, government, think tanks, and foundations play in the creation and implementation of health care policy are different. Having worked in each of these areas, Davis is able to appreciate some of the key differences. In government, she explains, one can often have the most day-to-day impact, since you are actually implementing policy. In academia, however, while some may feel they have the greatest freedom, one's ability to continue to study an issue or push for certain changes is highly dependent on your ability to obtain funding: long-term projects centered around writing a book or receiving a grant may stop when the grant or book contract is up. At the Commonwealth Fund, in contrast, Davis relishes the opportunity to work on bigger projects over longer periods of time. "In the foundation world," she remarks, "we have more influence because we can fund an entire body of research."

Maximizing the impact of the Fund is dependent on more than choosing the right research topics, Davis explains, and this constitutes the second core responsibility of her role. "It's getting the right work done, but then it's also getting it out to the right people who can use it properly." To do this Davis spends about twenty-five percent of her time traveling so she can personally communicate the results of the Fund's work. She frequently testifies before Congress and gives speeches to external groups, and notes that she is constantly assessing how the Fund can be more effective at packaging information or getting people's attention. Davis cites work by the Urban Institute as an example of the sort of research that she is particularly proud the Fund has both supported and helped communicate to actually shape policy: "The research done on Medicare prescription drug legislation at the Urban Institute played a major role in the commitment of at least $400 billion in funds over ten years to low-income people and those with catastrophic expenses, and federalization of prescription coverage for low-income seniors now covered by Medicaid."

One of the ways in which Davis achieves these two goals is by being closely involved with the rest of the health policy sphere, and one of the most important ways she does this is by serving on the boards and advisory committees of numerous other organizations. These have included serving on the Overseers' Committee for the Harvard School of Public Health, the Kaiser Commission on Medicaid and Uninsured, the Agency for Healthcare Research, the Quality National Advisory Council, and the Governing Council for the Institute of Medicine. These committees provide a setting where she can make heard both her own voice and the voice of her organization, as well as stay abreast of the latest developments in health care policy and research. Often, time is spent brainstorming and discussing potential issues and problems that she and others working in similar contexts will have to face in the future—problems that, while not seemingly pressing at the moment, are going to become significant issues five or ten years from now. In this way she and her colleagues play an instrumental role in setting the health policy agenda, by identifying and starting to build research on the issues we will face tomorrow.

REFLECTIONS AND ADVICE

To people interested in embarking upon similar career paths, Davis emphasizes the importance of adequate training, but also stresses that those interested in careers like hers need not follow her academic path. "I almost never recommend a traditional economics training," she explains. "I often just push a doctorate in a school of public health or health economics, or a Ph.D. in political science." As for her perspective on the benefits of clinical training versus those of training in public health, Davis is hesitant to recommend one over the other:

> I think that any terminal degree is good. It keeps you from feeling over your head. The question is how much stuff do you have to learn that you'll never use and that is totally irrelevant, and how much of it keeps you motivated and focused on the issues that really matter.

When reflecting on the influences that have shaped her career, like many leaders, she brings up the important role of mentoring. "When I think about my mentors," she says, "they've all been people I've worked for who spent time developing me." Particularly important was the role these mentors played in pushing Davis beyond her own perceived limits at an early stage in her career. "For one of my first speeches," she recalls, "I was asked to speak at the New York Academy of Medicine—a prospect I found totally intimidating." But she argues that chances like these are exactly the sort that mentors, whether they're university professors or professional supervisors, should encourage those learning under them to take:

> A lot of people are focused on what they need to get ahead. The thought that you would just sit around and just chat with someone who works for you—that's not something people do normally. But I think that it's good to encourage leaders to let people stretch and try themselves out. There is really a responsibility for leaders to make themselves available to people.

Finally, Davis points out the importance of work-life balance in achieving both success and happiness. While she spends a great deal of time and energy at work, this drive is self-generated, and not necessarily a function of the job. Most importantly, she always makes time to pursue the other activities she enjoys, such as pleasure reading (which she does every night for two hours), theater, running, and visiting with her daughter. She credits her striving to use every minute carefully with the balance she has achieved. "Eighty hours a week can be a lot of work," she notes, "but it's not every hour."

AFTERWORD

In 2012, after two decades at the Commonwealth Fund—eighteen years of which were spent as president—Davis stepped down, handing the reigns over to David Blumenthal.[1] She subsequently returned to her previous academic home in the Department of Health Policy and Management at Johns Hopkins University where she was named the Eugene and Mildred Lipitz professor and director of the Roger C. Lipitz Center for Integrated Health Care.

1   A profile of David Blumenthal can be found on page 84.

THOMAS P. DICKERSON

Former Chairman, Tullis-Dickerson & Co., Inc.

As the chairman of a private equity fund, Tom Dickerson's impact on health care stems from his firm's ability to both fund and advise health care companies across all stages of their development. Trained in both business and law, Dickerson explains in this profile why he believes that even the best education may not adequately prepare one for all aspects of a career. He elaborates on the merits of skills learned outside the classroom, including knowing how to communicate with and persuade other people. Dickerson also discusses why he finds investing in and working with health care companies to be particularly satisfying.

EDUCATION & TRAINING

1968–1971	B.A., Harvard University
1971–1974	J.D., Harvard Law School
1979–1981	M.B.A., Harvard Business School

CAREER PATH

1974–1977	Corporate Attorney, Coudert Brothers
1979–1980	Assistant Vice President, Office of Strategic Projects, W.R. Grace & Co.
1980–1985	Vice President, Investment Banking Division, Lehman Brothers
1985–1987	First Vice President, Corporate Finance, E.F. Hutton & Co.
1987–1990	Principal, Tullis-Dickerson & Co., Inc.
1990–1998	President, Tullis-Dickerson & Co., Inc.
1998–2009	Chairman, Tullis-Dickerson & Co., Inc
2008–2014	Chair, Board of Trustees, United World College-USA

Your background matters a lot less than your people skills. The partner with the most critical skill set in the firm went to a local college just down the road. She is absolutely brilliant at convincing hard-nosed CEOs that they really want to step aside. She has been an enormous asset to the firm for the past decade.

—Tom Dickerson

As chairman of a leading health care private equity and venture capital firm, Tom Dickerson's job requires him to make high risk investment decisions with the potential for even higher returns. His success depends on his intuitive ability—formed through years of experience—to choose the right companies and match them with a management team suited to their particular stage of development. With a background in both law and business, Dickerson also serves as director on the boards of a number of private companies and non-profit organizations.

Early Education

As a child, Dickerson lived mostly outside of the United States, and attended the United World College of the Atlantic, an international high school in Wales. He then received his bachelor's degree in economics from Harvard University and his J.D. from Harvard Law School.

After law school, Dickerson headed the U.S. national committee for United World Colleges, an experience that convinced him that what he wanted most was to "run something." This desire prompted a successful application to business school. Dickerson received his M.B.A., again from Harvard, in 1981. He went on to work in investment banking, corporate strategic planning and finally in the venture capital industry. Since 1987, Dickerson has served as a principal at Tullis-Dickerson & Co., a private equity firm that invests in biotechnology and health care companies.

"One Step Closer" to Hands-on Management

Dickerson views his own career as a clear progression from the periphery of the corporate world towards the hub of activity at its center. Ever since his fundraising efforts for United World, Dickerson has moved steadily closer to the type of hands-on management position he enjoyed there. He acknowledges, however, that he still has not reached that point. "You certainly don't run companies as venture capitalists," he concedes.

> But you're one step closer to running something, which has been a theme that I have headed towards over the past twenty or twenty-five years. So in a sense my notion of wanting to run something has always been interrupted or has come to rest one step before actually going out and running something.

Whether he will ever arrive at that destination remains an open question; his path towards corporate operations has always felt spontaneous to him rather than premeditated. In fact, Dickerson feels that being one level removed from daily corporate management actually suits his strengths in "multi-tasking over a variety of transactions." Drawing on his extensive experience, he candidly compares the roles of corporate executive and venture capitalist:

> The good news about running a company is that you're running something. The bad news is that, at the end of the day, you're just selling the same product over and over again. I've had CEO friends who have said to me, "I've had a great time with my company for seven or eight years, but now it's getting to be boring. I want to be a venture capitalist!" There's a trade-off between limiting yourself to a set of tasks which is related to one particular product or service, versus the more varied—but removed—advisory or consulting role that investment bankers and venture capitalists find themselves in.

For Dickerson, a career change from venture capitalism to corporate management is still possible, but for now he enjoys his work as an investor and observer.

Venture Capital: An Overview

Venture capitalists have been viewed as the risk-takers, the deal-makers, the sought-after men and women with the money—and therefore with the power—to save a company or to shut it down. While the fiscal glamour of venture capitalism is attractive to many professionals, Dickerson argues that the investment industry is widely misunderstood. Money is indisputably crucial to any successful enterprise, but what truly makes or breaks a company is not just its technology or even its product:

> The conventional wisdom is that venture capitalists come across fabulous technologies or ideas—Lotus, Genentech, eBay—and they go find the CEO, and they support that technology, and it's the technology that drives the success. The reality is the opposite. The reality is that there is an enormous amount of technology out there, probably five or ten percent of which could be converted into a successful company. But what really drives success is finding the right managers, and understanding that the skill sets that are required

to start a company are very, very different from the skill sets that are used to develop a company and take it public.

Ultimately a company will live or die by the talents and experience of the people who run it. According to Dickerson, the venture capitalist's responsibility is to ensure that the current management at the helm of a portfolio company is suited to the company's needs at that time:

> My metaphor for that is that back in high school, the folks who start companies would have been the geeks who sat in the chemistry lab, invented something and had enough of an attitude to start a company. The folks who take companies public are essentially cheerleaders. They don't have to understand the technology in detail. They just have to convince investors that this is a great deal and they have to buy this. And in my high school, the geeks were never on the cheerleading squad. It's a different mindset, not to speak of a different skill set.

But Dickerson's metaphor, as he acknowledges, makes his job look easier than it is—the differences between a start-up management team and a team suited to attract investors are a bit less transparent than those between "geeks" and "cheerleaders." He emphasizes that his ability to find a good match between a management team and a particular phase of a company has been honed through years of trial and error:

> What you really get as a venture capitalist is a second sense of how to recognize when the skill set of a CEO no longer matches the developing needs of a company, which is when you have to change the CEO out. And your ability to recognize that soon enough—that's really the critical venture capitalist skill. It's very touchy-feely, it's something you really can't learn in school—you learn it through ten years of experience.

Once Dickerson has decided that a management team is right, his next responsibility is to continue working with it. Cooperating productively with corporate executives is another crucial skill for venture capitalists. Dickerson explains that this can be a challenging but exciting part of the job, especially given the volatile combination of character traits that make up a successful executive:

> Entrepreneurs have very interesting personalities. To be a CEO, you really have to be both crazy and not crazy. You've got to be crazy if you believe that you and a desk are going to go up against General Motors and win. But you've also got to have your feet planted firmly on the ground, because if you don't understand in obsessive detail how much cash you have in the bank, and what you can reasonably accomplish before it runs out, then the game's over.

Working with such obstacles demands both patience and sound judgment. In Dickerson's opinion, the very same characteristics that distinguish top entrepreneurs can, if left unchecked, also bring about their demise. The venture capitalist is often in the necessary but difficult position of stepping between a talented CEO and a portfolio company to provide that check when the company's evolution, or its very survival, requires it:

> CEOs have to be extremely self-confident to the point of being arrogant—often wrong but never in doubt. And in a sense you want that. But at the same time it makes them at times fairly challenging to work with. So one of the frustrations is dealing with some potentially difficult people whom you are trying to lead to a rational conclusion, but because of their own personality they just cannot get there and can lose you a lot of money.

This kind of situation, in which the future of a company can ride on the venture capitalist's powers of persuasion, is one major reason that Dickerson emphasizes interpersonal skills as perhaps the primary ones in his line of work.

Dickerson notes that while the chances of successfully closing a truly lucrative deal in venture capital are low, the returns on such a deal are potentially spectacular: "Of ten deals, something like half of them go under," says Dickerson. "With two or three of them, you get two or three times your money back. And with one or two of them, you get ten times your money back." Of course, this latter possibility is the motivation for venture capitalists to risk their investors' money on fledgling companies. Meanwhile, venture capitalists must keep fundraising in mind as well, convincing new investors to entrust their money to them. Dickerson describes fundraising, along with lengthy workdays and frequent travel, as one of the more trying parts of his job. Still, he points out that many other professions share these drawbacks.

Dickerson is also quick to praise his profession, but recognizes that whether something is stimulating or not on a day-to-day basis depends on one's personality:

> Look, there's obviously nothing generically wrong with the tasks involved in being a corporate lawyer. In fact, there is a lot of personal and intellectual satisfaction to be derived in producing a well-crafted document. My wife, whom I met at the law firm, took to this stuff so much that she became the third female partner in the 130-year history of the firm. ... Whatever you end up doing, remember that you have to go into the office every day and do it from nine to five. You'd better like it.

As a venture capitalist, Dickerson is constantly "dealing with strategic big-picture kind of issues. There's so much variety in the job and you're dealing with relatively important problems." Dickerson also finds working with companies in the health care sector uniquely rewarding. A tremendous benefit of investing in medical and biotechnology companies is, he says, helping the fellow who's walking around out there today but who would have been dead six months ago if it weren't for one of our portfolio companies that's working on brain cancer. You get some satisfaction out of the fact that you're doing that rather than making a better cell phone.

Besides the personal gratification of advancing patient care, Dickerson is drawn to the health care industry because of his inherent interest in science: "Even at the kind of ten-thousand-foot level from which I understand science, over the course of the years I've picked up enough of it that my partners tell me I'm a very fast study in understanding what a company has developed." The nature of his work allows him to stay abreast of the very latest biomedical technologies. Moreover, Dickerson adds that unlike most other industries, health care is already a giant sector of the economy but still has much potential for growth—it makes, in short, a great investment.

Dickerson sees the essence of venture capitalism in its fast pace and its demand for constant multitasking. It requires, he says,

> juggling an enormous number of balls, because you've got several companies in different stages of the life cycle and because you have to keep up with the venture capital industry as well as the health care industry, not to speak of maintaining relationships with bankers and consultants who are critical to getting your job done.

Outstanding venture capitalists are those who have built the largest stores of experiential knowledge and who manage to keep track of the latest developments in their field. "There's a network of relationships that you have to build," says Dickerson, with his own career in mind. "So a lot of it is being on the phone, attending conferences, and remaining networked with what's going on in these various fields."

People Skills

Unlike a number of his colleagues who invest primarily in health care, Dickerson's formal training in science is limited. He suggests that qualifications other than a science degree, namely the ability to understand and persuade other people, often outweigh the importance of scientific knowledge: "I think that having a real intuitive sense for what goes on in a meeting—the hidden agendas, the underlying currents—and understanding what really motivates people as opposed to what they tell you motivates them is probably the critical skill set." To illustrate his point, Dickerson recalls the hiring process that his firm recently undertook to find a new associate with both a science degree and an M.B.A.:

> The critical question that we always asked in the interview was, "Describe to me a situation where you personally had responsibility for convincing either

a peer or a superior to do something that you wanted them to do, and how you went about doing it." The more the science background the candidate had, the more the response would take the form of, "My peer or superior didn't have data; I had data; I showed them the data; and the data convinced them of the correctness of my position." The people who had less of a science background created a much richer tapestry: "I thought about the personality of my superior, and I talked to some buddies he used to work with and all my peers about how I should approach this." It was a much more interesting, thoughtful, flexible kind of an answer.

MAINTAINING PERSPECTIVE

Dickerson's strongest advice for those beginning a career is that they should always approach decisions from a rational and open-minded perspective. He applies this advice to multiple aspects of his own attitude towards his work. For example, he admits that early in his career he too often sacrificed personal time with his family for additional hours in the office, regularly working up to 85 hours per week. He is no longer sure the sacrifice was entirely worthwhile:

> You know, I don't think I advanced any faster than I would have if I worked 70 hours a week. At the end of the day, it's about maintaining some sense of perspective or overview that it's okay to not kill yourself, because those last ten hours don't really add that much to your career, and they really detract a lot from your personal life.

He also urges young professionals to "maintain an overview" of the field in which they work. It is all too easy to become absorbed in details or to avoid challenging the status quo when still new to a profession, but Dickerson insists that stepping back to look at the big picture and risking the innovative suggestions that can result from such a perspective will be applauded. Demonstrating passion and creativity matters more than making mistakes: "People pay you not for your ability to grind out work but for your ability to think."

Dickerson believes that maintaining a flexible attitude is essential in any line of work. It will help to mitigate the surprises and setbacks inevitable in every career, and will allow one to make the best of every situation:

> Everybody worries an enormous amount about directing his or her career and taking control of it, but the reality is that stuff just happens sometimes over which you have no control. The game is as much recognizing the unexpected opportunity and seizing it as it is actually planning it out.

AFTERWORD

In 2009, Dickerson stepped down from his position at Tullis-Dickerson after over twenty years with the company. In the following years, he became increasingly involved on a volunteer basis with his former school, the United World College. Created during the Cold War with the hope of fostering cooperation among students from diverse international backgrounds, the UWC has evolved a great deal since Dickerson's 1968 graduation from its original—and at that time, only—campus in Wales. The organization now includes twelve campuses in locations around the world, including a United States campus in Montezuma, New Mexico. Dickerson served on UWC-USA's finance committee from 2004 to 2008, and from 2008 to 2014 as chair of its Board of Trustees. In that role, he helped to steer the organization through a transitional period in its fundraising and leadership.

LARRY DOSSEY

Executive Editor, *Explore: The Journal of Science and Healing*

Working at the crossroads of internal medicine and psychology, Larry Dossey is one of the nation's leading authorities on mind-body connections and complementary and alternative medicine. In this profile, Dossey explains how he successfully integrated alternative therapies into his internal medicine practice. He also reflects on the transition from clinical practice to the work as an editor, author and public speaker that has defined his career for the past two decades. Though deeply rooted in science and skeptical by nature, Dossey is convinced that mind-body therapies are a powerful remedy to certain medical conditions.

EDUCATION & TRAINING

1959–1963	B.S., University of Texas at Austin
1963–1967	M.D., University of Texas Southwestern Medical School
1967–1968	Intern, Parkland Memorial and VA Hospitals, Dallas, TX
1970–1972	Resident, Internal Medicine, Parkland Memorial and VA Hospitals

CAREER PATH

1968–1969	Battalion Surgeon, U.S. Army (Vietnam)
1969–1970	Staff Physician, Fort Carson Army Hospital, U.S. Army
1974–1992	Consultant in internal medicine, Dallas Diagnostic Association
1976–1988	Founder and Director, Biofeedback Laboratory (Dallas, TX)
1979–1980	Chairman, Internal Medicine, Medical City Dallas Hospital
1981–1982	Chief of Staff, Medical City Dallas Hospital
1986–1989	Adjunct Professor, Psychology, North Texas State University
1995–2003	Executive Editor, *Alternative Therapies in Health and Medicine*
2005–	Executive Editor, *Explore: The Journal of Science and Healing*

SELECTED PUBLICATIONS

Healing Words: The Power of Prayer and the Practice of Medicine. San Francisco: HarperSanFrancisco, 1993.

Healing Beyond the Body. Boston: Shambhala, 2001.

The Extraordinary Healing Power of Ordinary Things. New York: Harmony, 2006.

The Power of Premonitions: How Knowing the Future Can Shape Our Lives. New York: Dutton, 2009.

One Mind: How Our Individual Mind Is Part of a Greater Consciousness and Why It Matters. Carlsbad, CA: Hay House; 2013.

ADDITIONAL INFORMATION

Larry Dossey: www.dosseydossey.com

I used to believe that we must choose between science and reason on one hand, and spirituality on the other, in how we lead our lives. Now I consider this a false choice. We can recover the sense of sacredness, not just in science, but in perhaps every area of life.

—*Larry Dossey*

As a young boy in the plains of central Texas, Larry Dossey suffered from intractable, excruciating migraine headaches. The intermittent headaches caused partial blindness, nausea, vomiting, and terrible pain. His family took him to local physicians, but conventional scientific medicine did not relieve his suffering. This early experience with illness, and with the unfulfilled promise of a cure, launched Dossey on his improbable journey into medicine. The journey was improbable to begin with because nothing in Dossey's circumstances made medical school seem a likely destination. He and his identical twin brother were the first members of their family to graduate from high school, and Dossey went on to graduate at the top of his college class at the University of Texas-Austin, where he studied pharmacy:

> I simply had, for reasons that I can't articulate and have never understood, a fascination with physiology and biochemistry. Looking at the history of the family, I'm not sure where that came from. I cannot account for it.

But accounting for the unaccountable has been, in a sense, Dossey's vocation. His migraines continued into adulthood, and as his medical training failed to yield any lasting cure, Dossey began to push at the boundaries of his profession, seeking answers at the intersection of Western medicine and alternative therapies. A leading expert and prolific author in his field, Dossey is the recipient of many awards, including the Pioneer of Integrative Medicine Award (Aspen, 2004 and New York, 2007) and the Visionary Award of the Integrative Healthcare Symposium (New York, 2013).

FROM MIGRAINES TO MEDICINE

Dossey's interest in the life sciences led him to the University of Texas Southwestern Medical School in Dallas. During his first year of medical school, he was eating lunch in the cafeteria of Parkland Memorial Hospital when he heard the news that President Kennedy had been assassinated. He rushed to the Parkland emergency room, where Kennedy was taken, and found himself with a "front row view" of history. During the pandemonium, a reporter grabbed him and instructed him to guard the emergency room payphone with his life; the reporter had managed to secure one of the hospital phone lines and was corresponding with his press office in New York City. For the next three hours, Dossey himself corresponded with the New York newsroom staff, giving them real-time updates on the president's status.

While this was the most extraordinary event of Dossey's time in medical school, he experienced other successes and frustrations as his studies progressed. He excelled academically, and during his third year he decided to specialize in internal medicine because he enjoyed differential diagnostics. Around that same time, though, the headaches that had plagued him since childhood brought him to a moment of crisis:

> My migraines actually got increasingly troublesome in medical school, so much so that I tried to drop out of medical school because it had become an ethical issue for me. I thought it would just be a matter of time before I had one of these partial blindness episodes during surgery and I might hurt or even kill someone.

His faculty advisor refused to let him drop out, though, and assured him that the migraines would eventually subside.

NEW ROUTINES: SERVICE IN VIETNAM

Yet the headaches, which actually continued to get worse, were not Dossey's biggest frustration. By the time he had completed medical school and his internship, he was disenchanted with what he viewed as Western medicine's attempts to mechanize and reduce humans to biological and physiological specimens. An avid reader of East Asian philosophies, in particular Buddhist writings, Dossey had become increasingly discontent with his medical school's complete neglect of the psyche: emotions, attitudes, and consciousness. Furthermore, he was exhausted by the rigors of medical life: "The long work hours, sleep deprivation, and periodic moonlighting to supplement the poverty-level wages then paid to young doctors in training."

Needing an extended break from the routines of his profession, he volunteered to serve as a doctor in the Vietnam War. He spent the first of his two years of service as a surgeon for an airborne battalion in Vietnam. He was decorated for valor after he rescued the pilot of a downed chopper. Dossey acknowledges the award, but plays it off as an act of duty rather than an act of courage. As he puts it, "There is an old saying among soldiers that 'courage is what you call it later. At the time, it's just called doing your job.'"

During his military service, Dossey's "love affair with internal medicine was rekindled," and upon his return he entered an internal medicine residency at Dallas's Parkland Memorial Hospital in 1971:

> Living behind barbwire and sandbags for a year, going on army patrols, and flying around recklessly in rescue helicopters—my trusty companions for a year in Vietnam were an aid kit, stethoscope, an M-16 rifle, a 45-caliber pistol, and a flack jacket. I had a huge dose of adventure at that point in my life. It was precisely what I needed; it cleaned out my channels of boredom and drudgery, which I was feeling in my medical training.

BEYOND WESTERN MEDICINE

After the war, Dossey learned through a wide-ranging course of reading that biofeedback was a possible treatment for his relentless migraine headaches. Biofeedback trains a patient to perceive involuntary biological processes (blood pressure, heart rate, etc.) and manipulate them through mental awareness:

> By the early seventies, I had finished my medical training and had cycled through Vietnam, and biofeedback had emerged on the national scene as a therapy for classical migraine headaches. I ran all over the country learning how to do biofeedback, and it was practically a miraculous result—the migraine syndrome almost went away completely. I was astonished by that because nothing had worked conventionally in terms of medication or anything else.

Dossey was so impressed with biofeedback that he became a certified instructor in the technique and incorporated it into his private practice, which he set up in 1976. Although Dossey still practiced standard Western medicine, he used biofeedback and other mind-body techniques as complements. He also endorsed both Freudian and cognitive-behavioral psychotherapy, meditation, and spiritual healing: "My position was: There is no formula to plug people into. It just depends on people's temperament and personality and where they are in their own psychological life."

Physicians often sent their patients to Dossey's clinic if conventional medicine failed. Patients were receptive to his unorthodox suggestions, and as a result his clinic and biofeedback practice became so successful that he eventually stopped teaching biofeedback himself, instead hiring three biofeedback specialists to run that part of his practice:

> I had a parallel interest in mind-body approaches. I was running the biofeedback laboratory at the Dallas Diagnostic Association while practicing pretty typical internal medicine. Actually, I became chief of staff of this huge hos-

pital in Dallas. I mention that simply to illustrate that although I had some unconventional interests, my colleagues considered me to be a reputable physician. I managed to work in both worlds, and I did it respectably.

DIGGING DEEPER: TRANSITIONING FROM CLINICIAN TO EDUCATOR

As his knowledge of mind-body therapies grew, Dossey began to monitor the outpouring of mind-body research from the academic and medical communities. In the late 1970s, new and controversial ideas were being proposed about the interplay between consciousness and physics. Dossey read eagerly about the intersection of these two topics. He also attended lectures and seminars, and then wrote essays on his findings. One day, he looked at his tall stack of essays and realized what they amounted to: "I had literally written a book about the intersection of physics, consciousness, and medicine." He eventually turned his collection of essays into his first of nine books, entitled *Space, Time & Medicine*, which was published in 1982 and is still in print today. Dossey describes the period of its publication as a transitional one for his profession:

> It was a hugely exciting time to be in medicine. People were actually beginning to acknowledge that there might be such a thing as the mind. All of this stuff seems to be taken for granted now. When I was in medical school, there was considerable doubt whether we were justified using terms like consciousness.

A self-declared skeptic, Dossey became fully convinced of the mind-body connection only after a series of incidents, including a strange event that occurred one day in his office. He was in his clinic early one morning when one of his patients arrived in hysterics because she had had a dream that three white spots had formed on her left ovary. Convinced they were malignant, the woman demanded an exam. Her exam went fine, so Dossey requested a sonogram. The radiologist told Dossey the whole thing was ridiculous, but performed the procedure anyway. Fifteen minutes later, he came into Dossey's office to tell him that the woman had three white dots on her left ovary:

> This woman had had some sort of ability to see deeply in her body in the context of a dream; those sorts of things convince most open-minded people that we underestimate the nature of consciousness and what it's capable of. Even in the first two years of my medical practice, I had some sensational pre-cognitive dreams of medical events that would not be played out till later. They hadn't even happened at the time of the dream, which absolutely sobered me about the nature of consciousness.

After the publication of his first book, Dossey's professional life became hectic. He was working as both a physician and a writer-lecturer, and it became exceedingly difficult for him to juggle these roles. In 1987, after herniating a disc in his lower back, Dossey realized that something had to give. He underwent neurosurgery to alleviate his back pain, but the pain did not adequately subside and Dossey had to give up his clinical work in 1988:

> I thought I'd still be seeing patients into my seventies and eighties; I thought I'd be doing that for the rest of my life. To this day, my self-image is still that of an internist. I love it dearly, and I truly miss the patient interactions. It will always be a deep love of mine.

HEALING THROUGH PRAYER

After leaving clinical medicine, Dossey spent his time writing and lecturing about mind-body medicine. In 1993, he became enthralled with a double-blind, randomized, and controlled study conducted by a University of San Francisco cardiologist named Randolph Byrd. The study had suggested that long-distance prayer could aid healing:

> People receiving intercessory prayer by prayer groups around the country did better on several counts than people treated conventionally in the coronary care unit. I was confused by this study; I didn't know how to respond to it. It became clear to me that if this represented good science, then this had stunning implications for the nature of consciousness and how it works in the world. Here one saw an extension of the mind-body framework from the ability of consciousness to modify not just your body but someone else's from a distance.

Dossey was stunned by Byrd's findings because they contradicted his long-held belief that consciousness is private and impenetrable. Intrigued and confused, he conducted in-depth research into the topic. Having assumed he would only find a few other studies on intercessory prayer and its effect on healing, Dossey was floored when he came across 130 research studies, most of them scientifically grounded, that also demonstrated this phenomenon. Dossey, who prides himself upon being a man of science first and foremost, was so convinced by these studies that in 1993 he wrote a book about them: *Healing Words: The Power of Prayer and the Practice of Medicine*. The book became a *New York Times* bestseller and landed Dossey on the Oprah Winfrey Show and a number of other talk shows. At the time of the book's publication, only three medical schools in the country offered a course on spirituality in health; today, 90 medical schools do:

> I had accepted at this time that something valid was happening here and that's why I was willing to put my name on this book and take a public stance on it. That was not the best way at the time to advance your career in medi-

cine because this was incendiary, highly controversial stuff, against which some people would just go ballistic in opposition to it, and some still do. But what began as a heretical, truly blasphemous position has really generated a tidal wave of interest and even acceptance in some parts.

After the book's publication, Dossey became the executive editor of the journal *Alternative Therapies in Health and Medicine*, which he describes as the most subscribed-to peer-reviewed journal in its field. As executive editor, he enjoyed writing a bimonthly editorial on a topic of his choosing. In 2005, Dossey became the executive editor of *Explore: The Journal of Science and Healing*. When not absorbed with his work as a writer, he lectures at medical schools and hospitals across the country. He speaks to thousands of doctors each year about advancements in alternative medicine, with the goal of demonstrating to the medical community how attention to consciousness can be incorporated with good science and medicine:

> I think we underestimate the mystery and majesty of the world and our place in it, so I consistently pushed at the margins—particularly during the past ten years of my professional life. I think that we are at a pivotal moment in history when we are being forced by many of these findings to redefine the nature of consciousness and how it operates, from a local framework, to what I call a distant—or perhaps infinite—framework.

The Power of the M.D.

Dossey believes he is able to "get away with such outrageous claims" because of his life-long devotion to science and Western medicine. Publishers have told him that they publish his works not just because of the ideas he writes about, but also, in some measure, because he has a medical degree. Were it not for his credentials, he would have a much harder time gaining credibility in the scientific and publishing communities:

> I've had the immense satisfaction and fulfillment of seeing my work honored and embraced at the highest levels. Many writers never in their lifetime experience that kind of acceptance; I'm often speechless about the level of acceptance. If I'd been writing a script, I couldn't have written a better one.

ARNOLD M. EPSTEIN

John H. Foster Professor and Chair, Department of Health Policy and Management, Harvard School of Public Health; Former Deputy Assistant Secretary, Planning and Evaluation, U.S. Department of Health and Human Services

Arnold Epstein's diverse research has focused on how social and policy factors, such as the socioeconomic status of patients and payers' reimbursement systems and administrative policies, affect the quality of health care in practice. In this profile, he discusses the ambitions that led him to a medical career, and how he has tried to realize those ambitions through his research. He also reflects on his role in the Clinton administration's health care task force, his views on the influence of academic research on policy, and his work as an editor of the *New England Journal of Medicine*.

EDUCATION & TRAINING

1965–1969	B.A., University of Rochester (Mathematics and Political Science)
1967–1968	London School of Economics
1970–1972	M.A., Harvard University (Political Science)
1972–1974	B.M.S., Dartmouth Medical School
1974–1976	M.D., Duke University
1976–1978	Intern and Resident, Internal Medicine, Peter Bent Brigham Hospital (Boston)
1978–1979	Visiting Research Fellow, Oxford University, Department of Social and Community Medicine
1979–1980	Senior Resident, Internal Medicine, Peter Bent Brigham Hospital

CAREER PATH

1980–	Faculty positions culminating in Professor of Medicine and Professor of Health Care Policy, Harvard Medical School
1980–	Positions culminating in Senior Physician and Director, Section of Health Services and Policy Research, Brigham and Women's Hospital
1988–	Faculty positions culminating in John H. Foster Professor and Chair (1997), Department of Health Policy and Management, Harvard School of Public Health
1993–1994	Expert Policy Advisor, U.S. Department of Health and Human Services; Domestic Policy Advisor, The White House
2000–	Associate Editor, Health Policy, *New England Journal of Medicine*
2004–	Board of Trustees, and Vice Chair (2013–2014), Center for Health Care Strategies
2010–	Board of Governors, Patient Centered Outcome Research Institute
2014–2016	Deputy Assistant Secretary, Planning and Evaluation, U.S. Department of Health and Human Services

I would say that the link between research and change in policy is long and tenuous. There are many examples people could draw upon to say that the research we do provides context to the debate, informs us about which options are useful, tells us what the pros and cons are, and sometimes leads to wiser decision-making. It's also true that any particular investigator may often wait a long time before he or she is able to see the impact from his of her findings. But collectively, and some of us individually—we have done work that is important.

—*Arnold Epstein*

When asked to sum up the continuous theme in his complex career Arnold Epstein replies: "All things considered, if you can spend your time doing anything, wouldn't it be nice to do it to make the world a better place?" Inspired to enter a career in medicine by his belief that wisely administered health care policies could do just that, Epstein has been at the forefront of interdisciplinary research in health care policy for over twenty years. His research has focused on questions of access to care and quality of care for disadvantaged populations, asking, for example, how patients' socioeconomic status or race affects the likelihood of their being referred for a particular procedure, or how the payment policies of insurance companies or Medicaid affect quality of care.

Author of numerous articles and, with Joel Weissman, an award-winning book on health insurance, Epstein has held various positions at Harvard Medical School and the Harvard School of Public Health, where he became chair of the Department of Health Policy and Management in 1997. Over the course of his career he has mentored numerous trainees and young faculty; nearly a dozen of his trainees have served on the Harvard faculty. He was a member of the task force responsible for formulating a universal health care plan in the early years of the Clinton administration, and has since continued to serve in various advisory roles to the government. Since 2000, Epstein has been associate editor for health policy of the *New England Journal of Medicine.*

TOWARDS A CAREER IN MEDICINE

As a child growing up near New York City, Epstein had little exposure to the medical profession, and no early aspirations to become a physician. But he recalls that thanks to his father, an attorney who once ran for state office, "the world of politics and policy was the dinner table conversation" more often than not during his childhood. His extended family included other attorneys and some businessmen, and so Epstein saw himself heading for a career along these lines when he became an undergraduate at the University of Rochester.

During his undergraduate years, three spent at Rochester and one abroad at the London School of Economics, Epstein channeled his interest in politics into a political science major; his second major, in mathematics, gradually led him to focus on mathematical modeling in political science.

Epstein graduated from Rochester during the Vietnam War, but a favorable number in the draft lottery allowed him to continue his studies. After an intervening year spent teaching high school math in Massachusetts, he went on to pursue an M.A. in political science at Harvard. He continued to focus on mathematical modeling there; since quantitative study in political science was a relatively young field, he took a number of his courses in the economics department where quantitative methodologies were more thoroughly developed.

Epstein remembers his time at Harvard as a critical one in his own development, in large part because of a felt disconnect between his highly theoretical studies and the rapidly changing world around him:

> This was a period of great upheaval in the country with a schism in where the country was going, with the war and lifestyle, and it seemed particularly attractive to have a job in which if you did your work well, people were better off for it.

Increasingly, his work in political science felt like it would not lead to that kind of satisfaction. Epstein's interest in mathematics had always been at once intense and abstract. As an undergraduate, he remembers focusing mostly on "pure" as opposed to applied math, and his work in political science felt not very different:

> It was intellectually interesting in the way that mathematics... in the way that a mathematical problem would be interesting. And then here's why I left—it was boring, in that it was too ethereal. It just wasn't applied enough, practical enough, and at some point it did not seem to really matter.

At the same time as he began questioning the relevance of his M.A. studies, other influences began leading Epstein toward a career in medicine. While he says many factors were involved in the decision, he singles out as particularly important his conversations with his older sister's husband:

> My brother-in-law was a doctor and he was then in academic medicine, doing investigation, albeit in a different field than mine. He was, I think, pretty

important to me in terms of saying, "What I do is relevant." He didn't say it in a bragging way, just, "Medicine may be something you want to think about. It really matters to people. Health care matters." And so over a period of time I had a glimmer that health care might hold important challenges and be a place to make a positive impact in the world.

While Epstein now had one doctor in the family, he says that his lack of any close connection to the medical profession before this made his new career choice feel like a leap rather than an easy transition: "I didn't have a solid image of what it would be like to be a doctor.... I didn't even have a slight inkling." But he committed himself wholeheartedly, taking the courses in organic chemistry and biology that he needed to fulfill premed requirements even as he was finishing work on his M.A.

DARTMOUTH, DUKE, BOSTON, AND A YEAR "ON"

In 1972 Epstein began medical school in a two-year program at Dartmouth, designed to allow students to transfer elsewhere to complete their training. Epstein chose Dartmouth in part because he wanted a change of pace from Boston. He says the training he received was excellent, but when speaking of his time there his thoughts dwell on experiences outside of the classroom:

It's a wonderful place. I learned a lot at Dartmouth—it's a pretty unique atmosphere, because of its location, because it's rural, because it's cold, because they cherish winter. I learned a lot of really good things up there.

Probably the most important event of Epstein's time at Dartmouth was personal: he met his future wife there, Patricia O'Malley, a fellow medical student. In 1974 they transferred together to Duke University to complete their medical degrees.

Epstein chose Duke because he was looking for something "bigger and bolder, clinically," and the university gave him what he expected. While he knew he was interested in health policy, he remembers focusing primarily on medical science during these years, an emphasis suited to the strengths of a program Epstein describes as "orthodox," at that time, in its orientation toward clinical and biomedical science.

Less orthodox, in ways that have continued to shape Epstein's career, was the environment he found himself in during his internship and residency at Peter Bent Brigham Hospital in Boston (now Brigham and Women's Hospital). At Peter Bent, Epstein explains, clinical practice felt more consistent with thinking about larger questions of health care policy: "The interaction of clinical medicine and social problems was evident."

This interaction led, at first, to further questioning and exploration rather than professional focus. Epstein arranged this with his supervisor:

We [my wife and I] figured out that we didn't quite know what we wanted to do…so as an intern, I approached Marshall Wolf, who ran the program, and said, "Marshall, we're leaving after junior year, taking a year off"—or a year away, or a year "on," however you want to call it. I told him that I needed to figure out how to connect the things that were important to me in my work. And he said, "All right, that makes perfect sense, I'll help you in any way I can." And he did.

With Wolf's support, Epstein went to England along with his wife, where they found positions in the department of social and community medicine at Oxford and at University College in London, respectively.

Already during his time at Duke, Epstein knew that he did not want a career devoted entirely to clinical practice. In his year at Oxford, his interests began to focus on questions of health care policy, and he acquired a base of knowledge that he would build on in his research over the next decade:

> I read a tremendous amount that year, across a wide array of topics that generalists were working on. And it was crystal clear to me that I was much more interested in behavioral science issues, which today we call health services research, than I was in anything that had to do with clinical epidemiology.

In 1979, Epstein returned to complete his residency at Brigham, and in 1980 accepted joint appointments there and as an instructor at Harvard Medical School.

LAUNCHING A CAREER:
FROM "BROWNIAN MOTION" TO RESEARCH WITH A VISION

"Brownian motion" is the term for the random, rapid movement of a microscopic particle suspended in a fluid. This is the metaphor Epstein uses to describe the frenetic pace and quickly changing projects of his first years as a research physician. "It was opportunism and Brownian motion as I initially gained experience and skill in research." An idea of just how much effort this phase of learning the research process took may lie in Epstein's recollection that he initially spent about four half-days per week on patient care, not counting call duty and three months of inpatient attending, and the other fifty percent on his research; implicitly, these were long workweeks.

While Epstein's academic appointment was in Harvard's and the Brigham's department of medicine, he had his office during those years at the Harvard School of Public Health's Center for the Analysis of Health Practices, launched in the 1970s as part of HSPH Dean Howard Hiatt's effort to expand the boundaries of the academic study of public health. Epstein explains that effort as follows:

> Hiatt's vision was that there would be a merger between public health, clinical

medicine, behavioral science, epidemiology, engineering and applied mathematics that would integrate them much more than had heretofore been the case. And that was an important step that would advance the development of policy.

The Center was at the cutting edge of interdisciplinary work in the field, and it was amidst what Epstein remembers as a spectacular group of colleagues that he began to move his research from the opportunism that dominated the very early stage to a more coherent vision of his own.

Epstein describes this vision as a return to the combination of interests that had inspired him to go into medicine in the first place; he had never left this vision behind, but became increasingly able to integrate it into his research. Much of Epstein's research has examined how the social, economic, and psychological characteristics of physicians and patients—from beliefs and attitudes to race, insurance, and income—are related to health care practices and outcomes. Particularly important to his development during this period, he says, was his work on how poor patients were being affected by Medicare's new hospital payment system, which was organized around Diagnosis Related Groups (DRGs) or groups of patients deemed to have similar clinical conditions and thus to incur similar costs:

> I had been interested before in organizational issues. As DRGs were introduced in 1983 I started to study the hospital payment system, and it became clear to me there were some important things about that system as it applied to poor people. And that launched me into empirical investigation of those issues, and that in turn provided impetus for my thinking further about disadvantaged populations.[1]

Underlying Epstein's ability to conduct such research were the unrestricted grants he received during this period. He credits these with allowing him to rethink the nature and scope of his research, and mentions in particular the flexibility permitted him by a five-year award from the Kaiser Family Foundation as "a signal event."

FROM HSPH TO THE WHITE HOUSE—AND BACK

In the late 1980s, as Epstein's career was flourishing, the Center for the Analysis of Health Policy fell on hard times—sources of funding dried up, and the center would soon be dissolved. At the same time, Harvard Medical School created a department of health care policy. Its chair, Barbara McNeil, had frequently collaborated with Epstein in the past, and now offered him a position in the department.

Epstein worked there until 1992, when he went on sabbatical as a Robert Wood Johnson Health Policy Fellow in Washington, D.C. The fellowship, designed to allow mid-career health care professionals to interact with the federal government, came to Epstein at an opportune moment. Bill Clinton was elected to the presidency that November, and Epstein soon found himself working as part of the Task Force for National Health Care Reform led by Hillary Clinton. He remained in the administration through 1994. As a practicing physician with policy expertise, he worked on delivery system issues — particularly quality of care — in the proposal for universal health care that the administration sponsored.

While he had always intended to return to HSPH, Epstein entertained the idea of a longer stay in Washington to continue working on implementation of the Clinton proposal. When it became clear that the legislation was not going to pass, though, he knew his return would come sooner rather than later. Epstein acknowledges the sense of lost opportunity at this time: "Many have suggested that if something more modest had been proposed, or people had done things differently, something might have passed."

Yet despite this setback, he remembers his time in Washington as a productive one that gave him "enormous new understanding":

> I was able to concentrate just on health policy, and I learned a lot. I worked closely with numerous people from all walks of life in the government and in the health policy apparatus, who taught me a tremendous amount about how the policy world moves, day to day.

Epstein worked in the legislative office of Senator Edward Kennedy as well as in the White House during this time. His experience in government, he says, helped him better understand how policy research must mesh with politics in order to effect practical change.

Epstein says that as a researcher he is "probably more ideological than average," in that much of his research is motivated in some way by a vision of social justice. But he also emphasizes that the field of health care policy research is "more academically driven than ideologically," grounded in objective and measurable data. Though he found himself in the middle of the highly politicized debates over the Clinton health care plan, what he took away from these years was an appreciation of the necessity for pragmatic common ground:

> If you think about what the policy process can be like, it's often a shuttle back and forth between people with very divergent values who want to see different things, different outputs out of the system. And finding the common ground, from a policy point of view, is where politics and policy merge in part. Sometimes the ground is too far apart or there is intractable ideology: "We cannot compromise; we must have a market solution." "We cannot yield; we must have a regulatory solution." But it's often useful to ask, what are the goals you are really trying to achieve?

AN EDITOR'S VIEW OF THE PROFESSION

Epstein returned to Harvard Medical School in 1994. Three years later he shifted his primary affiliation to the Harvard School of Public Health, where he became chair of the department of health policy and management. In that role, he has divided his time between the administrative work necessary to guide the department and his own research, which has continued to focus on the relations among factors such as socioeconomic status and race and quality of care; Epstein has also written extensively about the pros and cons of "pay for performance," the impact of public reporting, and Medicaid policy.

Under Epstein's leadership the department has flourished. Three of the faculty members recruited under his tenure have won the outstanding new investigator award from AcademyHealth, the national organization for health services research. Two others have won MacArthur genius awards.

In 2000 Epstein added to his responsibilities when he became associate editor for health policy at the *New England Journal of Medicine*, a job he describes as both demanding and rewarding. He enjoys the "collegial" nature and the relative anonymity of much of his work at the *Journal*, which he describes as a contrast to the need felt in academia to do visible work that a university can easily measure: "In academia there is a lot of concern about what you get credit for. Over [at *NEJM*], it's 'we're only trying to make this a better journal'—and though my name will or won't appear on things where I have a lot of input, that's fine. That's just fine."

As with so much of his work, what he emphasizes about this position is its potential to create practical change:

> You're having a say on what's published in one of the most highly respected journals and one of the most well-read journals, and so you're having an impact on what people see and, to some extent, an influence on what people will work on. I don't mean to say that all of a sudden there is instantaneous change. We are a country with 250 million people or whatever we are these days, one voice among many—but you get heard, and over time move the ball just a little bit further.

This modest estimation of what having an impact means, and of the collective nature of work in health care policy, seem to balance the intense desire to change the world that attracted Epstein to medicine in the first place. Asked whether academic research is perhaps too frustrating a field for someone with this kind of desire, he avoids a simple yes or no; he talks instead, and in much detail, about a wide variety of people from different parts of the health care sector—congressional staffers, academics, CEOs, administrators for fellowship grants—whose work he sees as influential in the context of a system larger than any single player.

While Epstein writes editorials as an advocate for particular policies, he values just as much his role as a facilitator of robust debate—*NEJM*, he explains, is "a place where all points of view can have a hearing." More broadly still, he enjoys the vantage point his editorial position gives him over the profession as a whole: "You're reading constantly what people think of as their best work—it's a real opportunity." Since 2010 he has served on the Board of Governors for the Patient Centered Outcomes Research Institute. PCORI now funds approximately half a billion dollars per year of research activities related to comparative effectiveness. Epstein has been a prominent voice promoting work designed to improve health care systems.

Underlying Themes: Personal and Professional

Epstein has, from the very beginning of his medical career, seen himself as a generalist. Early in medical school, he was certain that he wanted a residency in internal medicine, and the desire for breadth of experience and flexibility has remained a constant for him:

> More than most people, I really like the combination and the transition intellectually, emotionally, between different activities. If I have the choice of great diversity in widespread challenges and the opportunity to move across disciplines or combine them versus feeling like I have extraordinary competency in one area—I'll take the former.

He has maintained this kind of diversity in his multiple roles as department chair, mentor, researcher, editor, and physician (Epstein has continued to see patients throughout his career). Epstein's comfort in such various roles may have something to do with the way he looks back on the stress he felt when choosing a career in medicine. He does not doubt that choice at all. However—perhaps appropriately for someone who has done research on how attitudes and beliefs can impinge on medical practices—he now feels that what most unifies a career has less do with the choice of profession than with the character traits of the person who practices it:

> Earlier in my career, I thought there were important decision points about whether or not to go into medicine. And now I think that there are underlying themes that define one's work, themes like how ideologically you are focused, whether you're people-oriented or more cerebral, theoretical or applied; in terms of problem-solving, whether you're socially oriented or more scientifically oriented. And I think that each of us has preferences along this line of themes, and no matter what job or profession one has chosen, most of us will work out a set of activities and responsibilities that fits those preferences.

Going Forward

In 2014, Epstein was called again into public service, taking leave from Harvard to serve as deputy assistant secretary and head the Office of Health Policy in the office of the assistant secretary for planning and evaluation in the Department of Health and Human Services. Epstein explained:

> We face an extraordinary opportunity now, as how we implement the Affordable Care Act and pursue delivery reform over the next years will likely affect the health care and health of millions of people. I believe the position I will assume will enable me to contribute meaningfully to progress in this area.

When not in Washington, D.C., Epstein resides in Lincoln, Massachusetts, with his wife, Patricia O'Malley, and occasionally with one or more of his three daughters, Kathleen, Rebecca and Elicia Epstein.

Note

1   Two articles from this period may be of particular interest to readers. Arnold Epstein et al "The association of patients' socioeconomic characteristics with length of hospital stay and hospital charges within Diagnosis Related Groups," *NEJM* 318 (1988): 1579–85, and Arnold Epstein, R.S. Stern, J.S. Weissman, "Do the poor cost more; a multihospital study of patients' socioeconomic status and use of hospital resources," *NEJM* 322 (1990): 1122–8.

Harvey V. Fineberg

President, Gordon and Betty Moore Foundation
Former President, Institute of Medicine
Former Provost, Harvard University

Beginning his career as a physician and researcher in the field of medical decision making, Harvey Fineberg went on to become a leader of some of the nation's foremost public health institutions. In this profile, he discusses what interested him in looking at medical issues from a public health rather than a clinical standpoint, and the motives that led him to a career focused on leading organizations.

EDUCATION & TRAINING

1963–1967	A.B., Harvard University (Psychology)
1967–1972	M.D., Harvard Medical School
1969–1972	M.P.P., Kennedy School of Government (KSG), Harvard University
1972–1973	Intern, Medicine, Beth Israel Hospital, Boston
1973–1980	Ph.D., Harvard University (Public Policy)
1974–1975	Intermediate Junior Fellow, Harvard Society of Fellows

CAREER PATH

1973–1981	Faculty positions culminating in Associate Professor of Health Services Administration, Harvard School of Public Health (HSPH), and Member of the Faculty, KSG
1975–1978	Director, Graduate Program in Health Policy and Management, HSPH
1982–1984	Professor of Health Policy and Management, HSPH
1984–1997	Dean, Harvard School of Public Health
1997–2001	Provost, Harvard University
2002–2014	President, Institute of Medicine, National Academy of Sciences
2015–	President, Gordon and Betty Moore Foundation

SELECTED PUBLICATIONS

Weinstein MC, Fineberg HV et al. *Clinical Decision Analysis.* Philadelphia: W. B. Saunders, 1980.

Neustadt RE, Fineberg HV. *The Epidemic That Never Was: Policy-Making and the Swine Flu Scare.* New York: Vintage Books, 1982.

Sepulveda J, Fineberg HV, Mann J, eds. *AIDS: Prevention Through Education: A World View.* New York: Oxford University Press, 1992.

Ross RH, Fineberg HV. *Innovators in Physician Education: The Process and Pattern of Reform in North American Medical Schools.* New York: Springer, 1996.

I like the quote that is attributed to General Eisenhower. He said, "Plans are useless, but planning is essential." I think the wisdom in that is that, yes, having a vision of where you want to be is a good thing to do, but also remaining flexible to take advantage of changing circumstance, or adapt when an opportunity arises or challenges come that weren't anticipated—that's pretty important.

—*Harvey Fineberg*

When you walk into the Great Hall of the National Academy of Sciences in Washington, you enter a monument to the impact of knowledge on society. At the apex of the hall's 56-foot-high dome, an image of the sun is surrounded by symbols of the planets and, beyond them, of eight representative sciences. In the inscription that encircles the base of the dome, one of the epithets given "to science" signals the presence of the Institute of Medicine, the division of the academy devoted to advancing health: "To science," reads the inscription, "conqueror of disease."

At the helm of the IOM sits Harvey Fineberg, a physician by training with a doctorate in public policy and a lengthy track record in public health. If the Great Hall is a space celebrating the mythic aspirations of science, Fineberg is well acquainted with its realities, and will explain that conquering disease happens not in a single battle but in numerous small steps, and through an understanding of the individuals and organizations that practice science on the ground, beneath the dome.

Fineberg has devoted his career to understanding complex decisions and the groups that implement them, organizing scientists, scholars, and students to achieve more collectively than they could alone. For most of his career—as physician, professor, dean of the Harvard School of Public Health, and president of IOM—his work has been centered in the fields of health policy and medical decision making. His love of intellectual breadth and interdisciplinary endeavors found perhaps its widest application during his term as Harvard's provost, a position that made him responsible for integrating research and educational efforts throughout the entire university. His research interests range from HIV/AIDS and other infectious diseases to the evaluation of diagnostic tests and vaccines and the ethical and social implications of new medical technologies.

MEDICINE AS A VECTOR

When Fineberg arrived at Harvard College as an undergraduate, he brought with him the desire to have a positive impact on society. He attributes this in part to his parents, and also recalls the early influence of a Boy Scout leader who was, Fineberg says, "a wonderful human being: an adult who was devoted to the social services." But the desire for a career in public service seems to Fineberg so much a part of who he is that its source is hard to pinpoint—as was the direction it would take him in when he entered college:

> I was always interested in people, so I always thought I'd have a service career. But if you said to me, "Is that going to be in teaching, law, medicine, or social service in some other way?" I would have said, "I'm not sure."

This uncertainty began to give way to a definite interest in medicine when Fineberg took a course taught by biologist George Wald: "The course was basically introductory biology—it was a natural science survey course and he was a gifted teacher, and the subject was intellectually gripping." From the beginning, medicine seemed to be not an end in itself but, Fineberg explains,

> a vector that promised both sides of what I enjoyed: making an impact on individuals and doing something that mattered in the world. And it was this biology class that actually crystallized for me that the vector was going to be medicine.

Fineberg completed his premedical course work while majoring in psychology, with a particular emphasis on physiological psychology. He completed a senior thesis on what may seem, given his subsequent career, an unlikely topic—the sleeping patterns of homing pigeons:

> I was interested in diurnal rhythms—it was related to navigation in birds, because to navigate you also have to know what time it is. In principle, you need some sort of clock. With pigeons, there was a dispute over whether or not they slept, because one of the great pigeon breeders who wrote the definitive work on pigeon breeding described the fact that whenever he walked into the pigeon roost they were always awake. I was interested in these questions, so I set up a design apparatus, measurement devices—and I found that they do sleep for very brief periods of time.

While Fineberg now thinks of his thesis topic as "a very arcane subject," his ability to master such subjects in all their technical detail, to grasp scientific research at its smallest and most basic level, would form the basis of his success in managing research at the largest institutional levels in years to come.

A BROADENING VIEW OF MEDICINE

While completing his senior thesis, Fineberg was accepted at Harvard Medical School, where he enrolled in 1967. He arrived at HMS in the midst of the widespread and fervent student activism that characterized the era, and found his interest in the social and political aspects of health care echoed by his classmates:

> Even in my first year—this was the late 1960s—there was a lot of student activism, and we as students prompted the organization of courses on the social dimensions of medicine. We found some faculty who were willing to teach these extra seminars. It wasn't framed specifically as a policy course—it was more about the dilemma of health care in society and how to solve it. But of course it was not removed from policy.

These student-initiated courses came to feature many of social medicine's most prominent figures, including Leon Eisenberg and Victor Seidel.

In 1968, the Kennedy School of Government (KSG) had just announced a new program in public policy, and invited interested HMS students to apply for a joint degree. Once Fineberg saw the list of faculty involved, he was immediately convinced that the program's emphasis perfectly suited his combination of interests. Fineberg hoped to take the year off between his second and third years of medical school to pursue the M.P.P. program, but to do so he had to clear it with the dean of students first:

> I had never actually met with the dean before, and I could see that on his desk in front of him was this folder. And as I was talking to him he was just looking through this folder, and looking at me, and looking down at the folder. And I was explaining to him what I wanted to do—that there was this program that had just come along in public policy, it was at the Kennedy School of Government, it had this wonderful faculty, and that I was thinking about taking a year off and applying to that program.

What today is usually seen as a worthwhile ambition to supplement an M.D. with an education in policy was, in the early years of the KSG program, a highly unorthodox departure—as Fineberg discovered when he found out what the dean was looking for in his folder:

> So after awhile he said, "Let me get this straight—you're thinking about taking off a year?" And I said, "That's right." And he said, "And you're not going to go into a laboratory?" And I said, "No, actually, I had been thinking about going into this program in public policy." And he said, "public policy"—and then looking through my records—"but your record here isn't all that bad!"

In spite of the dean's bewilderment, Fineberg received permission to take leave, and matriculated with the first joint M.D.-M.P.P. class at Harvard.

What Fineberg discovered in that program was a fundamental tension within policy making that has continued to absorb and challenge him ever since. Public health policy, he explains, offered a combination of "the softest science and the hardest problems"—"soft" not in the sense of weak or vague, but in the sense of being flexible enough to translate medical goals into societal realities:

> It's putting together the needs of people and all the intellectual tools and momentum that you need to analyze and understand the problem. And then from a very practical and pragmatic point of view, how do you motivate the will and capacity of a society to actually solve the problems? It's a sense of not taking things for granted, but looking for ways that you can actually have things get better.

After completing his final two years in medical school, Fineberg began his residency at Beth Israel Hospital in 1972.[1] There he made contact with Howard Hiatt, who had been Beth Israel's chief of medicine until his appointment as dean of the Harvard School of Public Health in the previous year. Hiatt saw in Fineberg the ambition and the broad interest in public health issues that he wanted to bring to his faculty, and invited Fineberg to join: "Howard called me in one day and said, 'You know you're interested in medicine and public policy—public health is the perfect intersection of those two, and we should have you here at the school of public health.'" Fineberg cut short his residency to take up the position, and began teaching there and at KSG in 1973; he was awarded a prestigious Intermediate Junior Fellowship at Harvard's Society of Fellows for the 1974–1975 academic year.

MAKING DECISIONS

After leaving his residency and joining the faculty at HSPH, Fineberg began pursuing a Ph.D. in public policy from Harvard's Graduate School of Arts and Sciences, an endeavor which took him eight years: "It was extended because I was doing clinical practice, teaching at two different schools and writing my dissertation all at the same time."

Fineberg's own research has spanned many topics, but central to his dissertation and much of his other work has been the concept of decision making. The science of decision analysis arose in business research in the middle of the century and gradually spread to other fields. It seeks to rationalize decisions that depend on extremely complex information by developing a model, sometimes a mathematical one, to reliably process this information.

Fineberg's work in the 1970s culminated in his co-authorship of the 1980 textbook *Clinical Decision Analysis*, which established the techniques of decision analysis in the field of medicine. Howard Raiffa—economist, pioneering decision theorist and one of Fineberg's teachers at KSG—emphasizes in his preface to the book the value of decision analysis for medicine, and gives examples of the kinds of factors that it can account for:

> Medical decisions are important enough and repetitive enough for us to try painstakingly to dissect the decision process. In doing this, there are some obvious pluses: we can systematically incorporate objective statistical data; we can elicit and combine the judgments of several experts; we can adaptively and systematically combine the experiences of others; we can calibrate the experts; we can correct for dysfunctional biases; we can elicit the preferences of patients for different medical outcomes.[2]

Fineberg's first major project in policy analysis was undertaken at the behest of Joseph Califano, then secretary of health, education and welfare (HEW).[3] Califano asked Richard Neustadt, a prominent KSG professor, to analyze the events of the 1976–1977 debacle surrounding the swine flu immunization program. Neustadt, in turn, enlisted Fineberg, his former student and now faculty colleague, to join him.

For nine months, beginning in March 1976, the federal government had sought to immunize the entire U.S. population against a strain of influenza thought to have the potential to create a deadly epidemic. The National Influenza Immunization Program encountered a series of unforeseen events: insurers balked at writing policies for the vaccine's manufacturers, who in turn demanded that the government cover their liability; no epidemic ever occurred; and the program was abandoned when immunizations were related to a severe side effect in a small number of vaccine recipients. The program was suspended just two months after full-scale implementation had begun, and was widely judged to have been mismanaged. In its wake, Califano wanted an outside expert analysis of what had gone wrong. He was particularly interested in the decision-making process, as he explains in his introduction to the report:

> I was impressed by the enormous difficulty that a lay official has in fulfilling his responsibility to make sound, balanced judgments about complex scientifically-based public health issues.[4]

The report was first published by HEW in 1978; an expanded edition, entitled *The Epidemic That Never Was: Policy-Making and the Swine Flu Scare*, was published by Vintage in 1982. The failed attempt to immunize every American against a new kind of influenza, wrote Fineberg and Neustadt, "was and is a trauma to the government officials most involved and to their scientific advisers. A year and more later, cheeks flush, brows furrow, voices crack."[5]

Yet Califano praised Fineberg and Neustadt precisely for turning attention away from this kind of embarrassment and towards methods for better handling such crises in the future:

Their narrative will prove enormously valuable to policy-makers in this Department facing difficult decisions in the future—and needing to steer by the light that a clear, objective history can shed upon their way. Indeed, this study can have great meaning for all citizens, within government and outside it, who are interested in the process by which large decisions are made—and who are eager to improve that process.[6]

Their study's conclusions, grounded in a meticulous reconstruction of events and dozens of interviews with the persons concerned, dealt not only with the slippery nature of medical knowledge about the likelihood of flu epidemics, but also with how to plan for the dissemination of that knowledge by the media and its handling among experts. It emphasized the need for, among other things, step-by-step and detailed discussion of evidence, a concerted effort to imagine possible outcomes in the short as well as long term, and the importance for tangible evidence of a threat in order to convince the public that a response was necessary.

Fineberg built on this success in subsequent years. In 1979, he co-founded the Society for Medical Decision Making, an academic association of clinicians and researchers dedicated to understanding and improving the way in which clinicians, patients and policy makers arrive at decisions. Fineberg's 1980 Ph.D. dissertation, "Medical Practices: Five Case Studies in Evaluation, Diffusion, and Policy Making," also made use of his expertise in decision analysis, as did a number of articles published during this period.

Fineberg finds the analysis of clinical decisions "deeply compelling in its own right, because these decisions matter so much and because they have this rich and very clear inclusion of values and likelihoods." More generally, though, he also sees the effort to better understand and make decisions as a constant element of his career: "I just see making better decisions and forming better decisions as a kind of endless quest, and that's a path I've been walking, no matter what I've been doing along the way."

BECOMING AN INSTITUTIONAL LEADER

In 1984 the president of Harvard University, Derek Bok, asked Fineberg to become dean of the Harvard School of Public Health. Fineberg, after some consideration, accepted the offer:

I felt that the school was a really important institution and I thought that I could make a contribution. I was attracted to the combination of importance and a conviction about my own potential to contribute. I would say that has been true at every step of my career.

Even while making the decision, Fineberg realized how deeply it would affect his life: "It meant a significant change in my daily work and my responsibilities and my relations to people." For this and other reasons, he identifies becoming dean of HSPH as the most significant turning point in his career:

> Prior to 1984 I was primarily a teacher, a researcher, a scholar in a field. This decision was an inflection point, because it was when I made the shift into administration of organizations. There was more difference in moving from that professorial role to a dean role than there was moving from a dean role to a provost role, or from either of those to the role as president of the IOM.

His new responsibilities did not come without a cost, however. Though Fineberg had left his residency to join HSPH, he had never given up clinical practice: he had continued to see patients as a general practitioner at two Boston-area health centers even as he fulfilled his academic duties. With most of his time as a dean now taken up by administrative work, he felt that he could no longer do so:

> My wife, who is a physician—an infectious disease specialist—said, "At this point, medical *practice* would be a good word for what you'd be doing." In fairness to the patients, I do think you need to be at a level of currency that just wasn't practical for me at that point.

This decision, however, was not a change of heart about the importance of patient care, or even about its satisfactions for him; caring for patients and work at the policy level, says Fineberg, "are both worthwhile, they are both important." But Fineberg explains that he had always felt that his primary interest and his best chance to make an impact lay at the interface between medicine and policy: "I was always interested in this interface. For me it was more a trajectory along that path intellectually from the beginning, and not a reaction to being unable to have an impact somewhere else."

Fineberg had had little administrative experience prior to becoming a dean. Yet he explains that this relative inexperience is not uncommon among academics appointed as deans, including those who prove to be successful. It is a job, he says, for which no preparation is quite sufficient:

> Very few people when they first become a dean have any basis to predict whether they'll be good at it. Nobody, practically, is trained to be a dean. So it's a little bit of speculation on the part of both those who appoint and those who accept.

Fineberg, then, learned how to be a dean only by becoming one. He took over the position from his friend and mentor Howard Hiatt, who in his twelve-year tenure had transformed the school and greatly expanded the disciplinary boundaries of the study of public health. Fineberg continued Hiatt's innovative work, presiding over the creation of a number of interdisciplinary centers at the school to study key areas of concern in public health. Perhaps the most notable of these was the Harvard AIDS Institute founded in 1988; Fineberg helped make HSPH a leader in the early fight against the disease, and acted himself as a public advocate for rational, humane treatment of its victims. Fineberg also presided over the growth of HSPH's faculty and a nearly fourfold increase in the school's budget, thanks in no small part to his success as a fundraiser.

The Public's Health

One advantage of getting an M.D. before going into the field of public health, Fineberg says, is simply that it makes it easier to explain to people what you do: "Often times you'll end up just saying to people, 'I'm a doctor.'" Communicating the nature of work in public health can be a bit more difficult:

> The question I am asked more than any other is "What is public health and how is it different from medicine?" And what it boils down to is that medicine has a different emphasis.[7]

In public health, medicine is only one of many tools employed, along with public education, nutrition, environmental protections and workplace safety. The main difference from medicine lies in the way public health professionals look at health problems: the physician looks at an individual patient, while the public health professional more often looks at demographic groups or at the entire population.

Fineberg clarifies the unique educational goals of his school by drawing an analogy: "If a medical school is akin to a school of law, then a school of public health is like a school of justice." While medical schools train physicians according to the best known methods, a school of public health works one step removed from this training and tries to reassess what "the best" is, in physician training as well as in fields like disease control and nutrition. The 1996 book co-authored by Fineberg, *Innovators in Physician Education: The Process and Pattern of Reform in North American Medical Schools*, attempts just this kind of reassessment, analyzing the redesign of medical education at ten leading American medical schools.

"One emphasis is not necessarily better than the other," says Fineberg of medicine and public health. "But in my heart of hearts, I really believe we will never in this world solve health problems one person at a time."[8] This conclusion about where he can most make a difference underlies Fineberg's longstanding desire to study and bring about change in health care policy.

> I knew what problems interested me: the problems of how you make health care work for people, of how you help people live healthier lives. And I was interested in solving them for everyone, or a large number of people. So I was always attracted to the social policy level.

BRIDGING DISCIPLINES

It was exactly the same rationale, Fineberg says, which motivated him to accept the offer to become Harvard's provost in 1997. Fineberg also felt like it was the right time for a change:

> At that point I had been dean for about thirteen years. I had it in mind that I should start being open to other things, because it's very easy for a dean to stay too long. Even if it seems that the incumbent might be best for the next year, when you take a five-year outlook, you see that the institution is better served by a fresh start.

The position of provost marked a new level of responsibility for Fineberg, as well as a departure from the field of public health. The office of the provost was created to oversee activities ranging across Harvard's many departments and schools, from KSG and HSPH to the Faculty of Arts and Sciences. Fineberg initiated programs designed to foster collaboration among these different schools—to facilitate, for example, the interaction of scientists from the chemistry department in FAS with researchers in the medical school. Fineberg worked on other issues of concern to the entire university community, such as information technology and faculty diversity, and put together a team to oversee the expansion of Harvard's campus in the years to come.

SWITCHING ACADEMIES: THE INSTITUTE OF MEDICINE

In 2002, Fineberg was asked by the council of the Institute of Medicine to become its seventh president. He had first become involved with the IOM in 1981 when he was elected as a member, and had since served as chair or co-chair of several of its committees. The IOM's offer was an attractive one for Fineberg, given the position's continuity with his seventeen years of experience managing large organizations; the decision to accept, he says, "was easy, because it is a unique, critical organization and again, I thought I could make a contribution."

The move to the IOM meant a return to medicine and public health after Fineberg's interdisciplinary administrative work as provost. On the other hand, it was a significant departure for him in other ways. Fineberg had spent the previous 38 years—as student, teacher and administrator—at Harvard, and so the move meant leaving a much-loved institution and moving with his wife to Washington, D.C. It also meant moving from academia into a different kind of institution.

Inaugurated in 1970 as a branch of the Congressionally chartered National Academy of Sciences, the IOM acts independently of, and in an advisory capacity to, the federal government and other organizations; its elected members and other expert volunteers do their work *pro bono*, as a public service. The IOM releases several dozen reports every year on health issues. The topics it addresses are as diverse as Fineberg's own interests—examples include the health of astronauts, the environmental effects of damp indoor spaces, lessons from SARS, nutrition labeling, childhood obesity, medication errors, advice to the Department of Defense on bio-warfare preparedness, the effects of post-traumatic stress disorder on returning veterans, and the effects of climate change on the spread of infectious disease.

While the range is wide, the IOM is also committed to a few ongoing programs of study for which the institute is particularly well known. The most famous of these is the IOM's quality initiative, which has brought the leading experts together in authoring a series of reports on the quality of health care in the U.S. These include the watershed 2001 report *To Err is Human*—best known for its estimate that as many as 98,000 lives were lost in the U.S. each year due to medical errors—as well as the follow-up report *Crossing the Quality Chasm*. These books have helped bring about a period of tremendous focus on quality in health care, and particularly on reducing medical errors. In recent years, the IOM has emphasized work to increase the value of health care, taking account of both quality and cost of care.

Fineberg took over as the head of the IOM at what he believed to be a particularly important time for the institute's mission: "To meet the public's health needs and to fulfill the promise of science for health have never been more compelling social goals," he wrote in his statement accepting the presidency.

To ensure that the IOM would respond effectively to opportunities on the horizon, Fineberg supervised the writing of its strategic plan for 2003 through 2008, the end of his first term as president. The plan set out a course for improvement in the IOM's work and operations, with the clear ultimate goal of increasing the impact of the institute's work. Its mission statement reads simply: "The Institute of Medicine serves as advisor to the nation to improve health."[9]

Fineberg's character and experience are reflected across the strategic statement. It emphasizes the need for IOM to take "an ecological and systems view" of its work—to understand each project in its "interdependencies" with others—and to use the resource of its diverse membership to conduct multi-disciplinary research where needed.[10] It stresses the importance of actively searching out topics of investigation not yet well understood, or not receiving due attention from policy makers, and of taking an active role in discerning emergent health care problems. It asserts the value of deliberately conducted, detailed self-evaluation for the institute—a theme in much of Fineberg's work on decision analysis: "A spirit of self-inquiry and learning should be a hallmark of how we conduct our work."[11]

The plan implicitly lays out a pragmatic definition of what "vision" in public health means: not just a set of lofty goals—though there is no shortage of these—but also a constant vigilance with regard to the conditions for their implementation, from simple timeliness to world-class technology, from effective communication with the media to, at a thoroughly human level, the need for the institute to be "a recurring source of professional delight for its members."[12] The report's ethos, then, squares with that which Fineberg has brought to each of his administrative positions. "I think that vision is wonderful," he explains, "but it's not enough. If you're going to have an impact, you also have to help transform the organization."

In 2008 Fineberg was elected to a second five-year term as President of the IOM. Among the topics addressed by the IOM during Fineberg's tenure were AIDS prevention, physical education in schools, the evaluation of new medical technologies, and the priorities for research to reduce harm from firearm-related violence. Among the achievements of his presidency was the leadership role the IOM took in the field of comparative effectiveness research. CER is designed to help patients and clinicians make more informed decisions about a patient's care based on actual evidence and data, and is therefore closely related to Fineberg's lifelong interest in understanding decision making. Believing in the value of such information to help both improve the public's health and reduce the cost of care, in 2009 Congress appropriated $1.1 billion in federal support for CER as part of the American Recovery and Reinvestment Act of 2009. The IOM was asked to take a leadership role in guiding this effort, and in 2009 released a report establishing a working definition of CER, prioritizing potential CER research topics, and identifying the resources needed to create an ongoing research program in this field.

DECIDING, ENABLING, AND LEARNING

Reflecting on the interests and goals that have unified his career, Fineberg comes up not with a single answer but, understandably after a career that has encompassed such various achievements, with a series of them. One thing he is entirely sure of is the motive that has remained constant for him through each of his major career moves:

> Accepting a new position has always been a choice not in terms of what I was good at, but about where could I make the most contribution at that time. That is the question I ask myself whenever I am deciding whether or not I am going to do something: where do I go to make the most contribution?

Fineberg also acknowledges the great pleasure he has found in each new set of challenges, and the way in which each has allowed him to grow. Asked to sum up his role in a single word, Fineberg demurs at some perhaps too obvious choices—leader, innovator, builder of institutions—and in favor of something more surprising:

> If I had to give myself one word, my word would be "learner"—I've always felt from everything I've done that I've gotten more out of it than I was able to give. My life has been a continuous learning experience, and I love learning.

The relationship between what Fineberg has given and what he has received—between what he has contributed and what he has learned—is not, of course, one of opposition. As a leader and administrator, he has understood how much one depends on the other. Fineberg's insistence in his strategic plan for the IOM that "a spirit of inquiry and learning should be a hallmark of how we conduct our work" also very much reflects his own goal for himself.

Another unifying theme Fineberg identifies is one that links his work as a Ph.D. student to his later career as an administrator:

> I guess I would say that the integrating web for me is more around making good decisions. Now that's not exactly a profession, that's not exactly a career. But what I've been interested in intellectually, and practicing personally, has been really around the question of making better decisions.

From his early work as a student and analyst of decisions to his later career, making immensely consequential decisions himself, Fineberg has never understood decisions as singular acts of will on the part of an executive. To read his account of the swine flu affair is to see decisions as above all processes, series of events that play out within and between organizations. To decide means first to understand this process in all its interpersonal complexity, and to produce a desirable outcome requires not so much giving orders as responding appropriately to others' feedback as the process unfolds.

Those other people are often foremost in Fineberg's mind as he discusses the satisfactions of his work. He mentions the pleasure of running across former students who are now in leadership positions themselves. "There are times," he adds, "when you may have an impact that you're not aware of. It's really a happy day when one of those becomes evident later from someone."

In Fineberg's final attempt to sum up his career, he almost disappears behind those other people—the organizations and countless individuals to whom his work has in some way made a difference:

> A common feature of what I have done is enabling: it was true for students, for my colleagues, as dean, as provost, and it's true now as president of the IOM. The people who work for the IOM now are doing a public service, and I'm trying to enable that. So maybe the whole job is about amplifying. Maybe my whole life has been one large amplification.

Notes

1   Beth Israel Hospital became Beth Israel Deaconess Medical Center after it merged with
    Deaconess Hospital in 1996.

2   Howard Raiffa, preface to Milton Weinstein, Harvey Fineberg et al, *Clinical Decision Analysis*
    (Philadelphia: W. B. Saunders, 1980).

3   The Department of Health, Education and Welfare was the predecessor to the Department of
    Health and Human Services, and was renamed in 1980 when the Department of Education
    was established as a separate department.

4   Joseph Califano, introduction in Neustadt and Fineberg, *The Epidemic That Never Was:
    Policy-Making and the Swine Flu Scare* (New York: Vintage, 1982), 4.

5   Ibid., 13.

6   Ibid., 6.

7   As quoted in Robin Marantz Henig, *The People's Health: A Memoir of Public Health and Its
    Evolution at Harvard* (Washington, D.C.: John Henry Press, 1997), 2.

8   Ibid., 3.

9   Institute of Medicine, "Strategic Vision 2003–2008," July 2003, 2.

10 Ibid., 3.

11 Ibid., 7.

12 Ibid., 10.

MARYANN F. FRALIC

Emerita Professor and Director, Corporate and Foundation Relations, The Johns Hopkins University School of Nursing

Across a long career in nursing administration and education Maryann Fralic has worked in a wide variety of roles, from staff nurse to senior hospital executive and from professor to management consultant. In this profile, she discusses how she has managed to balance the professional and family commitments that she values. She also discusses the virtues of the flexibility constantly demanded by the nursing profession, her contributions to nurse training and education, and her views on the importance of nursing executives to the health care system as a whole.

EDUCATION & TRAINING

B.S.N., Duquesne University
M.N., University of Pittsburgh (Nursing Administration and Cardiovascular Nursing)
Dr.P.H., University of Pittsburgh (Health Services Administration)

CAREER PATH

Staff Nurse and Nurse Supervisor, McKeesport Hospital
Faculty member, McKeesport Hospital School of Nursing
Assistant Director of Nursing, Braddock General Hospital
Chief Nursing Officer, Braddock General Hospital
Senior Vice President, Nursing, Robert Wood Johnson University Hospital
Clinical Associate Dean, Rutgers University College of Nursing
Chair of the National Advisory Council on Nurse Education and Practice of the Health Resources and Services Administration, Department of Health and Human Services (HHS)
Vice President for Nursing, The Johns Hopkins Hospital and Associate Dean, John Hopkins University School of Nursing (JHUSN)
Professor and Director, Corporate and Foundation Relations, JHUSN
Consultant, Robert Wood Johnson Executive Nurse Fellows Program
Executive Advisor, Nursing Executive Center, Advisory Board Company

SELECTED PUBLICATIONS

"Nursing Leadership for the New Millennium—Essential Knowledge and Skills." *Nursing and Health Care Perspectives.* 2001; 20(5):260–265.

Fralic MF, ed. *Staffing Management & Methods: Tools & Techniques for Nursing Leaders.* San Francisco: Jossey-Bass; Chicago: HealthForum, Inc., 2000.

ADDITIONAL INFORMATION

Institute for Nursing Leadership: www.nursingleadership.org
John Hopkins School of Nursing: www.son.jhmi.edu

I think it is wrong to so precisely plan a career. If you are focused only on the track that you are on, you will miss seeing other opportunities. You will be busy looking ahead only at what your goal is, and although peripheral things may be happening that are really quite wonderful, you will never see them—you will not recognize them. Allow for some serendipity.

—Maryann Fralic

Maryann Fralic tends to emphasize good fortune and the support she has received from others when discussing her career. These modest emphases may belie the extent to which she has herself provided such support, both to her family and to her profession at large, over the course of a career that has embraced every aspect of nursing, from clinical practice to education and administration. In her many professional roles, she has done innovative work on aspects of nursing as varied as improving the practice of nurse executives, managing day-to-day issues in patient care, and making competency in financial skills a part of nursing education at the Johns Hopkins University School of Nursing, where she is a professor and the director of corporate and foundation relations. Fralic also holds positions with the Advisory Board Company and the Robert Wood Johnson Executive Nurse Fellows Program, and is an internationally respected author and lecturer in health care and nursing administration.

"I'd like to say that I always had this calling," Fralic remarks of her career in nursing, but the way events have unfolded for her perhaps owes more to her openness to new and challenging options than to any long-term vision. "It happened that choosing nursing was absolutely the right thing," she says, "but I can't claim ownership to any master plan on that."

EARLY CAREER

After attending a diploma school of nursing in a hospital, Fralic went on to get her baccalaureate degree in nursing, a move that was unusual since the overriding trend at the time was for nurses to be hospital-educated. After college, Fralic began working at McKeesport Hospital, a large community hospital outside of Pittsburgh. Much to her surprise, she was asked to be a hospital nursing supervisor at the age of 22. Though she was at first intimidated by the expectations of her new position, she was thrilled to have received the confidence and trust of those working above her, and ultimately she found she could succeed.

The job was extremely demanding. At the time, it was customary for the nursing supervisor to take responsibility for the entire hospital, and for a wide variety of tasks in addition to all the clinical duties. These tasks included admitting patients, assigning beds and rooms, releasing bodies in the morgue, securing and scheduling staff, and working in the pharmacy to fill prescriptions twice a night. Fralic remembers the working environment as "crazy," but at the same time notes that, at a young age, she acquired the ability to work under pressure while juggling many responsibilities:

> I had a mentor…but when she was off, I was it. And that was kind of shocking—that I was it—but I was forced to learn to make decisions, to assume responsibility, and to develop a resilience that's really essential as you move from one responsibility to another. So, you could be handling a labor room without staffing for the night shift one second; the next second, there's a bomb scare; after that there's a drug needed that's out of stock in the pharmacy. It is a frenetic role, but it builds confidence in such an amazing way.

Fralic found that she thrived on "busy-ness," and that informed her approach to many other career and family challenges that she would face in the future.

FAMILY AND WORK, BALANCE AND SEQUENCING

While she was working as nursing supervisor, Fralic got married, and a year into her marriage she became pregnant. At the time, the assumption was that nurses could not work in the hospital during pregnancy, so Fralic became a part-time faculty member in the school of nursing. After her experience as a supervisor, teaching seemed to be a natural next step. She taught until her son was born; she later had a daughter as well. With the growing pull of family and personal life, she and her husband decided together that she would take time off from her career to stay at home with the children until they entered school. Regarding the push-and-pull of parenthood and career, she remarks:

> You really need balance. There are times in your career when your personal life has to be first, and other times when the career is first. There's a time to devote to family, there's a time when your career is the most important, there's a time when your husband's schedule is, when your children's activities are—you need to bend around that. In our family it was always give and take.

Despite the challenge, Fralic feels to this day that choosing to take time off and put her personal life first was absolutely the right decision. Laughing energetically, she quotes Lily Tomlin: "You can have it all … but you just can't have it all at once."

Striking a balance was no less challenging when Fralic returned to work after her years off. She addressed these difficulties in part by hiring a house-keeper, even though finances were tight at the time. This allowed her to maintain an active role in her children's lives; she insisted on reserving time to help with homework and to be there for them in other ways.

Fralic came to believe that her ability to identify the need for outside help was crucial to establishing a balance: "Everyone's not married with children," she says, "but whatever your circumstances are, you somehow need to know that there's something or someone around you that provides support." Indeed, Fralic experienced what a difference such support can make. With the help and encouragement of her family, she was able to pursue her master's degree full-time when her children were enrolled in school, and ended up earning a joint degree in nursing administration and cardiovascular nursing.

ADAPTATION AND GROWTH

Fralic points out that nursing has been a wise career choice because of the inherent value and importance of the work, and because of its unusually flexible nature: "One can have many different careers within a nursing career. You can move in and out. You can decide that you want to be a critical care nurse one day, and later you can be a researcher, and next, you can be work-ing as a nursing expert for a pharmaceutical company." And since there is such high demand for nurses, many hospitals eagerly retrain them even after they have taken several years away from the profession. But, she adds, the flexibility works both ways, since nurses have to be able to switch gears with ease to work well in their varied roles. This means, in turn, that they are often able to succeed outside the traditional boundaries of the profession:

> Nurses are educated to do really thorough objective assessment, analysis, plans of action. There is a rigor to what we call the nursing process…. It is a core competency in the background that makes the profession attractive in so many ways, because you bring that process along with you to whatever it is that you choose to do. For example, in addition to hospital nursing, nurses make good entrepreneurs, they make good IT people, they make good law-yers, and they are wonderful in consulting firms. … They are great in the man-aged care organizations where they are doing case management. They make excellent federal legislators—there are several in Congress right now. There's literally no limit, and there aren't many professions that can offer that.

While nursing has always remained at the center of Fralic's career, within the boundaries of her profession she has experienced a high degree of variety and flexibility. After completing her master's degree, Fralic learned that Braddock General Hospital, a small community facility in Pennsylvania, was advertising for an assistant director of nursing. She applied for the position and was hired. After several years there, her supervisor decided to leave and recommended that Fralic take her place as chief nurse.

At first, Fralic balked because she felt that the time was not right, that she was not ready and needed time to grow into the position. But the CEO of the hospital was so encouraging about the promotion that he urged Fralic to take advantage of the opportunity. She recalls him saying, "You must always learn to take advantage of opportunities when they present themselves." She never forgot the phrase, and she passes it on when others are at key turning points. In the end, she accepted the offer. As with her first job, she was again faced with a number of initially intimidating responsibilities, but she viewed them as a way of gaining invaluable expertise. In this case, Fralic found that the skills she had already acquired "could not have been a better training ground for a career in executive nursing."

Fralic's writing career also started at Braddock, and much like her initial decision to become a nurse, it was totally unplanned. From her new position as the hospital nurse executive, she was eager to communicate the staff's high-quality work in patient education. She made a cold call to the editor of the *Journal of Nursing Administration*, and he suggested she write up the program for publication; it became the first of more than 50 subsequent publications. A few months later, Fralic was offered a spot on the journal's editorial board, which marked the start of decades of collaboration in professional publishing.

Fralic remained in the demanding position of chief nurse for about five years, at which point she decided to resign so she could begin doctoral study. Her children were then teenagers in middle and high school, and she wanted to be able to spend more time at home and to accommodate their needs. She chose to pursue her doctorate in health services administration because she felt it would allow her to have a greater impact than in her previous positions:

> I knew that clinical nursing was not where I would be most valuable and where I could make the best contribution—and I always have seen executive nursing practice as being able to meaningfully influence clinical care, and to support so many nurses and so many patients.

After completing her doctorate, Fralic hoped to find a position as a chief nursing officer (CNO) in an academic hospital setting. Since her children were away at college by then, she looked at positions outside of her home state of Pennsylvania, and ultimately interviewed at New Jersey's Robert Wood Johnson University Hospital. She was offered the position, and accepted with her husband's strong support, despite the fact that the change meant keeping two houses in two different states.

Although she initially worried that she might not have made the right choice, she discovered in time that it felt like a perfect fit. She was able to put her administrative training to use, and at the same time assumed a joint appointment as associate dean at Rutgers University School of Nursing. Despite accumulating a lot of frequent flyer miles traveling between New Jersey and Pennsylvania, she was very satisfied by her life at work.

Fralic remained at the Robert Wood Johnson University Hospital for ten years. She was then recruited to work for the Johns Hopkins Hospital in Baltimore, and knew the position was right for her as soon as she looked into it: "I was captivated by the history and the values of Hopkins—that was it. That was the place for me at the time."

DAY-TO-DAY WORK AT HOPKINS AND ELSEWHERE

Fralic was employed as vice president for nursing at the one-thousand-bed Johns Hopkins Hospital, and held a joint appointment as associate dean for the Johns Hopkins University School of Nursing. As a member of the senior executive team, she was focused on supporting the clinical care of patients.

A typical day might start with a medical staff meeting at 7:00 a.m., then rounds, perhaps interviews, later a planning session for recruitment strategies, and then meetings with department heads to resolve any problems that had arisen during the day. The time would go by quickly, and since there was often no chance to spend more than a few minutes on any one project, much important work had to wait until the formal business day was over: "You get a lot of your work done past 5:00 p.m.," explains Fralic. Overall, though, she believes her work was focused on essentials. her primary job was ensuring that nurses at the bedside could provide high-quality patient care. Fulfilling this responsibility, she believes, required a great deal of commitment, and she emphasizes that such commitment from nurse executives matters to the way the health care system functions as a whole:

> You have to really love the job—just like any other top-level job. The requirements, the challenges, and the pressures are enormous. You have to really know that's all part of the territory and to be challenged by it. There's a whole lot of keeping your skill set sharp. I believe that if nurse executives do not have skills at the level that the other vice presidents at the table have, then patients lose—because that means they are not going to be successful at making the kind of case that needs to be made, so that patients can always receive high-quality care.

A hospital's chief nurse often has a budget in the tens of millions of dollars, larger than that of many corporations. In terms of financial responsibilities and concerns, many parallels can be drawn between this position and that of the CEO for a private company. At Hopkins, the nurses number in the thousands; the vice president for nursing is expected to maintain a viable administrative model, and to make effective, efficient use of resources.

After spending five years at the Johns Hopkins Hospital, Fralic stepped out of operations and moved to the Johns Hopkins University School of Nursing as a professor. At that time, she also began working as executive advisor at the Advisory Board Company in Washington, D.C., a research and best practices company for hospitals. During this time, she explains, the company had "programs for CFOs, CEOs, and others, but not for Chief Nursing Officers." The company's Nursing Executive Center was created with her help; it counts over one thousand CNOs as members, and over ten thousand nurse managers have passed through its training program, called the Nursing Leadership Academy.

Further expanding her commitment to executive education, Fralic also accepted an offer to work as a consultant with the Robert Wood Johnson Executive Nurse Fellows Program, which provides leadership development to executive nurses who have demonstrated outstanding capabilities. She believes the program is unique, and helps fill a critical void:

> Usually when you get to be a dean or a vice president, nobody is interested in developing you. They figure if you don't know what to do, you shouldn't have the job, right? Well, this goes the other way. It says, "Let's take our bright successful people and prepare them for national impact, national leadership." It's such a sterling program that the Robert Wood Johnson Foundation has funded. I am proud to be part of it.

PRESENT AND FUTURE GOALS

Fralic has continued to set priorities at the cutting edge of her profession. At Hopkins, she was instrumental in establishing a course at the Johns Hopkins School of Nursing called "The Business of Nursing," the first of its kind. Financial skills, Fralic explains, have not traditionally received much emphasis in nursing education, despite their increasing relevance: "We are so good at identifying the clinical implications of what we do. But today, cost is also important, as well as quality, and vice versa. We are not used to thinking that way, but that is our new reality."

In each of her three professional roles—at Hopkins, the Advisory Board Company, and the Robert Wood Johnson Program—Fralic has focused on the need for quantitative methods in research and in practice:

Nursing has great potential for very positive economic impact, whether it is doing effective case management and keeping patients out of hospitals, or having advanced practice nurses in the home with high-risk newborns to save inpatient days in a neonatal intensive care unit. All of these nursing actions have a significant cost impact. The goal is to interpret and communicate the data in a way that the business world respects. The power of quantitative research is that it can influence practice, policy, and quality patient care.

A BALANCE OF GOALS AND CHOICES

Fralic has found it overwhelming at times to have so many goals and interests in her work, education, and private life. With regard to the early days of her career and her search for balance, she again quotes Lily Tomlin: "If I knew what having it all meant, I would have settled for less!" But she says this with mild irony, not at all in earnest. Fralic has made sacrifices both professional and personal, but by no means does she feel that these have been wasted.

In all of her current roles, she strives to be a positive influence in the lives of nurses, students, and other health professionals, working hard to ensure their optimal performance and their satisfaction with their work. She has seen innumerable successes, as well as inevitable setbacks, and feels fortunate to have the chance to impart her knowledge and experience to others:

> You need that feeling around you that somebody will be there to help you be successful because they care about you. I have had that gift, and I work hard to provide the same for others. It takes lots of people and lots of support to make a person successful. Anybody who believes they're just great and that's how it happened—that's nonsense.

In 2012, in recognition of her career-long dedication to shaping the future of the nursing profession and cultivating nursing leadership, she was awarded the American Organization of Nurse Executives 2012 Lifetime Achievement Award.

Robert S. Galvin

Chief Executive Officer, Equity Healthcare, The Blackstone Group
Former Director, Global Healthcare, General Electric

As the director of global health care at General Electric for fifteen years, Robert Galvin has been at the forefront of developing and implementing innovative strategies for meeting health care needs while managing health care costs. Galvin, who after college began a career as a writer and poet, discusses what led him initially towards clinical medicine and eventually into the intersection of medicine and business. He also discusses the Leapfrog Group and other employer-based initiatives he has been involved in that promote health care quality.

Education & Training

1968–1972	B.A., University of Pennsylvania
1977–1981	M.D., University of Pennsylvania
1981–1984	Resident in Internal Medicine, University Hospital/ Boston University Medical Center
1995	M.B.A., Boston University School of Management

Career Path

1984–1990	Private Practice Physician, General Internal Medicine
1985–1995	Coordinator and Director, Inpatient Service, Internal Medicine Teaching Program, North Shore Medical Center
1988–1996	Physician Advisor, North Shore Medical Center
1990–1992	Medical Director, General Electric (GE), New England Region
1992–1995	General Manager, Health Care Operations, GE Aircraft Engines & Regions
1996–2010	Director, Global Health Care, GE
1999	Co-Founder, the Leapfrog Group
2001–	Positions culminating in Professor Adjunct of Medicine, Yale School of Medicine
2001–2004	Vice Chairman, Washington Business Group on Health (WBGH) (now the National Business Group on Health)
2003	Chairman, the Leapfrog Group
2010–	CEO, Equity Healthcare, The Blackstone Group

Additional Information

Catalyst for Payment Reform: www.catalyzepaymentreform.org

The Leapfrog Group: www.leapfroggroup.org

The Blackstone Group: www.blackstone.com

I love health care. I still have this belief that it's really about patients, and that even what I do now is, on a very large level, to get these systems centered around them. Whether it's a decision I have to make in a half hour about whether to quarantine people for SARS in Taiwan or whether, when we go to union negotiations, we're going to spend X million more dollars to cover more drugs, it's just a larger scale, but to me it's the same focus.

—*Robert Galvin*

From aspiring poet to senior executive at one of the world's largest corporations, Robert Galvin's career has seldom advanced along a straightforward path. He has repeatedly discovered passion and success in what appeared to be mere necessity: working as a nurse's aid to support his writing, he became a medical student; pushed by his senior medical partners back into the business world he had left for poetry, he became a health care executive. For fifteen years as director of global health care at General Electric, Galvin was responsible for the company's $3 billion in annual health benefit expenditures, and oversaw a provider network including 220 clinics, 500 physicians and nurses and one million patient visits annually. As co-founder of the Leapfrog Group, Galvin has also become a leader in major employers' efforts to promote and improve the quality of health care in America.

A CREATIVE START

Having grown up in Cleveland as the son of a corporate CEO, Galvin recalls being immersed in business culture from his youth. This environment initially led him to pursue an undergraduate degree in business:

> At dinner conversations, while as a kid you might be bored to death, you can't help but absorb it because you're sitting there. All that my dad and his relatives talked about were business operations, mergers and acquisitions, and bonds. So I went to Wharton.

After arriving in 1968 at Wharton, the University of Pennsylvania's business college, Galvin had a change of heart about working in business:

> I had written a little bit in high school in the late 1960s. And now business seemed boring, and writing seemed like a passion, and I thought it would be fun to follow my passion. So I wrote.

Galvin left Wharton and enrolled in the University of Pennsylvania's Arts and Sciences program, graduating as a creative writing major. He began to pursue a career as a writer, focusing mostly on poetry and short stories but also taking on journalism assignments to cover his costs. To supplement his income, Galvin found a job as a nurse's aid in the psychiatry department at the University of Pennsylvania Hospital, a position that offered him two key benefits. First, the psychiatry ward provided endless stimulation and material for his writing. Second, his boss, an aspiring academic psychiatrist, needed help with his own writing, and called upon Galvin to assist him.

During this time Galvin became increasingly convinced that while writing was his truest passion, he did not have the talent to succeed in it professionally:

> You don't make money publishing poems and stories—or at least I didn't. So I had to decide. I remember competing for this big poetry prize, and this guy who was running my poetry group—C. K. Williams [now a Pulitzer Prize winner]—was much better than I was and he was competing for the same prize. And it became clear that I was 'ok'—I mean, I was good—but if he and I were going to compete for the same prize, then I'm not in the game. You know as a musician or an actor that you could play in the group, but you know when somebody's Coltrane or Olivier, and I just was not on that level.

Reconciled to his talent's perceived limits, Galvin began considering other career options. The psychiatrist that he had been writing for suggested that he consider medicine—something Galvin thought might provide the type of challenge he was seeking. He also considered law school, business school and graduate school in psychology. His deliberations largely ended after seeking some advice from a noted authority on career choices:

> I called this guy, a Ph.D. in psychology, found his number and called him up. He was the guy that had written the book on choosing careers. We had a couple of long talks on the phone. I called him again and said, "I'm having a lot of trouble making this decision. Can I come and follow you around for a day?" And he said "no." I said, "What do you mean, no?" He said, "My research has shown that people make big decisions based on whim, and they actually know what they really want to do." And I said, "In that case, I'm going to medical school." So, he said, "You just made your decision."

Galvin recalls hanging up the phone and thinking his choice was ridiculous. He debated the decision for a few days but ultimately decided to go with his instinct. In retrospect, he realizes that he "did what a lot of educated people do when they're afraid to make decisions. [He] stacked them up here and there, [he] could have talked [himself] into or out of anything."

After spending a year completing all of his pre-med requirements and taking the MCAT, Galvin applied to medical school. He was rejected from two or three state schools, which were looking for traditional candidates, but was accepted at Penn, Stanford and Yale. Galvin enrolled in the University of Pennsylvania Medical School in 1977.

FALLING IN LOVE WITH MEDICINE

One of the distinct challenges faced by Galvin has been reconciling his diverse set of interests with the sometimes narrow focus required for medical training. He insists, however, that he never regretted going to medical school. What started out as "a great intellectual challenge" developed into a deep love of medicine and caring for patients: "I fell in love with internal medicine in medical school."

After medical school, Galvin began his residency in internal medicine at Boston University Medical Center. He had applied for a cardiology fellowship at Boston's Beth Israel Hospital, but just before starting it he went to Brockton Community Hospital to complete an unpopular rotation in general medicine. It was there that he came to a surprising realization:

> I was going to go into cardiology because I just kind of liked it. I was interested in the cardiology fellowship at Beth Israel in Boston, and then I went to a community hospital to do the rotation that no one wanted to do from the big academic medical centers. And I fell in love with general internal medicine. At Penn, all you saw were things like rare forms of Huntington's disease—quaternary care at best.

Quaternary care (the most complicated medical and surgical care) did interest Galvin, but at Brockton he discovered that his vocation lay elsewhere. What he now found most compelling were the human interaction, physical activity, and sheer excitement of primary care:

> There were all these heart attacks and PEs [pulmonary embolisms] and GI [gastrointestinal] bleeds. And I thought it was just great. Quaternary care was a great challenge, but this was a lot of fun. You could actually do something— it was action. If you got a variant of Huntington's chorea there is not much you are going to do. It's intellectually interesting to understand the pathway, but when you have an MI [myocardial infarction, i.e. heart attack] you put lines in.

EARLY YEARS IN PRACTICE: 1984–1990

After completing his residency, in 1984 Galvin joined a five-physician private practice in general internal medicine in the North Shore region of Boston. At that time, managed care was beginning to have a significant impact on the Boston region, due in large part to the high employment rate and the presence of large data and computer companies along the North Shore. As a result, physician group practices increasingly needed to negotiate contracts with managed care organizations (MCOs) in order to prevent patients from leaving their practices in favor of participating physician practices who could offer them the lower out-of-pocket fee:

> The contract plan [MCO] would come to us and say "Do you want to do business with us?" and my partners would go, "No," and then they would say, "Well do you know that we have General Electric and that's maybe 30% of your patient base? And your competitors across the street are joining." Remember, it used to be you had to pay a lot of money at the door for a deductible, and suddenly, it was a $3 co-payment. So patients, as much as they liked you, left.

With these changes imminent, the responsibility for understanding and negotiating the business contracts fell to Galvin:

> I'm in practice, I've got big gaps in my schedule, and all of a sudden Harvard Community Health Plan is up there, Tufts is up there, Blue Cross, and so the partners said to me, "Look, you've got free time, you went to Wharton, you do the contracts." They said, "You've got a business background." And I said, "I don't really. I never wanted to do that."

As a junior partner in the group, however, Galvin had little choice, and so he took charge of negotiating the group's managed care contracts—a move that proved to be instrumental in shaping the rest of his career:

> I don't know if it was the genes, sitting around the dinner table all those years, or something else, but I really took to it. After having no idea what I wanted to do at age 20, there I was at age 35, having done nothing in business, not wanting to do this, and trying to get out of it. And then I sat down and did these contracts and started renegotiating. And I just took to it.

From 1985 to 1990, Galvin became increasingly involved with the intersection of business and health care. He served as an advisor and teacher at the North Shore Medical Center in Salem, Massachusetts. His teaching responsibilities included instruction in internal medicine and developing the health care management curriculum. As an advisor, he helped North Shore with their efforts at vertical integration in the mid-1990s, which eventually led to their merger with Boston-based Partners HealthCare in 1995. He was also actively involved in their utilization review process and began the introduction of a total quality management process for their resource utilization.

JOINING GE

In 1990, Galvin made the most significant move of his career to date. Deciding to leave full-time clinical practice, Galvin was recruited by the executive search firm Witt/Kieffer to a full-time position as the medical director for the New England Region for GE. Up to this point Galvin had been a physician involved in business; this move made him a businessperson involved in medicine.

The switch from clinical work to administration was at first difficult for Galvin, because at the time "that wasn't what doctors were supposed to do." When he first left the physician group in 1990 he was still practicing, seeing the free-care patients at the hospitals and supervising residents, but he felt pressure to "get out of clinical practice, because back then, you were either a clinician or you did administrative stuff." The amount of time that he spent with patients gradually decreased, until by 1996 he was spending only one day a week in the clinic. Although Galvin had reservations about leaving clinical care, the leap to business proved rewarding:

> It's substitution. The kind of interaction with patients you find really wonderful, but as much as I gave up there, I got in business challenge, so I felt it was never a negative. I missed it, but business is fabulous. It's great. I love what I do. So for everything I lost in not having those relationships with patients I picked up in having incredible challenges in business.

In 1992 Galvin stepped up to serve as the general manager of health care operations for GE's Aircraft Engines and Regions, which put him in charge of 30,000 covered lives and over $100 million in health care expenditures. In this role, Galvin developed point-of-service health plans, a variation on the traditional HMO model of managed care, for several new markets. He also led an employer-sponsored study of health outcomes, and became increasingly involved in employer-sponsored efforts to improve health care quality, co-founding the Massachusetts Healthcare Purchaser Group in 1993 and the Massachusetts Health Quality Partnership in 1994. These projects paved the way for his later work with the Leapfrog Group.

During this period, Galvin also completed the executive M.B.A. program at Boston University, which he believed would give him additional credibility and expertise in the business world. He was also accepted to and considered attending the full-time M.B.A. program at Wharton, where he had been an undergraduate.

In 1996, Galvin's responsibilities at GE significantly expanded when he became director of global health care for all of GE—the company's most senior health care position. His belief about the M.B.A. proved right: Galvin recalls then-CEO Jack Welch telling him, "I can't believe I'm giving a doctor a billion dollars to manage...at least you have an M.B.A."

Galvin's new position made him one of the senior executives working among the 500 employees at GE's worldwide corporate headquarters in Fairfield, Connecticut, representing GE's 325,000 employees in 50 countries. He describes his role as two-fold: part CEO of a health insurance company, part medical director for the company. In the CEO role, Galvin managed GE's health expenditures for its employees—GE, like many large companies, is self-insured and so acts much like a health insurance company—and was responsible for a $3 billion annual budget. In this capacity, Galvin focused primarily on trying to develop benefit packages that promote the right behaviors, and a reimbursement strategy that promotes quality and improvement in the delivery system.

In his role as medical director, Galvin oversaw a large network of clinics and physicians who deliver primarily occupational and walk-in care to GE's employees across the globe. Combining these two roles, he also served as an advisor to the company for several of its medical and health care-related businesses. Galvin also continued to see patients in his role at GE, spending a few hours a week practicing clinical medicine either at the clinic at the GE headquarters in Fairfield, Connecticut, or through phone consultations. He served as the personal physician to some of the firm's most senior executives.

GE itself is a conglomerate of thirteen businesses which range from aircraft engines to light bulbs to financial services. Several of these businesses serve the health care industry: in particular, GE Medical Systems, which sells advanced diagnostic imaging equipment and accompanying software to hospitals and health care providers, and Healthcare Financial Services, which provides financing to health care providers. Until the 2005 sale of its Medical Protective Corporation to Berkshire-Hathaway—and thus during much of Galvin's tenure—GE was also among the leading providers of medical malpractice insurance in the U.S.

ADVOCATING FOR QUALITY

Throughout the 1990s, Galvin was extensively involved with the efforts of large employers, who consider themselves the purchasers of health care services for their employees, to improve quality in the health care system. This interest culminated in 1998 when Galvin co-founded the Leapfrog Group, a collection of employers who work to encourage safety and high-quality patient care in the American health care industry. In 2003 Galvin served as chair for the group, which has grown to represent 150 employers and 33 million covered lives.

Galvin has also been active in the application of Six Sigma to the health care industry. Six Sigma—which refers to the number of standard deviations between the norm and the error-rate at the highest levels of quality believed to be attainable—is a management initiative that was applied to every component of GE's businesses. Galvin became a spokesperson for the application of the principles and methodology of Six Sigma to health care delivery:

Six Sigma is an approach to making quality better, and I happen to think it's well suited for health care because it's quantitative and it speaks the doctor's language. There are similarities with other approaches such as TQM [total quality management] or CQI [continuous quality improvement], but they examine variation around a mean. With Six Sigma, it's unambiguous—you either have a defect or you don't. Fixation on the control phase also makes it an appropriate quality methodology for health care.[1]

In addition to his involvement with the Leapfrog Group, Galvin has been an active board member of the National Commission on Quality Accreditation, the Strategic Framework Board and Strategic Advisory Committee of the National Quality Forum, the Council of Health Economics and Policy, and the Commonwealth Fund Task Force on Academic Health Centers. He has also been actively involved in, and served from 2001 to 2004 as vice chairman of, the Washington Business Group on Health (later renamed the National Business Group on Health). NBGH is a coalition of businesses pursuing quality in health care, with a somewhat stronger health policy focus than the Leapfrog Group. Galvin has written more than 50 publications on a range of issues including the application of Six Sigma to health care and the role of employers in health care quality.

In 2009, Galvin continued his efforts to organize health care purchasers when he founded Catalyst for Payment Reform, a group that counts several Fortune 500 Companies and state government purchasers among its members. CPR seeks to promote "value-based" payment reform—payment plans that reward improvements in quality and efficiency, rather than quantity of care as in the fee-for-service model. At a press conference in 2013, CPR announced the results of a study showing that only 11 percent of current health care payments are value- rather than volume-based; the group has set a goal of raising that number to 20 percent by 2020.[2]

CURRENT ROLE AND THOUGHTS ON THE FUTURE

In 2010, after fifteen years as the head of health care at GE, Galvin stepped down to accept a position as CEO of Equity Healthcare at the Blackstone Group. In this role, Galvin's objectives are very similar to those he worked towards at GE: using corporate purchasing power to both help improve quality while containing costs. The Blackstone Group is one of the world's largest and most successful investment and advisory firms, with 1,800 employees across 24 offices and more than $200 billion in assets. A significant part of their business is in private equity, and they invest in a portfolio of companies which collectively employ 730,000 people worldwide. Like all companies, the companies in Blackstone's private equity portfolio struggle to provide high quality health care at a reasonable cost to their employees and families. Blackstone's Equity Healthcare program was established to help their portfolio companies meet this challenge. As Galvin explained at the time of his appointment:

> Equity Healthcare is one of the most innovative efforts within corporate America to deal with the rapidly increasing cost of health care, while at the same time improving the health and well-being of the affected employees and their families. I am excited about leading this effort and making it a model for best-of-class health care delivery in the United States.

Equity works with over 40 portfolio companies with a combined health care spending of about $2 billion annually. It focuses on helping its companies transition to a model of responsible consumerism, in which reduced costs stem from better decisions made by individual patients. The approach combines higher first-dollar payment by employees with extensive communication and advising from providers. Early results have been very positive: under Galvin's leadership, Equity's innovative strategies have produced substantial savings, shaving 3–4 percent off of benchmark trends.

Galvin's new responsibilities at Equity have reduced the time he has available for direct clinical care: "I no longer go out on a white coat," he says, but notes that he still participates in the diagnosis and other aspects of at least a hundred cases per year. His work as an executive still feels continuous with his experience as a physician, and Galvin cannot imagine working in any field other than health care:

> I really like running a big organizations. I think it's my natural talent, and I find it very challenging. Every day is a new set of challenges, but I love health care. If someone offered me a job that would make sense from here, but was not health care, it wouldn't really interest me.

Note

1 "Healthcare Executive Insights: Interview with Robert Galvin, M.D. Director of Global Health Care, General Electric." April 2002, accessed at www.gemedicalsystems.com.

2 See Julie Miller, "Moving Toward Value," *Managed Healthcare Executive*, Apr. 1, 2013 (at managedhealthcareexecutive.modernmedicine.com) for a more complete account of this study.

RAYMOND V. GILMARTIN

Former Chairman, President and CEO, Merck & Co., Inc.
Adjunct Professor, Management Practice, Harvard Business School

As the first CEO to come from outside the company, Gilmartin ran Merck during a time of considerable controversy and uncertainty in the pharmaceutical industry. As a visible leader in the public policy discussion surrounding the cost and accessibility of drugs, in this profile Gilmartin discusses his philosophy for guiding Merck during a time of intense public pressure. This profile highlights a career trajectory defined by a strong interest in strategy and a profound sense of responsibility for continuing Merck's legacy.

EDUCATION & TRAINING

1959–1963	B.S., Electrical Engineering, Union College
1966–1968	M.B.A., Harvard Business School

CAREER PATH

1963–1966	Development Engineer, Eastman Kodak
1968–1976	Management Consultant, Arthur D. Little
1976–1980	Vice President, Corporate Planning, Becton Dickinson and Company
1980–1982	President, Becton Dickinson Division, Becton Dickinson and Company
1982–1984	President, Medical Group, Becton Dickinson and Company
1984–1986	Senior Vice President, Becton Dickinson and Company
1986–1987	Executive Vice President, Becton Dickinson and Company
1987–1989	President, Becton Dickinson and Company
1989–1992	President and Chief Executive Officer, Becton Dickinson and Company
1992–1994	Chairman, President and CEO, Becton Dickinson and Company
1994–2005	Chairman, President and Chief Executive Officer, Merck & Co., Inc.
2006–2012	Professor of Management Practice, Harvard Business School

PAST POSITIONS

Member, President's Export Council

Trustee, American Enterprise Institute

Chairman, International Federation of Pharmaceutical Manufacturers

Director, General Mills, Inc.

Director, Microsoft Corporation

Member, Business Roundtable

My career has been a series of learnings at each step of the way—what options were available to me that I never knew about before? It was a question of expanding my knowledge of the options available to me. My approach to all of these things was to have a sense of potential—I didn't know what I was going to do next, but it would be something else that would help me grow. The idea is pursuing personal growth as an approach to life.

—Raymond Gilmartin

As you walk into the lobby of Merck's worldwide headquarters in White-house Station, New Jersey, you come face to face with a life-sized sculpture of a child leading an adult with a stick.* The accompanying placards explain that this scene—a blind adult following a child—was common two decades ago in villages afflicted by the parasite that causes river blindness. In 1987, Roy Vagelos, then chairman of Merck, set a powerful example for the pharmaceutical industry when he decided to distribute Merck's drug Mectizan free of charge to help eradicate river blindness in developing countries.[1] Since it began, the program has grown to reach 30 million people annually in more than 30 nations.

To Raymond Gilmartin, this statue represents the first part of a dual legacy he feels responsible for upholding. The other part of this legacy is Merck's research—what he describes as a "legacy of scientific excellence." As chairman, president and CEO of Merck, Gilmartin was responsible for running an organization with more than $20 billion in annual sales and more than 63,000 employees across the globe. Assuming leadership of the company in 1994, Gilmartin oversaw the introduction of life-changing drugs such as Crixivan for AIDS and Singulair for asthma. During his tenure, Merck received worldwide attention for establishing a world-class HIV/AIDS treatment program in Botswana; he also continued to manage Merck's groundbreaking river blindness treatment program in Africa.

---

* Raymond Gilmartin was interviewed for this profile in 2004 before his decision to step down as Merck's CEO in 2005. A postscript, based on an additional interview conducted in 2007, is included at the end of this profile.

EARLY FRAMEWORKS

Growing up in a small town on Long Island's south shore, Gilmartin was the first person in his family to attend college. He discovered his aptitude for conceptual and theoretical thinking at Union College in Schenectady, New York, where he took classes in mathematics and science and ultimately earned a degree in electrical engineering. His grasp of conceptual frameworks, fostered during college and solidified during his years at Harvard Business School, has been at the heart of his decision-making process ever since:

> I remember Professor Craig, who taught Laplace and Fourier transforms. His point was that the way to succeed in his course was not by learning to do the problems in the back of the chapter—because those will be the only problems you can do—but to understand which equation applies to the problem you are trying to solve. What is the theoretical and conceptual framework? And once you have that down, the problem will solve itself. I am always asking, "What is the theoretical framework I need to apply to solve this problem?" To this day, I think that way.

At Union College, Gilmartin assumed leadership roles as the captain of the wrestling team and president of his class. He sought diversity in his experience, a hallmark of Gilmartin's approach to life:

> At Union College, when the computer arrived at school in the early 1960s, they offered an elective to engineers in computing, but I turned that down. Instead, my elective was the history of the English novel with English majors on a Saturday morning.

After graduating from Union College in 1963, he declined an offer from Proctor and Gamble and instead joined Eastman Kodak as a development engineer. At Eastman Kodak, Gilmartin knew immediately that he was interested in pursuing a career in management, but a brief stint in the army interrupted his plans.

A TRANSFORMING EXPERIENCE

After being away on active duty in the army for six months, Gilmartin returned and discovered that a fellow engineer at Kodak with a similar background had received a full-tuition fellowship to Harvard Business School. Still interested in a career in management and intrigued by HBS, Gilmartin applied, and in 1966 started the M.B.A. program with a full-tuition fellowship. Having married a year earlier, he and his wife arrived in Boston with little more than Gilmartin's fellowship money:

> We lived then as we do now: with the sense that, no matter how satisfied we may be at any given time, the two of us feel that whatever we are doing, it will

not be the last thing we will do. There will always be another possibility—undefined—but another possibility.

With little money and a new marriage, the decision seemed like a risk. Taking it, however, would prove invaluable from both a personal and professional standpoint:

> Business school was a transforming experience. The educational transformation was that when you're an engineer at an undergraduate or entry-level position, the answer is in the book. The transformational experience at Harvard Business School was all of a sudden recognizing that there really was no answer in the book. It was all about how to think about a problem—how to gather the data and think about it. It was realizing that, "Yes, I am capable, and equally adept as anyone else at assembling this data, and arriving at the best possible judgment given the information available"—no longer looking to the book for the answer.

Ready to use his newly learned skills, Gilmartin accepted a position with Arthur D. Little, a management consulting firm in Cambridge, Massachusetts. Gilmartin feels the position was a very strong choice for him: "It was a tremendous learning experience—like a post-graduate course for my M.B.A. program. Basically it was eight years of solving problems, which built upon the frameworks learned at HBS."

MOVING INTO HEALTH CARE

By 1976, Gilmartin realized the problems he faced as a consultant were becoming repetitive, and that his learning had stopped. That year, Gilmartin was offered a position as head of strategy by one of his clients—Becton Dickinson (BD), a manufacturer of needles, syringes, and other medical supplies. Both the position and the company's mission appealed to Gilmartin:

> I went to BD because it was an interesting company but also because of the kind of business that it was—technology, science and health. I liked the business from the standpoint that we could do important things. For instance, BD really developed the whole field of flow cytometry [a technique for measuring the amount of DNA in cells], which was essential to unraveling the immune system and understanding HIV/AIDS and a range of other immune diseases. It had a high impact—it was a good business to be in.

His first position was essentially as an internal consultant, but BD's senior management made it clear that they wanted Gilmartin to run an operational division within three years. While it actually took five years, in 1980 he took over the flagship division of BD, which manufactured needles and syringes. After that initial promotion, Gilmartin's career began advancing rapidly, and he became senior vice president and then executive vice president. Within eleven years of starting, he was president of the company, and within a few more years he was chairman and CEO as well.

During this time, Gilmartin continued to pursue innovative strategies, working with well-known academics such as Harvard's Michael Porter to develop frameworks for BD's global strategy:

> A connection very early on was with Michael Porter at HBS. He credits me with being one of the first to recognize the importance of having an integrated global strategy—although it was actually one of the people I worked with at BD, who was a former Harvard Professor. In the 1970s, this was new thinking—up until that time, people thought more about multinational strategy, with different strategies tailored to different regions of the world. This was when people really started thinking in terms of *integrated global strategies.*

This work put Gilmartin at the forefront of new management theory, which would later make him an attractive candidate to lead a global pharmaceutical company like Merck.

THE DECISION TO MOVE TO MERCK

In 1994, Gilmartin had no intention of leaving Becton Dickinson, so when an executive recruiter contacted him to discuss an opportunity at an unspecified company, Gilmartin initially refused his offer:

> I said to him, "I like what I am doing. I run a very complex company—multidivisional, different kinds of businesses. Running something four times the size is not what I am looking for, and, therefore, let's not have lunch because I don't intend—even if I am fortunate enough to be offered the position—to leave Becton Dickinson." And he said to me, "I really think you should think twice about that because the company is Merck, and it is on an extraordinary path."

Gilmartin agreed to take a few days to think about the offer, and get back in touch with the recruiter that next weekend:

> At a prearranged time on Saturday I called him back and told him that I couldn't do it. I had just made some changes in management. The new team was just getting underway, and the timing was just not good. I knew it was an extraordinary opportunity, but I just couldn't take it.

Gilmartin's refusal of the position was based on his sense that he had not fulfilled his responsibilities to BD, but over the next few days his thoughts changed:

> The following Tuesday night I said to my wife, "You know, I'm really breaking a cardinal rule. I'm acting as if, if I leave Becton Dickinson, the place will collapse." I had reached the point at BD that I had reached previously at Arthur D. Little. I could see what I was going to be doing over the next few years. I

was even thinking of the possibility of retiring at 57 to do something else, but to me the timing wasn't right, and I would not be fulfilling my responsibility to the company.

After thinking about his role at BD further, Gilmartin realized that he did have a strong successor there, and that grooming that successor was an important part of his responsibility to the company. This realization made him comfortable with the thought of moving on, so he contacted the headhunter about the position at Merck. Gilmartin became Merck's president and CEO in 1994, and was named chairman of its board of directors later the same year.

INHERITING A LEGACY

Gilmartin was the first Merck CEO to come from outside the pharmaceutical industry, or even from outside the firm. Some outsiders expressed concern that he was not a research scientist. He believes the board selected him nonetheless because of his knowledge of the health care industry, his familiarity with managed care (a major concern for Merck at the time), his track record of running a large company and his innovative thinking about global strategy at BD.

Gilmartin found Merck exciting because of its reputation for cutting-edge science and the strong values for which the company had become known. Roy Vagelos, Gilmartin's predecessor, had won Merck worldwide attention for the Mectizan program for river blindness. A close friend of Gilmartin's added to his sense of that legacy:

> I have a friend who is a research physician who did an internship at Merck while he was at medical school, and I spoke with him shortly after accepting Merck's offer. First, he couldn't believe that his friend—a mere mortal—was going to be the CEO of Merck. He then went on seriously to tell me what an extraordinary legacy I was being given, and all the great breakthroughs that Merck had done in terms of science. And it goes back a long way—from figuring out how to mass produce penicillin or being able to synthesize cortisone, which hadn't been possible before. So there are these great breakthroughs that continue. He said, "You should recognize how important that legacy is and what Merck is capable of doing."

Gilmartin remembers this discussion vividly, and took its message very much to heart.

While Merck's scientific reputation was a strong factor in Gilmartin's decision, another attraction was the set of challenges the company was facing. At the time, Merck was confronting a range of difficulties including declining stock price and departing leadership:

I took on Merck in part because of the challenge—because of all the things that were going on. For seven years Merck had been the "Most Admired Company in America," as named by *Fortune* magazine, and now it had lost that distinction. They had bought Medco, which many people in and outside the company questioned.[2] The share price was way down, executives were leaving, and managed care was coming. And I was the first guy from the outside.

This was exactly the type of challenge Gilmartin was seeking. He explains that his tendency is to see virtually all problems as opportunities, an optimistic outlook that he uses his children's words to explain:

My kids say to me, "Dad, you're the kind of person who doesn't think anything bad has ever happened to him in his entire life." One can view that as denial of reality. But I prefer to think of it as seeing challenges and problems and turning them into opportunities.

This confidence in his ability to handle the future is manifest in Gilmartin's profoundly calm and even-keeled personal demeanor, and it was with this confidence that he moved into his new position at the head of Merck.

THE IMPORTANCE OF NOT BEING A "HERO CEO"

Central to Gilmartin's approach to leadership was his firm belief that companies are not helped by the so-called "hero" or "celebrity CEO," a high-profile leader who leads unilaterally and becomes synonymous with the company. This is bad for the company, he argues, and bad for the employees as well. Leading a firm is a team effort rather than the work of any one individual:

When I came to Merck, a fellow I was on a board which advised me to try to stay off the cover of business magazines. Because I alone wouldn't deserve it, and the people I worked with wouldn't like it. You've got to keep that perspective: you provide leadership, but you are working with a lot of other people who provide leadership. It is everybody in the company that combines to contribute to the success.

This belief shaped the way in which Gilmartin assumed his role as the head of Merck:

The first thing I did when I arrived at Merck was to interview executives at different levels at the company and ask them two questions: "What are the major issues we face?" and, "If you were me, what are the major issues you would focus your time on?"

Gilmartin's next move was to assemble a team of talented leaders, which he selected entirely from within the company:

The next thing I did was to assemble a management team. I made some significant changes, but they were all Merck people, so I was able to tap into the institutional talent and knowledge that was here. And we built a team. That was the first step: to get the leadership in place—leadership that would be seen by the rest of the organization as not only talented and competent, but sharing the values and culture of the company, which would inspire confidence and trust. Given all the uncertainty at the time, this was a key step.

After putting the right team in place, Gilmartin began working with them to set a clear direction for the company's future strategy, which guided the firm in its development during the late 1990s:

We made a whole series of important decisions. We got out of several businesses that were specialty chemical, not pharmaceutical, exited the generics business, reaffirmed the fact that breakthrough research was more important now than ever before, and communicated this message heavily to the company.

THE PHARMACEUTICAL INDUSTRY UNDER FIRE

Gilmartin led Merck at an extraordinarily difficult time for the pharmaceutical industry. With intense pressure domestically and internationally for more affordable drugs and health care, and with global epidemics such as HIV/AIDS threatening many populations, Gilmartin's leadership integrated a strategic understanding of Merck's development needs with broader public policy issues:

By working together in 1994, we set a very clear direction for the company.... And the clear direction is, that in order to really respond to the needs of society out there, we have to continue to come up with drugs that are novel—that are based on new knowledge about the pathways of disease, that are better than what is there now. But increasingly, we must be able to offer that breakthrough, that novelty, at affordable prices.

To achieve these goals, Gilmartin had to make tough choices, including decisions regarding layoffs and cost-reduction:

What we're doing is fundamentally lowering the cost-structure of the company, by doing things that have already been done in a lot of other industries, to meet the needs of more affordable medicines.

As the pharmaceutical industry has faced stricter price controls abroad, a dwindling product "pipeline"—fewer drugs in various stages of development—and intense competition among its major companies and from generic manufacturers, a wave of mergers has occurred involving virtually every significant pharmaceutical firm except for Merck:

I have been very clear that we are not going to merge with anybody. There is no large-scale merger that would add to our pipeline or to our long-term growth. In addition, we have a unique culture and capability that would only be undermined by a merger, as has happened to other companies. We're in a business where we make big bets, where most things you're betting on don't work, but the few things that do, win. It's almost like broad-scale venture capital, and when they do work out there is a huge payoff. Drug discovery doesn't occur in a smooth predictable fashion—it comes in spurts.

Internally, Merck focused its objectives for the second half of Gilmartin's term on securing the capabilities to support their strategy:

We are in the midst of a revolution in how research will be done in the biosciences, which is being driven by the knowledge of the human genome, and by advances in drug discovery tools. What we are working on is staying on the leading edge—if not opening up the leading edge—of science. This means locating ourselves where great science is being done, such as building labs in Boston, San Diego and Seattle. It means continuing to recruit top talent. It means transforming our relationships with the biotech industry, which we view not as licensing and business development, but as a scientific initiative, led by our scientists. These relationships exist across the continuum of scientific research—from early-stage basic science to later-stage compounds—and we consider internal and external research as a continuum.

PATIENTS AND PROFITS

On top of the table in Gilmartin's office is a glass case containing a copy of *Time* magazine from August 18, 1952. On the cover is a picture of George W. Merck, the company's modern founder, along with the quote: "Medicine is for the people, not the profits." The full quote concludes: "The profits follow, and if we have remembered that, they have never failed to appear." Gilmartin displays the magazine because he believes it summarizes his own approach to the issues facing Merck and the larger pharmaceutical industry. He considers himself ultimately accountable to the patients, not the shareholders, and believes that if he focuses on meeting their needs, the shareholders will reap the greatest financial rewards. He explains how this philosophy applies to the public policy challenges in the industry:

Merck likes to operate in the area of high engagement with important needs—how to get medicines to the developing world for HIV, how to deal with the perception that intellectual property is a barrier, how to deal with prescription drug coverage for Medicare. Rather than focus on our short-term self-interest, we are trying to do what is best in terms of public policy. We know that if we get that right, we will prosper.

That's the way to focus ourselves on the long-term goal—not just on what's good for us in the short term. The way to deal with these kinds of major problems is to offer solutions, and engage with others to get these solutions done. Many view this approach as the slippery slope, and they end up wanting to defend the status quo. They get driven into damage control and acquiescence. But if you seek to do the right thing—which is the philosophy ingrained in this company—then one of the benefits is that you can preempt solutions that are damaging, such as price controls and erosion of intellectual property. It's a question of giving up your short-term self-interest in the expectation you can succeed over the long term.

Gilmartin offers Merck's efforts to address the global HIV epidemic as an example of this long-term strategy. To foster "a transformation of awareness," Merck established a major research project in Botswana, which has one of the highest infection rates in Africa; its goal is to discover the best way to deliver treatment to those suffering from AIDS:

> We are attacking HIV across the full spectrum—from prevention of transmission to treatment with anti-retrovirals. We train doctors and nurses, build up facilities to provide care, and build up the health care infrastructure for delivering HIV care and treatment. I was in Botswana, and I visited an AIDS treatment center and a groundbreaking for an orphan daycare center. It really brings it to a personal level. We are on our way to treating 110,000 people, who are going to live instead of having an almost certain death sentence, and who will be around to raise their children. There is a deep level of satisfaction for me in terms of what Merck is capable of doing.

Gilmartin derives a broader lesson from this satisfaction, one he would offer as advice to future health care leaders:

> This goes back to the George W. Merck quote that I pulled out when I arrived at Merck. My advice to students is to try to make a contribution without worrying about the reward. Contributions are always recognized at some point. At the same time, conduct yourself to the highest standards of ethics and integrity, and treat everyone, particularly those who work for you, with dignity and respect. It's not only the right thing to do, but you'll find that you'll be able to attract great people to work for you, and they will try to make you successful. Secondly, when you get into trouble—which you will from time to time—others will come and bail you out, often in ways you don't even know about. It is sort of a formula for success: strive to do the right thing, and the rewards will follow.

COMING UNDER PERSONAL FIRE

In late 2003, Merck faced increased scrutiny from Wall Street. Its stock price had lost significant value, its pipeline of new drugs appeared less than robust, and it faced patent expirations in the coming years on several of its most profitable drugs. Gilmartin, who was at the time the longest-serving

CEO among the major pharmaceutical companies, came under particular scrutiny, most notably in a *Wall Street Journal* article that ran in October 2003.[3] The article noted that a Wall Street analyst had made the unusual move of suggesting Gilmartin step down, a suggestion seconded in the article by one of Merck's powerful board members. Criticism focused on the fact that Merck, unlike other major drug makers, was refusing to merge with other pharmaceutical firms, a move that could have boosted short-term profits. Instead, Merck was staying focused on the discovery of new drugs, a lengthy and uncertain process that takes on average more than ten years.

Gilmartin responds to this criticism by underscoring the vital importance of maintaining a long-term view, even during difficult times:

> All businesses go through cycles and have rough periods. Although short-term performance cannot be completely ignored, it's particularly important during these tough times to stay focused on the long term. This is particularly true in the pharmaceutical industry, where timeframes are typically ten to fifteen years.

In early 2004, *Fortune* magazine ran an article that was similarly quite critical of Gilmartin, accusing him of fostering a scientific "culture of arrogance."[4] The argument was that by focusing the firm on the discovery and development of "breakthrough" medicines—drugs designed to treat previously untreated conditions, or treat conditions with significantly higher efficacy— he was hurting the firm's short-term profitability. Other drug makers were boosting their cash flows with so-called "me-too" drugs—drugs developed in response to successful breakthrough drugs, typically with minor changes in the structure or delivery to avoid patent constraints, and produced to capture a share in an already existing, lucrative market.

Gilmartin responds straightforwardly to this criticism: "If arrogance is defined as only working on breakthrough drugs, then I am guilty as charged." As he explains, Merck has a history of hiring world-class scientists, and world-class scientists are not motivated by the challenge of copying existing drugs. Gilmartin explains that while he does not like such press, he does not let it sway him from doing what he feels is right.

HOPES FOR A LEGACY

While Gilmartin has not given much thought to what he will do after he leaves Merck, he has given considerable thought to how he wants to leave the company. If he is able to fulfill his responsibilities to Merck, he explains, he will be able to walk out the door without regret. He emphasizes that it is important to the firm for a retiring CEO to move on completely: "Don't linger. It is important to your successor as well. Don't stay on the board." As he did at BD, he feels particularly committed to the goal of grooming those who will succeed him in leading Merck.

Gilmartin hopes he will be remembered for having furthered Merck's own legacy of scientific excellence, which he believes can ultimately have a profound impact on humanity:

> I would like to feel that I had fulfilled my responsibilities to continue Merck's legacy of scientific excellence. I would like to think that I have been able to do that—that it is a stronger research organization today than it was ten years ago when I arrived. The world desperately needs an HIV vaccine, which Merck has been working on for fifteen years. Merck has the scientific capability, I believe, to ultimately discover and develop that vaccine. And I would like to think that I played some small role in building and maintaining the scientific excellence to be able to accomplish that.

POSTSCRIPT[5]

In September 2004, Merck voluntarily withdrew the arthritis drug Vioxx® from the market after a study linked the drug to increased risk of heart attack. Gilmartin explains what his thinking was in making this decision:

> My direction to the Merck organization, and in particular the head of research, was that whatever decision is made, whatever we do, we need to be guided by what science says is in the best interest of the patient. Merck ultimately concluded that it was in the best interest of patients to voluntarily withdraw Vioxx®, particularly in light of the alternative drugs that were currently available.

In leading Merck through this turbulent time Gilmartin succeeded in having the board select an internal successor at a time when the company might have been susceptible to selection of a "hero" or "celebrity CEO." True to one of Gilmartin's firmly held tenets of leadership, his successor, Richard Clark, had been a highly effective CEO of Medco Health Solutions, and Gilmartin felt that he "would be able to continue the values and cultures of the Merck company." With the announcement of Clark's appointment in May 2005, Gilmartin left the board of directors and moved to an outside office. Gilmartin served as a special advisor to the board of directors until his retirement from Merck in April 2006, at which time Gilmartin joined the faculty at Harvard Business School.

Despite the lack of sales and profit growth in the last years of his tenure at Merck, Gilmartin feels that he did not waiver in his commitment to scientific excellence: Merck doubled its research budget from $2 billion in 1999 to $4 billion in 2004, even as the company suffered significant losses related to Vioxx. Gilmartin explains that he chose to take the hit elsewhere and stay on track with an accelerated research budget.

This commitment to discovery under Gilmartin's leadership has in fact yielded a number of new products, both novel medicines and vaccines, over the past several years; a 2008 article in *Fortune* on Merck's financial recovery said that "the seeds of Merck's resurgence were planted on [Gilmartin's] watch."[6] In 2006 and 2007 Merck introduced the cervical cancer vaccine, Gardasil; Januvia, a novel approach for treating type 2 diabetes; and a novel treatment for a rare form of skin cancer, Zolinza, an orphan drug with the potential for broader application. In 2009, the FDA approved Isentress, a first-in-its-class drug for treating HIV. Gilmartin explains that these products have increased the recognition on Wall Street that Merck has a late stage pipeline that will contribute to significant future growth, leading analysts to be much more optimistic about the worth of the company.

Finally, in terms of leadership, the hopes that Gilmartin stated before leaving Merck appear to have come true. Gilmartin's successor is well regarded, and Gilmartin believes that Merck continues to benefit from the commitments to patients and scientific excellence and the investments in research that he championed throughout his tenure as CEO.

Notes

1   The story of Roy Vagelos, Raymond Gilmartin's predecessor at Merck, is told in Roy Vagelos and Louis Galambos, *Medicine, Science, and Merck* (Cambridge and New York: Cambridge University Press, 2004).

2   In 1993 Merck acquired Medco, a pharmacy benefit management company. The company was spun off as an independent entity in 2003.

3   Peter Landers and Joann S. Lublin, "Merck's Slide May Dislodge Company's CEO," *The Wall Street Journal*, 30 October 2003, Eastern edition.

4   John Simons, "Merck's Man in the Hot Seat," *Fortune*, 23 February 2004.

5   This post-script was written in 2007 after Gilmartin's decision to step down as Merck's CEO.

6   John Simons, "How Merck Healed Itself," *Fortune*, 7 February 2008.

JOHN GLASER

Senior Vice President, Population Health, Cerner
Former Chief Information Officer, Partners HealthCare

John Glaser is one of the leading experts in the field of medical informatics, and focuses on development and implementation of clinical and administrative information systems. As the CIO of a large, integrated delivery system, he feels strongly that a broad-based education, including publishing and leadership positions, provides the best preparation for a career in IT. He discusses the path that led him to the field of health care IT, his strong belief in the pivotal role of IT in the future of health care, and how this belief combined with his passion for the subject have led him to become a world-renowned leader in the field.

EDUCATION & TRAINING

1972–1976	A.B., Duke University (Mathematics)
1980–1984	Ph.D., University of Minnesota (Medical Informatics)

CAREER PATH

1977–1980	Analyst, Research Triangle Institute
1984–1988	Manager, Health Care Technology Management Unit, Arthur D. Little
1988–1995	Vice President of Information Systems, Brigham and Women's Hospital
1995–2010	Vice President and Chief Information Officer, Partners HealthCare, Inc.
2009–2010	Advisor to the National Coordinator for Health Information Technology, U.S. Department of Health and Human Services
2010–2015	CEO, Health Services Business Unit, Siemens Healthcare
2015–	Senior Vice President, Population Health, Cerner

SELECTED PUBLICATIONS

The Strategic Application of Information Technology in Healthcare Organizations, 2nd ed. San Francisco: Jossey-Bass, 2002.

Wager, Karen A., Frances Wickham Lee, John P. Glaser. *Managing Health Care Information Systems: A Practical Approach for Health Care Executives*. San Francisco: Jossey-Bass, 2005.

Glaser J, Foley T. "The Future of Healthcare IT: What Can We Expect to See?" *Healthcare Financial Management*. 2008 Nov; 62(11):82–8.

"Implementing Electronic Health Records: 10 Factors for Success." *Healthcare Financial Management*. 2009 Jan; 63(1):50–2, 54.

I will die someday. And if I had thirty seconds when I could look back on my life, what I would want is to be as madly in love with my wife as I am now; I want my daughters to have lives as blessed as mine; I want the people who I work with to say I inspired, taught them, and led them well; and the organizations I work for to be different and better because I was here.

—*John Glaser*

One might expect the blog of an executive leading one of the health care industry's most advanced IT divisions to focus on technological developments, changes in the industry, or the impact of the Obama administration's emphasis on electronic recordkeeping. John Glaser has written about all of these things in his occasional contributions at HIStalk2.com, a health care IT news site, but a column from the spring of 2009 also praises "one of the greatest inventions of all time": the three-by-five card. "No batteries. No worries about an operating system crash. Easy to read. You can drop it down the stairs and it doesn't break. And you don't need to stay in the lines when you write on it." Glaser's own card, which he uses as a simple organizing tool for his day, includes items like "budget" and "staff e-mail," but also a reminder that he needs to help his adult daughter fix up the back yard of her Boston condo and a line reading "NWT Frm": "I have no idea," Glaser wryly confesses, "what this means."

The column, with its sense of humor, its easy reference to a life beyond work and its acknowledgment that computers can be frustrating as well as liberating will surprise only those unfamiliar with Glaser, whose career has unfolded at the intersection of evolving technology and the all too human organizations that depend on it. An optimist about technological progress, Glaser has also been attuned to the fact that new technology can create new problems and difficult periods of adjustment for people who often work best when they don't have to stay in the lines.

In the mid-'90s, as vice president and chief information officer during the formation of Partners HealthCare, an integrated delivery system based in Boston, Glaser was responsible for centralizing all of the affiliates' existing clinical, telecommunications, and administrative information systems. He kept Partners on the cutting edge of health IT developments throughout his fifteen-year tenure there. Glaser is considered one of the world's leading experts on the role of IT in health care, and advises, consults and teaches on the subject across the globe. In 2002, he received the *CIO Magazine* 20/20 Award for being one of the world's twenty most significant leaders in IT management across all industries.

FINDING DIRECTION

When people tell Glaser they want to do what he does, he can't help but reflect on the irony of such a wish: "When I got out of college, I didn't know what to do." His unique combination of interests, which would later lead him to integrate the fields of medicine, management science, social science and conventional information technology, had only begun to coalesce.

Glaser graduated *magna cum laude* from Duke University. Unlike many of his colleagues in the field of health care, however, he studied mathematics—a concentration he chose without a long-term goal in sight. When, upon graduation, he discovered he did not enjoy math enough to become a mathematician, he found himself somewhat at a loss. He held a variety of odd jobs, hitchhiked across the country and finally—after a three-thousand-mile trek which ended in Panama—was motivated to return to North Carolina by a woman he had met at Duke. The move proved opportune: still drawing on his mathematics background, Glaser began work as a programmer/analyst for the Research Triangle Institute. Much of Glaser's work focused on the National Medical Care Expenditure Survey. He enjoyed the health care-related work so much that he applied to the Ph.D. program in medical informatics at the University of Minnesota.

MIXING SKILLS WITH PASSION

Once enrolled, Glaser continued to search for an academic path that would accommodate his many interests. Even in a Ph.D. program, he says, "It took me six months to get a feel for what I wanted to do." Most of his classmates were physicians who had an interest in computer science. Glaser, on the other hand, had little medical background and was not content to limit his studies to medical and IT-related topics. He took courses in sociology and political theory and attended many classes at the business school. Glaser knew that only a career path integrating his skill with hard numbers and his passion for health care and management science would be interesting enough to pursue.

Glaser made one more stop between his doctoral program and his work at Partners. After receiving his Ph.D., he accepted a position at Arthur D. Little, where he became manager of the Health Care Technology Management Unit. As manager, Glaser's responsibilities consisted largely of developing the company's consulting practice, which centered on health care information systems. It was ultimately the amount of travel the job required that led Glaser to leave. He wanted to spend more time with his young family, and he wanted to see if he could actually implement the advice that he had dispensed as a consultant.

Glaser thus accepted a position as vice president of information systems at the Brigham and Women's Hospital, where he was influential in developing and installing cutting-edge clinical and administrative information systems. When the Brigham teamed up with Massachusetts General Hospital to establish Partners HealthCare as a multi-hospital system, Glaser assumed the role of vice president and chief information officer. In this position, he works on system-wide strategy and implementation, and is ultimately responsible for the technical, financial and operational management of system-wide information technology projects and ongoing operations. One of his main tasks was to merge all of Partners' existing information systems, telecommunications and medical records departments so that they could be accessed from 52,000 devices at 110 locations. He describes merging the information systems across Partners as a three-step process: "One, establishing a direction; two, working out the new management mechanisms and the kinks that arise during mergers; three, monitoring ongoing strategy and operations."

THE IMPORTANCE OF A SOLID BACKGROUND

The curriculum Glaser recommends for today's information technology students is in many ways a reflection of the curriculum he pioneered for himself as a Ph.D. candidate, including courses and curricular emphases traditionally found in business programs or the social sciences. His recommendations are quite broad, comprising at least five different categories: writing and communication skills; health care and health policy; statistics; accounting; and management information systems (the management of information technology projects and data and the establishment of governance structures).

Glaser also recommends courses in computer science because it teaches an appreciation for the sophistication and complexity of the field. His emphasis on learning to speak and write well has a more pragmatic justification:

> It's terribly important to be able to effectively say to a group of administrative and clinical leadership, "This is what I think we should do and why," and convince them. But most people don't come out of graduate school knowing how to write or speak very well.

It is also clear from Glaser's description of his path that he has drawn on his own quantitative background as an undergraduate math major. While Glaser has demonstrated that it is possible to seek out this kind of breadth for oneself, he also believes that IT as a field is showing trends in this direction.

The Future Impact of IT on Health Care

Glaser also highlights three changes in IT that have taken place since his own entrance into the field:

> One is that technology has gotten a lot better; it's cheaper, easier to use. The second is there's now a generation of folks coming through who just expect it to be easier, expect it to be present; and that wasn't the case years ago. The third is the understanding in the industry that you can make demonstrable and significant organizational improvements using IT.

Glaser identifies the delivery of remote care and physicians' access to patient information as two areas of health systems information technology that he thinks will develop in the future. Already, Glaser says, information technology has made it possible for medical professionals to gain remarkably complete information about a patient's allergies, medications, medical history and previous care providers, even from other hospitals. Even with an integrated delivery system, this is a hard task. Glaser believes that perfecting such a system is one of the long-term goals for the field of information technology. He also predicts that IT will help care providers to manage the knowledge they need to make decisions by helping them select the optimal intervention for their patient from among hundreds of options.

Glaser also suggests that improvements in IT will make remote care, also known as telemedicine, a much more immediate option for many patients. This development will allow physicians to monitor at-risk patients while the patient remains at home, or enable doctors to offer diagnoses to patients hundreds of miles away. Glaser predicts that wider use of remote care will occur in the very near future. The advantages of such technology could include an increase in the feasibility of outpatient treatment for many patients, and reliable medical care for people in parts of the country far removed from medical specialists.

Personal Dedication, and the Importance of Contributing to your Field

Glaser does not choose to map his career out in the long term, particularly since his entrance into the field was not preceded by years of careful planning. He chooses to take a short-range view of his professional options, and is motivated by his passion for the field and his innate sense of leadership.

Glaser's involvement in IT goes well beyond his position at Partners— he holds positions on the boards of many other organizations throughout the health IT sector. When he speaks of managing his various time commitments, he again gives a threefold answer: "You have three fundamental approaches available to you. One is you delegate a lot, second you ignore certain things, the third is that you put in long hours."

Motivated by the important effects that he believes his team's work will have on the health care field, Glaser spends the evenings that follow his eleven- or twelve-hour workdays writing for various trade journals. He writes primarily because he feels publishing is a form of leadership; he also believes that his organization is in a unique position to lead. "Why do you write?" he asks. In response to his own question, he reiterates his answer to the question "Why do you work so hard?":

> Because you are actually thinking of ideas and experiences that will help others—if you believe that your work and thoughts can guide others, you will work after-hours when you could be doing something else. I believe that if you can lead then you must lead.

AFTERWORD

In May 2009 Glaser began an eleven-month appointment as an advisor to David Blumenthal (p. 84), President Obama's National Coordinator for Health Information Technology, where he advised Blumenthal on national efforts to adopt electronic medical records. Then, in 2010, Glaser accepted a position as chief executive officer of Siemens Health Services Business Unit. In this role he leads a staff of more than 4,500 employees and is responsible for leading Siemens' global health care IT business including product development, strategy, financial performance and customer satisfaction.

Philip H. Gordon

Surgeon, Author and Editor
Past President, American Society of Colorectal Surgeons

A leading practitioner and author of perhaps the most respected textbook in his subspecialty of colorectal surgery, Philip Gordon is a professor of surgery and oncology at McGill University. In this profile, he discusses the events leading to his specialization, and his involvement with the specialty's professional societies. He also discusses the approach behind his textbook, and the challenges of explaining his particular subspecialty to high school students.

Education & Training

1960–1962	Undergraduate Coursework, University of Saskatchewan
1962–1966	M.D., University of Saskatchewan
1966–1968	Junior Intern, and Assistant Resident, Jewish General Hospital, Montreal
1968–1969	Assistant Resident, Pathology, JGH
1968–1969	Demonstrator, Department of Anatomy, McGill University, Montreal
1969–1970	Senior Assistant Resident, Surgery, JGH
1970–1971	Chief Resident, Surgery, Montefiore Hospital, Pittsburgh, PA
1971–1972	Chief Resident, Surgery, JGH
1972–1973	Fellow, Colon and Rectal Surgery, University of Minnesota, Minneapolis
1973–1974	Honorary Assistant in Surgery, St. Mark's Hospital, London, England

Career Path

1974–1987	Clinical Assistant, Assistant and Associate Surgeon, JGH
1978–1989	Lecturer, Assistant & Associate Professor of Surgery, McGill University
1982–1986	Founding President, Canadian Society of Colorectal Surgeons
1987–	Senior Surgeon and Director, Division of Colon and Rectal Surgery, JGH
1989–	Professor of Surgery (1989–) and Oncology (1992–), McGill University
1993–	Vice Chairman, Department of Surgery, JGH
1994–1995	President, American Society of Colon and Rectal Surgeons
1999–2000	President, American Board of Colon and Rectal Surgery

In terms of training, you have to aim for the top, recognizing that very few people are going to get to the top. Alfred Lord Tennyson said that you hitch your wagon to a star and you're sure to go far. The reason for that is that if you put an average person in an average program, he's going to come out average. You put an average person in an above average program, and they're going to come out above average. Obviously if you have a very skilled individual, a very bright, eager individual in a very good program, they're clearly going to come out on top. You rarely ever get to the top of everything that you want. But if you don't aim for something better than where you are, then you'll go nowhere.

—*Philip H. Gordon*

Philip Gordon is one of North America's preeminent colorectal surgeons. In his over three decades of service as an instructor, researcher and practicing surgeon at McGill University and Jewish General Hospital in Montreal, Gordon has advanced his chosen subspecialty on multiple fronts. In his research and surgical practice, he has made progress in the treatment of colon cancer and other diseases, and is responsible for multiple innovations in surgical technique. One of the first Canadian physicians to restrict his practice to colorectal surgery, Gordon led the way in establishing the subspecialty there. He became founding president of the Canadian Society of Colon and Rectal Surgery, and was instrumental in winning official recognition for the subspecialty from Canada's Royal College of Physicians and Surgeons. Gordon has also played a leading role in the American Society of Colon and Rectal Surgeons, which made him the first non-U.S. citizen to become its president in 1994. Along with Santhat Nivatvongs, Gordon is the author of his subspecialty's most widely respected textbook, now in its third expanded edition. Gordon's career provides a model of the diverse interests and achievements that can be encompassed within devotion to a medical subspecialty.

EARLY INTEREST IN MEDICINE

Though Gordon's medical training would take him from Saskatoon, Saskatchewan to London, with several stops in between, he grew up quite far away from the center of anything. Gordon spent his childhood on a farm near the town of Brooksby, which is near Melfort—which, in turn, is not all that far from Regina, the capital of Saskatchewan.

Gordon first became interested in medicine in high school, in part as an extension of his interest in science. He recalls that his interest was very definite, but was not caused by any single transformative experience: "It just seemed like a reasonable career path." (Gordon's mother remembers that as a child he enjoyed sewing things up, and sees this as a sign that he would become a surgeon; Gordon insists he has no recollection of this himself.)

Gordon went to college just hoping he would be admitted to medical school—no other options seriously appealed to him. He applied to only one medical school, the University of Saskatchewan, and was admitted during his second year of college. As a result, he left the university and went straight to medical school at the age of twenty.

Although he notes that his college education was a bit narrower than it might have been, he has no regrets about going to medical school so young. Deepening his education in medical science at an early age was, he believes, a worthwhile exchange for the academic breadth he missed out on:

> If you were to take an extra year or two to get an arts degree, which I don't have, instead of getting my colorectal fellowship, the two can't be compared, although they take the same amount of time. Obviously, having an arts degree would have given me a broader base, but I don't believe it would have helped me significantly in my career.

Gordon's career, though, did not take a direct path into the specialty that has since come to define it.

CHOOSING A SPECIALTY: FROM OBSTETRICS TO SAINT MARK'S

After earning his M.D. in 1966 from Saskatchewan, Gordon moved east to Montreal for an internship at Jewish General Hospital, with the intention of specializing in obstetrics. After a required preparatory year of general surgery, also completed at JGH, Gordon moved on to Michael Reese Hospital in Chicago for a residency in obstetrics and gynecology in 1968. Obstetrics appealed to him in part, he says, because it seemed like an unusually "happy specialty":

> Obstetrical patients are really the only patients in the entire hospital that are happy they are in the hospital. They are not sick. They are happy people. I liked the idea of working with people who are happy they are there.

On a personal level, Gordon did enjoy being involved in the births of new children, but he soon found that, on a procedural level, obstetrics was not a good fit for his interests:

> During the weeks while I was doing deliveries, and with the patients who were having babies, I didn't seem to get as excited, because of the repetitive nature of it. And after I delivered my second set of twins and was not terribly excited about it, I wondered how I would feel about delivering singles at two o'clock in the morning ten years later. So I realized that maybe that was not a specialty I was cut out for.

Somewhat to his surprise, he found that the procedures he found most interesting were the Caesarian sections: "I realized that what excited me wasn't specifically the Caesarian sections, but the idea that I was back in the operating room, and in a surgical milieu. It made me realize surgery was for me."

Gordon was granted permission to leave his residency in Chicago. He returned to JGH in Montreal, where he spent a year studying pathology and teaching anatomy before beginning a residency in surgery in 1969. Wishing to broaden his experience as much as possible, he chose to spend the fourth year of his residency at Montefiore Hospital in Pittsburgh: "It was important in my mind that one has exposure to a variety of procedures and a variety of surgeons, and this allowed me to see an entirely new world."

It was during this year in Pittsburgh that Gordon first began to consider sub-specializing in colorectal surgery. His reasons for this were at first quite practical. Gordon knew he wanted to work at a major hospital in a large city, and he happened to learn that the chief of surgery back in Montreal was interested in taking on more specialists in this particular area: "I felt that if I got my extra training in colorectal surgery, I would stand a much better chance of getting a staff position at the Jewish General Hospital."

After a final year of surgical residency at JGH, during which Gordon was chief resident in the program, he began pursuing his new subspecialty energetically, first with a fellowship in colon and rectal surgery at the University of Minnesota in Minneapolis, and then for part of a year at St. Mark's Hospital in London. "St. Mark's", Gordon explains,

> was the Mecca of colon and rectal surgery—really the first hospital in the world that restricted itself to only colon and rectal surgery. And therefore many individuals who had specialized in colon and rectal surgery were there, and spending time with some of the most prominent people in the world was to me a very important part of my training.

In 1974, Gordon returned to the department of surgery at McGill and JGH, where he would rise through the ranks over the next two decades, becoming a full professor of surgery in 1989 and, thanks to his work on colon cancer treatment, professor of oncology in 1992.

DELICATE WORK, AND THE POTENTIAL FOR A MESS: PRACTICING COLORECTAL SURGERY

While Gordon's reasons for pursuing colorectal surgery were initially pragmatic, he has since come to greatly appreciate the work of his subspecialty. The greatest satisfactions of his work, he explains, lie in the way a successful surgery can utterly transform a patient's health. This is true not only in cases of the most life-threatening illnesses, such as colon cancer, but also for those that present less severe threats but can nonetheless ruin a patent's quality of life—"diseases that people often make a lot of fun of as long as it is on someone else's bottom," says Gordon.

> We see patients with severe inflammatory bowel disease who have lost an enormous amount of weight. They are very ill, they can't eat, and they have severe bowel dysfunction. After removing the severely affected bowel, these patients are walking into your office looking fit and healthy. It is enormously satisfying.

Gordon, who over the course of his career has been responsible for many innovations in surgical procedure, sees an additional satisfaction in working at the cutting edge of his field, and enjoys being able to help patients through "procedures that not a lot of other people are doing or are capable of doing."

He mentions the procedural aspect of his work as a satisfaction in itself. While the surgeries he performs may not be as apparently delicate as those of, for example, an ophthalmologist, the need to operate with great care is no less pressing to him:

> If you are a delicate and skilled surgeon, who is not a ripper and a tearer—and you can spell that as "tearer" or "terror"—you can do colon surgery in a relatively bloodless fashion. It can be very precise. And the challenge is even greater than in some other kinds of surgery, because the opportunity for things to get very messy is quite great.

Gordon also notes, with pleasure, that his specialty provides more opportunities for relationships with patients than one might expect—the relationship goes well beyond "when you're asleep, I'll see you," he explains:

> We make sure we follow all of our patients, so we do have long-term relationships with them. Certainly the cancer patients are followed by us, because it is important to detect early recurrences. And the decision-making process that goes into deciding whether a patient needs an operation is an opportunity to get to know the patient. It is not the paternalistic "you need this operation now"—today we tend to present patients with options, if there are options, and have them participate in the decision-making process.

Advancing the Subspecialty: Professional Societies

Eager to build on the training in colorectal surgery that he had received in Minneapolis and London, Gordon made a concerted effort in the early years of his career to keep up with the latest advances in his field. This meant traveling to the conferences where new developments were presented months or even years before reaching publication. This, in turn, led to increasing involvement with the professional societies connecting with physicians in his field, most notably the American Society of Colon and Rectal Surgeons (ASCRS). "It seemed," Gordon recalls with a degree of understatement, "that one could be a little more interested in the activity of the society and in new research developments if one was involved in its committees."

Gordon became, in fact, intensely involved, devoting prodigious amounts of time and energy to committee work in the ASCRS: "It seemed that if one were to spread the gospel, if you will, and have others recognize the importance of the specialty, that one could best do that through the societies." In the Canadian context, his work was perhaps still more pivotal. One of the first Canadian physicians to restrict his practice to colorectal surgery, Gordon took the lead in promoting his subspecialty within the medical community and seeking official recognition for it. In 1982, he became founding president of the Canadian Society of Colon and Rectal Surgeons, an organization he had worked to establish and which he has continued to serve in various roles ever since. In 2001, the CSCRS named its annual lectureship the Philip H. Gordon Lecture in honor of Gordon's contributions.

Even as he was founding the CSCRS, Gordon's role in its American counterpart continued to grow, and he became the first non-U.S. citizen to be named its president in 1994. In the same year, Gordon was elected to the board of the American Board of Colon and Rectal Surgery, the organization responsible for professional certification in the subspecialty, and once again became the first non-U.S. citizen to be its president in 1999.

While Gordon's work in these professional societies has inevitably taken time away from his clinical practice, he believes this has been a worthwhile tradeoff, and is proud of his role in the subspecialty's growth over the past decades. Nor does he feel his work in this regard is altogether finished. At his home institution, McGill University, he is part of the largest group of specialized colorectal surgeons in Canada, but still finds himself struggling to overcome a "fossilized thought process" within the university bureaucracy in his efforts to establish a training fellowship in the subspecialty there.

Writing the Definitive Textbook

Despite all these considerable achievements, the one that Gordon is most proud of, and probably the one he is best known for, is his authorship (along with Santhat Nivatvongs) of the widely acclaimed standard textbook in his field, *Principles and Practice of Surgery for the Colon, Rectum, and Anus,* first published in 1992 and released in an updated third edition in 2007.

The initial idea for a textbook came in the early phase of Gordon's career, during his fellowship in Minneapolis, when he realized that some of the standard works in the field were not up to date. The project became more concrete, Gordon explains, after a conference presentation in 1976. His first book, *Essentials of Anorectal Surgery,* co-authored with Nivatvongs and Stanley Goldberg, "was born in a hotel room in Baltimore after speaking at a meeting. I sat down after speaking and wrote a table of contents." At the time, Gordon recalls, "there had not been a book written or published in the U.S. for twenty years prior to that on anorectal surgery, and there seemed to be a very large void."

Gordon was invited to update and expand that first book to include material on the colon as well, and the new book became the first edition of *Principles and Practice.* Gordon sees the book as his greatest achievement in part, he says, because of the sheer amount of effort involved in putting it together. His wide-ranging involvement in the professional societies, along with work writing, editing and reviewing for various journals, helped to make this effort possible, keeping him abreast of the latest developments in the field. But much effort also went into presenting the textbook's material in a way that took into account legitimate differences of opinion within the field. To write a definitive textbook, Gordon made sure he gave other voices in the field their due respect:

> There are some books on a surgical subject that may be written as a "how I do it" book. The textbook that we wrote was more encompassing, and I felt that it was important to convey the ideas of different individuals on how a certain disease arises, or the different ways in which they think that particular disease should be treated. That makes it a lengthier proposition, there's no question about that, but I think that it's fair that you give other people in the field the respect they deserve in terms of how they feel this should be handled.

This approach has made the textbook not only a valuable procedural guide, but also a valuable reference to the range of literature in its field. For Gordon himself, it also proved to be a rewarding if exhausting way to stay up to date on a wider range of knowledge than an ordinary professional life would encompass. "Writing the book," he says, "is far and away the best form of continuing medical education you could have."

LOOKING BACK, AND GIVING BACK

Gordon's intensive work in these diverse aspects of his profession—

clinical practice, professional organizations, and publication—have been, in themselves, immensely rewarding. But the time they have each demanded came at what he feels to be a certain price:

> All of this took me away from my family, and my kids grew up without me being as involved as I'd like to be or maybe think I should have been. It kept me away from my wife as well, not necessarily away by five hundred miles or two thousand miles, but if I spend the night in my study working on whatever manuscript or book chapter or professional society organizational work that I was trying to put together, I wasn't spending the time with them. I would have liked to have a better balance. I would do it differently if I could do it over again.

In terms of his career itself, though, Gordon has few regrets. What comes to mind first as he thinks back on it are not so much errors that he would like to correct as opportunities he may never have seen at all: "It would have been nice to have been exposed to a number of individuals to choose as mentors at a much younger age than I was," Gordon reflects. He emphasizes the importance of circumstance in determining one's career, and urges students to seek out the best training possible so as to maximize new opportunities—even and perhaps especially the opportunities they cannot foresee. Gordon has experienced first-hand how important such opportunities can be, in some cases playing the role of mentor himself:

> I had one resident who came to me and said, "Until I met you my life was perfectly organized. I'm a fourth-year resident and I have a job after I'm finished at this, and everything was fine. But now that I have spent three months in your service, I want to be a colorectal surgeon and I'm really all mixed up." And so it's a matter of who you may be exposed to that tends to dictate where you're going to go.

As a professor, then, Gordon has been able to provide his students with some of the opportunities he may have missed out on. He has also tried to do so for even younger students by participating in JGH's Hospital Opportunity Program for Students since 1987. In HOPS, medical faculty lecture about their work to interested high school students. "We give them an idea of what we do in our specialty," Gordon explains, "and I do it in a graphic form."

Perhaps inevitably in a specialty sometimes referred to by younger students as a "butt-doctor," Gordon also uses humor to get his message across. For instance, he commissioned a song entitled "Working Where The Sun Don't Shine (The Colorectal Surgeon's Song)" which he plays for his audiences. It has become popular worldwide, receiving over 100,000 hits on the Internet.

But this ability to take himself but not his work lightly is, at bottom, one more way of serving his community and investing in the future of the specialty he has done so much to advance. As he explains, the HOPS program gives students an opportunity he feels he lacked:

> [T]he opportunity to know what the specialty is about. They have the opportunity to ask individuals "what is this all about?" and can then make more informed decisions about their future careers. I certainly never had an opportunity like that—and I do it because I think it's important.

Jane E. Henney

Home Secretary, Institute of Medicine
Former Commissioner, U.S. Food and Drug Administration
Former Provost for Health Affairs, University of Cincinnati

Jane Henney was the first woman appointed to be commissioner of the FDA. In this profile, she discusses the path that led her from an early interest in education into medicine, and how she has been able to combine both of these interests in many of her subsequent positions. She also reflects on how the experience of growing up in a small town prepared her for some of the managerial challenges she has overcome in the health care sector.

Education & Training

1965–1969	B.S., Manchester College
1969–1973	M.D., Indiana University School of Medicine
1973–1974	Intern, Medicine, St. Vincent's Hospital
1974–1975	Resident, Internal Medicine, Georgia Baptist Hospital
1975–1976	Fellow, Medical Oncology, M.D. Anderson Hospital and Tumor Institute

Career Path

1976–1985	Commissioned Officer, United States Public Health Service
1980–1985	Deputy Director, National Cancer Institute
1985–1991	Acting Director, University of Kansas Mid–America Cancer Center
1988–1991	Vice Chancellor for Health Programs and Policy, University of Kansas
1992–1994	Deputy Commissioner for Operations, U.S. Food and Drug Administration
1994–1998	Vice President for Health Sciences, University of New Mexico
1998–2001	Commissioner of Food and Drugs, U.S. Food and Drug Administration
2001–2003	Senior Scholar in Residence, Association of Academic Health Centers
2003–2008	Senior Vice President and Provost for Health Affairs, University of Cincinnati
2008–2012	Professor of Medicine, University of Cincinnati
2014–	Home Secretary, Institute of Medicine

Additional Positions

Board Member, The Commonwealth Foundation
Member, The China Medical Board
Board Member, GoVibrant
Board Member, Cigna

Many of the things that you want to get done in a senior health policy position are not done in a day. They're done over months or years or a lifetime. One needs to be able to take satisfaction out of the long term. Knowing you are a part of the action rather than needing to take credit for the whole is crucial to leading a complex organization. If you can come to terms with long-term, shared rewards it is possible to have a greater impact on your work and people's health.

—*Jane Henney*

Trained as a medical oncologist, Jane Henney has spent most of her career as a manager and administrator of health care institutions across the United States, most prominently as commissioner of the Food and Drug Administration from 1998 to 2001. Henney came to the FDA well prepared: she had spent many years furthering cancer research as a clinical monitor and manager at the National Cancer Institute, and had overseen the development of major health care initiatives in positions at the University of Kansas and the University of New Mexico. After leaving the FDA, Henney became the senior vice president and provost for health affairs at the University of Cincinnati.

FROM AN EDUCATION MAJOR TO A PRE-MED

Since many in her family were teachers, Henney pursued a major in education upon enrolling in college in 1965. Her natural proclivity for the sciences led her to gain teaching experience by tutoring pre-meds and serving as a lab assistant in biology courses. During her four years at Manchester College, it became clear to Henney that, while she would always want to be involved with education, her primary vocation was to become a physician.

She sought advice from the heads of the chemistry and biology departments at her school, and received mixed feedback. The chair of the chemistry program counseled her against going into medicine, because the two women he knew in the field were unhappy and had sacrificed their personal lives for their careers. The chair of the biology program said to her, "Well, why not?" She followed her biology professor's advice:

The experience taught me a few things. One is that I'm very selective in the advice that I'm willing to accept. And two, when you want to take on the impossible, listen to the voice that says, "Why not?"

THE DECISION TO PURSUE MEDICAL ONCOLOGY

Henney's inspiration to go into medicine originated with the family physician in her hometown. Although she planned to follow his path into general medicine, her exposure to oncology while attending medical school at Indiana University, along with a family friend who had suffered from breast cancer, soon changed her mind:

> I found that the patient population I was intellectually attracted to was the cancer population, because of the intricacies of the disease. I was also drawn to cancer patients emotionally. Every one of them faced a serious disease with courage. I was told it was a very depressing field, but I didn't find that at all.

Henney did not see oncology as a specialization that would take her away from the general medicine she had originally intended to practice. Because medical oncologists are privy to every aspect of their patients' care, she would be able to act as a primary care physician to her patients while still pursuing the specialization that most appealed to her.

During her residency, Henney also became involved in oncological research; this interest led her first to the M.D. Anderson Hospital and Tumor Clinic for a fellowship, and later to the National Cancer Institute.

DIRECTING BIOMEDICAL RESEARCH

Henney went to the National Cancer Institute (NCI) intending to stay there for two years, after which she would return to laboratory research at an academic medical center. She initially took a position as a drug monitor for investigational drug studies[1] largely because her husband had received a job offer in Washington, D.C.

Although Henney started her career at the NCI as a drug monitor, she subsequently became the project officer for many studies related to breast cancer. These included the Fisher and Bonadonna studies, two pivotal research projects that had a decisive impact on therapeutic treatments for breast cancer. Henney next became the special assistant to Vincent DeVita, then the division director. This promotion gave her responsibility over a wider range of activities in the Division of Cancer Treatments:

> Dr. DeVita worked very hard, and expected everyone around him to do so as well. Those six years that I worked for him, I worked seven days a week, every day of the year. He had a couple of good rules: Rule number one: "If you see a project you want to work on, do it. I will ask you to do a lot of things, but if you see something else that you want to take on, it is fine with me." And rule number two: "Five minutes before you think you're going to get yourself in real trouble, would you at least tell me?" My work portfolio expanded and I was always assured of a backup.

When DeVita was asked to become director of the entire institute, Henney continued on as special assistant to the division director and also filled in as acting division director and deputy director of the NCI:

> So, at the one time, I was special assistant to a division director, I was an acting division director in another division, and the deputy director of the Institute. The joke was that my desk should be on the elevator so I could ride from floor to floor trying to do my job.

While Henney was first able to develop her managerial skills during this time at the NCI, her understanding of management stemmed from a much earlier period. Growing up in a small town, Henney had observed the organizational skills and attitudes needed to be effective in a community:

> If you wanted to get things done in the small town like the one where I grew up, you had to be able to work together even if you didn't like one another. If we wanted to build a new baseball park or gas line for the city, or get city water rather than well water, we had to come together as a community. These are lessons you learn over and over again in managerial positions. It's how to bring out the best in people. To bring together talented people from diverse backgrounds and interests and get them to work on something bigger than they could do if they were doing it alone. I think that's some of the trick—the art—the skill of management.

IMPACT THROUGH EDUCATION

Despite her success at the NCI, Henney decided to return to academia. She wanted at once to influence the medical education that students received and to be at the forefront of technology and research:

> I wanted the experience of running a health sciences center with a school of medicine, nursing and pharmacy. I wanted to be part of shaping the future. After all, academic institutions are all about the future. The students are future health professionals, the research is the discovery of new knowledge, and the health care delivery system in an academic health center needs to be not only state-of-the-art but a platform to design and develop tomorrow's care. It's really about doing today what the future is going to be about for everyone else.

While at the NCI, Henney was recruited by the University of Kansas to become an associate vice chancellor. In this position, she was asked to develop centers of excellence in cancer, environmental health and aging. She also led an interdisciplinary training program involving scientists from the University of Kansas Medical Center and the Kansas State University biology department.

Two years later, when the dean of the medical school departed, she was asked to become interim dean. Henney notes that neither her prior work as a researcher nor her skills as a clinician could have fully prepared her for this new role:

> If I would have been solely focused on research or clinical practice, I would have been no more qualified to be a dean than a man on the moon. A lot of the responsibility of being a dean is to understand what the faculty members are trying to accomplish and see how they can fulfill their goals. Since that had been what I was doing, it made "deaning" easier. I had been getting prepared for a job without realizing it!

While acting as dean, Henney made decisions regarding faculty promotions and tenure, helped to mediate a state-wide malpractice crisis, and initiated a reorganization of management and leadership in several departments of the medical school that were struggling.

A RETURN TO GOVERNMENT

In 1992, when Henney received a call from the FDA commissioner, David Kessler, the idea of returning to government was far from her mind. After six years at Kansas, she was so entrenched in the academic environment that she assumed he had called to talk about the research that her university was doing:

> All I could think of was, "How did we screw up, what's gone wrong in our clinical trials operation, how do we deal with the press, what is this all about?" I was not thinking good thoughts when I got that message.

In fact, Kessler had called to offer her a job as his deputy of operations at the FDA. With his own work focused on national policy issues, he needed an experienced clinician and manager with a background in government to oversee the agency's daily internal functions. Henney had been recommended to him as someone with senior government experience and strong managerial skills:

> Kessler started out by saying, "You don't know me, but I want to come to Kansas City and talk to you about a job." All I could blurt out was, "I've got a job!" And he said, "Well, I know that, but I want to talk to you about a job at the FDA." I said, "Well, I'm perfectly happy in my job here, and if I was to take another job it would be in academia—not government. I enjoyed my time in government, but right now I'm committed to academia." Well, he was one tenacious fellow. Finally, I told him to come out and tell me about the job, and then I'd give him some recommendations about who he could interview for it—because I wasn't interested.

After a personal visit from the FDA commissioner and a lengthy six-hour discussion that made clear the reservations and requirements of both parties, Henney agreed to take the position. Ultimately, she feels that she excelled at the FDA: she recruited new leadership to direct the different centers at the agency and reorganized much of the daily work that was done there. "I was involved in a number of controversies of the time, but I thrived on the operations part of the job," she recalls.

The "Dream Job"

After two years at the FDA, Henney was recruited to be the first vice president for health sciences at the University of New Mexico. With her passion for academia and interdisciplinary research, she felt as if she had been offered a dream job. The regents at UNM had decided to reorganize all the components related to health care at the university into one organization. Henney was recruited to implement a vision of UNM's Academic Health Sciences Center:

> Unifying a medical school, college of nursing, pharmacy and all of the hospitals and clinics into a cohesive organization wasn't necessarily something that everyone thought should be done, but it was what I was recruited to achieve. Fortunately, the leadership at the schools, clinical operations and hospitals had enlightened self-interest. They didn't necessarily want to be a health center, but knew that if they had to, they ought to be the best one they could be. To do that, their success depended on my success, and my success was going to depend on their success.

Henney set out to engage everyone in discussions and retreats to plan strategy and map out the direction that they wanted the health center to take. Watching the health center evolve was rewarding to Henney: she loved being able to build an institution from the ground up. She feels she helped make the center a success, and that its impact is broad, positive and tangible:

> The faculty and staff at the health center believed in a real way that they were trying to improve the health of the people of New Mexico, whether they were in research or seeing patients in a clinic or trying to train the next generation of pharmacists. There was an energy in that faculty and staff that said, "We're making a difference for the people of New Mexico." You could feel it. When people are that value-congruent and that tied to a singleness of mission, it makes everything else go a little smoother.

One of Henney's top priorities was to reach out to community members and make sure they knew that the health center was there for them. Under her leadership, the health sciences center developed research programs concentrating on issues significant to New Mexico residents. The center also worked directly with the state legislature to tackle widespread health concerns in the community: "We created a health care delivery system. The job was not only satisfying, it was fun."

BACK TO GOVERNMENT

Henney's next job offer came from Secretary of Health and Human Services Donna Shalala (profiled on page 418). Shalala asked Henney if she would be willing to be recommended to the president as the next FDA commissioner. While honored by the offer, Henney was still reluctant to give up the work she loved at UNM: "I said to Secretary Shalala, 'Donna, I'm sitting at my desk looking at the Sandia Mountains in my dream job. I don't think I'm interested.'" But Henney also knew she could have a significant impact on the FDA:

> I thought, "There's only one FDA, there's probably only one opportunity like this. I would go back essentially to my own team of people. I'd be able to, for whatever time I was there, be effective from day one. I know how the agency works. Most commissioners coming in have never stepped a foot inside that agency. And I can make a difference."

Nominated by President Clinton and confirmed by the U.S. Senate, Henney became the first woman to head the FDA. Perhaps the greatest controversy during Henney's tenure concerned the FDA's approval of RU-486, a therapeutic alternative to surgical abortion. Yet this was one event among many other accomplishments that received less attention. For example, Henney improved the efficiency of the agency's approval process for drugs and medical devices. Her efforts also led to a revision of labels for non-prescription drugs, making it easier for consumers to find the information needed to use these products safely. She improved food safety through national surveillance programs and stricter importation standards, implemented new programs to assure the safety of the blood supply, and developed new programs to reduce smoking among young people.

THE COST OF MANAGEMENT

While Henney has few regrets about her career, she is keenly aware that her choices have entailed both personal and professional sacrifice. She misses, for example, the contact with patients that she gave up to pursue a career in health care management:

> I went into medicine to see and treat patients. Through everything I've done in my leadership and managerial career, I have always been able to have the satisfaction of knowing that some aspect of my job or the decisions I make would at least in part impact patients. It's just the human interaction—the conversations you have with patients, how you do or don't make a difference in their lives—that I miss.

In 2003, Henney moved to Cincinnati to take on the position of senior vice president and provost for health affairs at the University of Cincinnati;

her husband, Bob, remained in Washington, D.C. "It's back to marriage by boarding pass," says Henney resignedly, remarking that she and her husband have lived in different parts of the country for as many as eight and a half years at a stretch. Henney says that both she and her husband have been willing to sacrifice time together for the chance to take on interesting career opportunities, though such lengthy periods of separation have been far from easy. She credits her husband with making room for her career: "I have been able to have a lot of freedom of selection because Bob's been so supportive." Citing philosophical differences with the board of trustees and the president, Henney stepped down in 2008 from her administrative roles at the University of Cincinnati, where she continued work as a professor of medicine teaching in areas including public health and biomedical technology.

When Henney is asked about the biggest personal sacrifice she has made, she talks about the strain of distance on family relationships, but not in the context of her marriage. Instead, she discusses the difficulties of being separated from her close-knit nuclear family. With the exception of one sister, Henney's entire family is still in Indiana, while Henney herself has not lived there since her medical internship. In many ways, she says, it would have been easier if she had built a practice in Indiana, or had lived close enough to return every few weeks for a weekend family gathering. But her family, like her husband, has been extremely supportive of her career.

Henney cautions students and young professionals against granting their career any false importance or primacy in their lives:

> Careers are really important, but they're not the most important thing in life. If you have to put them on hold for a while or restructure and rebuild them, there's time. But there's not time to go back and fix broken relationships with family or with friends, or to lose your integrity. Careers can be set aside for a time if you need to. You can come back and redirect them, or watch them bounce even higher than they've been before. And some of those other things, unless you're paying attention to them all the time, you can never restore.

She suggests that many young women, in particular, are discouraged from taking time off to raise a family because their careers might not be the same afterwards. But she believes that such fears are, in the long term, unwarranted:

> I think if a person wants to take time—three, five, seven years—to raise a family, that person's career might not be the same as it was before: of course it isn't. But it doesn't mean that very successful people haven't been able to put their career on ice and come back.

LEARNING TO ACCEPT WHAT'S COMING TO YOU

Part of Henney's success stems from pursuing the opportunities that came to her, even if that meant accepting jobs with responsibilities and challenges that she had never previously undertaken. She was always able to observe and learn from the people she was working with and the situations in which she found herself:

> I think it's very hard for people who are early in their career or at midpoints in their careers to really believe that if someone asks you to do a job, it's because they really believe you can do it. You know, we get this crazy notion in our head that we won't be able to do it or they're trying to set us up, or, "I could never do that, they're just flattering me." I have had to learn this simple truth time and time again. But I know that I would never ask anybody to do a job where I thought they couldn't do it, so it should follow that people don't ask me to do jobs that they don't think I can do. I might not have known how to do every aspect of it, and that's one of the thrills of the job is to learn new things—as well as new things about yourself.

Note

1. The former director of the NCI, Andrew von Eschenbach, is profiled on page 442.

Steve Hochberg

Director, Solar Capital Ltd
Founder and Managing Partner, Ascent Biomedical Ventures
Senior Vice Chairman, Mount Sinai Health System

Steve Hochberg influences the future of medical technology by identifying, funding and helping direct early stage companies. In this profile, Hochberg discusses why he decided to apply his early experience in finance and "turnaround" management to entrepreneurship in the health care industry. He also discusses his work in the non-profit sector, most notably with the AppleCare Foundation, which he co-founded in 2003.

EDUCATION & TRAINING
1979–1983   B.B.A., University of Michigan
1987–1989   M.B.A., Harvard Business School

CAREER PATH
1985–1986   Associate, Alex. Brown and Sons
1986–1987   Associate, Bain and Co.
1989–1992   Associate, Sigoloff and Associates
1992–   Managing Director, The Ascent Group, LLC
1993–1995   President, Physicians' Online, Inc.
1993–1997   President, Advanced Health Technologies Corporation
1997–2003   CEO, Eminent Research Systems, Inc. and CEO, Clinsights, Inc.
2002–2004   CEO, Biomerix Corp.
2003–   Co-Chairman, AppleCare Foundation
2004–   Managing Partner, Ascent Biomedical Ventures
2011–2013   Chairman of the Board, Continuum Health Partners
2013   Senior Vice Chairman, Boards of Directors, Mount Sinai Health System and Icahn School of Medicine
2013–   Partner, Private Transactions Team, Deerfield Capital Management

FURTHER INFORMATION
Ascent Biomedical Ventures: www.abvlp.com
Turnaround Management Assoc: www.turnaround.org

If someone asked me what I do I'd say I'm a health care venture capitalist and entrepreneur, but health care to me is nothing more than an industry like financial services—we primarily use the same technologies. And technology is technology—whether it's applied to computers and software or it's applied to blood diagnostics and new therapies. It's just more fine-tuned in health care. The have-your-cake-and-eat-it-too part of this is that you go to bed and feel like you're doing something that will make a difference and at the same time will generate above average returns for your investors. I don't think there are many other opportunities like this one.

—Steve Hochberg

Steve Hochberg has been creating, running, and investing in companies at the cutting edge of technology, from early personal computers to contemporary biotechnology, for over thirty years. He is best known as the founder and managing partner of Ascent Biomedical Ventures, a venture capital firm specializing in the start-up and development of companies in the medical technology sector—companies that Hochberg often runs himself during their start-up phase, when he finds the challenge of running a company most exciting. In the past, he has co-founded Biomerix Corporation; Clinsights, Inc.; Eminent Research Systems, Inc.; Advanced Health Technologies Corporation; and Physicians' Online. He is also co-founder and co-chairman of the board of directors of the AppleCare Foundation, a non-profit organization that focuses on emergent health care issues.

A BEGINNING IN BUSINESS

Steve Hochberg started his first business in the early 1980s, before he had even graduated from college. In fact, during his undergraduate years at the University of Michigan, Hochberg started several business ventures to help pay off some of his tuition bills. Although he cannot pinpoint a specific influence or event that encouraged him to pursue accounting and finance in college, he believes that his desire to succeed in business was influenced by the experiences of his family: "The early failures of my family's businesses helped motivate me to be successful at it." Immediately after graduation, Hochberg threw himself into his first large-scale entrepreneurial endeavor:

I graduated from college in 1983, which is the time that IBM first started shipping out a product known as the personal computer. So, what we did was provide software and other supplies to large corporate buyers. It was based right on campus, and we just rented out some office space and built it into a distributor of products and services. I did that until 1985, at which point we sold the primary assets and shut down the business.

The slowdown in the market for PC software introduced Hochberg to the business cycle and its characteristic fluctuations in demand.

After this experience, Hochberg sought a more traditional position at Alex. Brown & Sons as an underwriter of technology offerings in San Francisco. After less than a year on the job, he found himself somewhat unhappy:

I went from being my own boss to working for a firm that only did underwriting and M&A [mergers and acquisitions]. It was a good learning experience—but it wasn't being an entrepreneur, and it wasn't my thing. So, literally, my boss there made a phone call to Bain and Co., I interviewed there and I started at Bain the next day. It was almost like being traded.

Bain & Company, a management consulting firm, seemed at first like a better fit for Hochberg. His focus was again on technology, and it was at Bain that he began to learn about health care technology. Yet while this new field fascinated him, his work at Bain was ultimately unsatisfying. For Hochberg, working for someone else would never provide the excitement of running his own company. Quickly recognizing that he needed a change, Hochberg applied to business school.

TURNAROUND MANAGEMENT

Hochberg enrolled in Harvard Business School (HBS) in 1987, and within his first few weeks he had started another business—this time a not-for-profit. Although his previous five years of experience were in technology, Hochberg had become fascinated with the "turnaround" business, and focused his new project around this concept:

The not-for-profit was called the Turnaround Management Association. Today, it has 6,400 members and is a flourishing enterprise. It was designed to train professionals about how to deal with businesses that are in trouble—lawyers, accountants, finance specialists, and general managers. The idea was to create a training program for people to earn a certification in turnaround management. I was very satisfied with this project, from co-founding it to running the organization. It was based in North Carolina, but I ran it out of my dorm room on the business school campus.

Hochberg combined his studies at HBS with his growing business. He proposed an independent learning course where he would research what defined a successful turnaround. Defining a turnaround as a company that had two years of losses followed by two years of gains, he researched every publicly traded company that followed that pattern:

> I came up with a thesis that there were two key variables that differentiated successful turnarounds from unsuccessful ones. One is whether or not the company was in an industry that was susceptible to economic cyclicality, and two was whether the industry was growing. And based on the analysis, there were only two industries that had constant growth and no cycle—the food industry and health care.

Hochberg thought back to his first business cycle experience, when he had to shut down his computer software business due to a slowing market. He knew that working in health care, with its constantly growing demand curve, would allow him to circumvent the ups and downs inherent in most industries. Hochberg saw the health care sector as a chance to work at the forefront of technological innovation—it was a great business opportunity: "I had no interest in health care up until that point. Doing something good was important to me, but I wasn't going to be a care provider. I was going to be in business."

In 1989, Hochberg graduated from business school and went to work for Sigoloff and Associates in turnaround management:

> It wasn't being an entrepreneur, but it was as close as you were going to get while working in a professional services firm. We'd get dropped into these companies that were in the midst of major crisis and we'd assume general management responsibility. We were making decisions across all functions of the business.

Since the businesses for which Hochberg consulted were in financial distress, he and his colleagues were often forced to include layoffs among other cost-cutting measures. Hochberg found such responsibilities hard to bear. After two years, he decided that he would be much happier "hiring, rather than firing people," and left Sigoloff and Associates to launch his first health care technology business.

START-UPS AND TURNAROUNDS

Hochberg found that the skills he used in turning businesses around were very similar to those needed to start a company:

> In both instances, the businesses don't have a lot of cash. While a turnaround typically has a franchise or a customer base that they can leverage, there's still the whole issue of cash management and resource allocation. It's almost the same in a start-up.

What Hochberg finds different and more exciting with start-ups is the need for creativity, the chance to build an organization up from an idea:

> I am motivated by the ability to create—that's what gets me going, the creativity that goes into picking ideas and building them into businesses. I always need to have more then one venture going on because, if the business is successful, at some point the businesses get where they're beyond the creative phase. They go into the management phase, and that's where I like to step out of the role as CEO and take a more passive one, or see new ownership. I don't want to give up my creative energy.

Knowing this about himself, Hochberg has started up numerous health care endeavors, usually juggling several at a time. His first health care start-up was Physicians' Online (POL), an interactive, online medical reference provider launched in 1992. He recalls that, at the time, few people had even heard of the Internet, and few professions had taken advantage of its possibilities: "We built one of the first on-line communities—it was over 230,000 physicians at a time when everyone said that doctors never use the computer." POL also proved technologically challenging: Hochberg had to move the user-base from a private network to the Internet when the underlying technology was still new.

In 1995, Hochberg's interests turned from medical reference to medical technology. He spun out a company from POL called Med-E-systems, which was a Web-based clinical data collection service for practicing physicians. This company merged with Advanced Health and went public in 1996, which was Hochberg's first experience with an initial public offering, or IPO:

> It was exciting—there's nothing like watching an idea you had turn into a ticker symbol on the exchange. Still, managing a public company was not ideal for me. It wasn't what I aspired towards.

At this time, Hochberg recognized an opportunity to match his technology background with the needs in the field of clinical research. He started his next venture, Eminent Research Systems, a clinical research organization, in 1997. Eminent focused exclusively on helping medical device companies bring their products through the clinical trials process and ultimately to market. Staying within the clinical research sector, Hochberg also started Clinsights, an Internet-based company with tools for gathering and disseminating medical research. In 2003, both Eminent and Clinsights were sold to Pharmaceutical Product Development.

INVESTING IN EMERGING HEALTH CARE TECHNOLOGIES

As a result of his experiences with Eminent and Clinsights, Hochberg had learned enough about managing clinical trials and new medical devices to feel comfortable investing in start-up medical device companies. In the late 1990s, he began providing seed capital to a half-dozen different groups:

Two of these companies have already been sold, one is going to be sold or shut down in the next few days, two are in process and one is my own—it's called Biomerix, and I'm now the CEO. As I look at the five that I seeded but didn't run, it's tough because I like to be in control. One of the things that has evolved having built these companies as an entrepreneur is that I like to make my own decisions.

Hochberg is also a founder and managing partner of Ascent Biomedical Ventures, where he focuses on making investments in biomedical companies that he controls. From 2004 to 2013, ABV has seeded 29 startups, with only two failures to date (a high rate of success in the high-risk field of venture capital). In 2013, ABV continued to grow as it merged its investment activities with Deerfield Management, one of the largest investment firms in the country to focus exclusively on health care. Aside from personal preference, Hochberg has found another compelling reason to control the health care companies that he invests in: "I get better returns for my investors when I make my own decisions. I have made them money every time that I've been in control."

Though Hochberg enjoys making decisions, he relies heavily on clinical partners and medical experts to guide him in areas in which he is not trained. Without a medical background, Hochberg has developed the ability to look for consistent responses from medical experts to help filter out less pertinent information:

I think that it's good, but not necessary, to be in this field and have a medical background ... I go to seminars and read publications and speak to experts— you just learn from experience.

CONVERGENCE

For Hochberg, the most exciting endeavors are those based on distinct concepts that converge to create a new opportunity:

The opportunities that I am attracted to are really those where there is a convergence of events or technologies. Biomerix, for instance, is a convergence of devices and drugs and integrating them together. The challenge and the complexity of working on next-generation, leading edge technologies or information are exciting to me.

With this in mind, Hochberg set out in 2003 to launch his first not-for-profit in more than a decade. The AppleCare Foundation, co-founded by Hochberg, focuses on emergent health care issues. These issues include new health risks, such as SARS; old health risks that have a sudden re-emergence, such as anthrax or plague; and existing health issues that suddenly intensify, such as childhood obesity. While most of these issues are related to disease or societal factors, AppleCare has responded to the health-related aspects of other kinds of crises as well:

> After September 11th, there was no such thing as an expert in preparedness for a continuum of biological, chemical and nuclear emergencies—it was a convergence of clinical and industrial technologies, and a matter of funneling them together. So we [AppleCare] published a *New York Times* bestseller book called *The Survival Guide: What to do in a Biological, Chemical or Nuclear Emergency*. By putting it all together, we made the information accessible to both doctors and laymen.

Hochberg is proud of his work with AppleCare: "Most of our initiatives are ideas that I have put forward—I feel particularly good about that." He also finds the same kind of excitement in his work for AppleCare that he does in his business ventures: "For-profit or non-profit, it doesn't matter to me. Of course the financial rewards are greater in for-profit, but the work is the same."

STILL LOOKING FORWARD

While Hochberg's restless drive to create new businesses has brought him much success, it has at times left him overworked and overcommitted:

> My greatest regrets are the times when I was first starting out, and I was so motivated to create, but I had too many balls in the air. I was juggling too much, and I was too stressed. That rubs off on your home life. Modulating the amount of new projects I take on has always been the most difficult thing for me.

Today, with two daughters, Hochberg believes that he is better at acknowledging his limits. He finds his schedule remarkably flexible. He rarely works weekends and makes sure he has time to be with his children and pursue his outside interests: "Since I'm on my own, I have built my organizations with people who I can off-load to, so my work is flexible."

As a creator, Hochberg points to establishing the first on-line community of doctors as one of his most satisfying achievements. He also feels proud when the information collected and disseminated from one of his clinical research companies makes an impact on the health care system:

> Having our data be converted into manuscripts and presented at conferences, watching adoption increase as a result of the work we've done, tracking the first 10,000 patients with drug-eluting stents—it is all great. Ultimately, improving health care has been extremely satisfying—they have all proved to be worthwhile initiatives. In the end, it's producing something that people value and use.

Hochberg is also particularly proud of the biomedical products developed by Biomerix, a health care technology company that he helped to found, and where he remains chairman of the board. The company's base technology is a proprietary biomaterial designed to mimic the extracellular matrix. While the material was still in its early phases of development, Hochberg already had high hopes for it:

> It has the most promise and the most challenge. We've been dealing with new chemistry, the FDA, new technology, and clinical issues: How do you design the product to be clinically effective, but also so that the clinician can use the technology?

Today, the material has FDA approval for use in the surgical repair of hernias and rotator cuff injuries, with still further applications on the horizon.

Most recently, Hochberg spearheaded the massive undertaking of merging two of New York City's largest health care providers, Continuum Health Partners and Mount Sinai Hospital and Medical School. Named chairman of the board at Continuum in 2011, Hochberg led negotiations for the merger of the two companies into the Mount Sinai Health System in 2013. With seven hospitals and over $6 billion in annual revenue, Mount Sinai is now one of the largest private, not-for-profit health systems in the country.

In assessing the value of any new technology before he commits his investors' money, Hochberg thoroughly evaluates the risks and returns of each possible company or idea. He encourages those who aspire to entrepreneurship to learn early on how to evaluate and navigate risk:

> Understand risk. People say, "You must be a risk taker because you start businesses." But in some ways, I would say I'm not a risk taker. I not only have partners who are experts in the particular technology, but I assess if what I'm doing is overly risky and whether I'm ultimately comfortable with that. People may have a great idea, but translating it into a successful venture within our health care system which has regulations, physician adoption, and patient acceptance issues—you really need to make sure that you've adequately assessed all this. When we started Physicians' Online, people said doctors won't use the Internet, but I had a large group of doctors who told me what barriers would need to be overcome so that they would. In the end you want to be in a position where you can say, "There is no risk other than execution."

Ralph I. Horwitz

Director, Institute for Transformative Medicine, Temple University
Former Dean, Case Western Reserve School of Medicine
Former Chair, Internal Medicine, Yale School of Medicine

Ralph Horwitz is considered one of the pioneers of modern clinical investigation, largely because of the advances he has made in fundamental research methodology. In this profile, he discusses the early clinical experiences that motivated him to become involved in basic research, and the value of collaboration in research. He also reflects on the desire for new challenges that, after decades at Yale, led him to seek out institutional leadership roles first at Case Western and then at Stanford.

Education & Training

1965–1969	B.S., Albright College
1969–1973	M.D., Pennsylvania State University College of Medicine
1973–1974	Intern, Internal Medicine, Royal Victoria Hospital of McGill University, Montreal, Quebec
1975–1977	Fellow, Robert Wood Johnson Clinical Scholars Program, Yale University
1977–1978	Senior Resident, Massachusetts General Hospital, Boston, Massachusetts

Career Path

1978–2003	Co-Director, Yale Robert Wood Johnson Clinical Scholars Program
1982–1994	Chief, Section of General medicine, Department of Internal Medicine, Yale University School of Medicine (SOM)
1994–2003	Chairman, Department of Internal Medicine, Yale SOM
2003–2006	Dean, Case Western Reserve University School of Medicine
2003–2006	Director, Case Research Institute
2006–2011	Chair, Department of Medicine and Arthur Bloomfield Professor of Medicine, Stanford University
2011–	Senior Vice President for Clinical Evaluation and Senior Advisor to the Chairman of Research and Development, GlaxoSmithKline

Selected Publications

Concato J, Shah N, Horwitz RI. "Randomized controlled trials, observational studies, and the hierarchy of research designs." *NEJM*. 2000; 342: 1887–1892.

Viscoli CM, Brass LM, Kernan WN, Sarrell P, Suissa S, Horwitz RI. "A clinical trial of estrogen-replacement therapy after ischemic stroke." *NEJM*. 2001; 245: 1243–9.

Horwitz RI et al. "Internal medicine residency redesign: proposal of the Internal Medicine Working Group." *American Journal of Medicine*. 2011.

When I went to medical school, I didn't understand the versatility of a medical degree, or the diversity of careers that one could pursue. I viewed the faculty who were teaching me as very different from what I had envisioned for myself. Accomplished Ph.D. scientists were teaching me about things that didn't seem directly related to medicine. At that time, I didn't have a good sense for the opportunities open to physicians in academic medicine.

—*Ralph Horwitz*

A leading innovator in clinical research in the early years of his career, Ralph Horwitz has devoted his energies for much of the past two decades to institutional leadership: first at Yale, where his many years of service culminated in his chairing the Department of Internal Medicine; then at the Case Western Reserve University School of Medicine, which he guided through a crucial period of growth; and finally at one of the nation's flagship departments of medicine at Stanford. The transition from a focus on clincial research to broader leadership roles is, for Horwitz, less improbable than it might seem. Looking back on his career, he is keenly aware of how his own entry into academic medicine and research was made possible by a system of medical education flexible enough to allow him to pursue his own interests as they evolved. In his leadership roles, Horwitz has sought to create institutional structures that will foster for present-day students and physicians the innovation that has characterized his own career in research. His leadership at these institutions has also tightened the intellectual and organizational links between basic research and its clinical applications. Horwitz sees these links not just as practically necessary but, for researchers, as intellectually motivating. Having distinguished himself as a medical scientist, Horwitz has never lost sight of the clinical practice that, as a young medical student from a working-class family, he thought would be his own primary field of activity.

EARLY ASPIRATIONS IN MEDICINE

Horwitz grew up in a family "where there weren't any professionals," but from a young age his parents, a five-and-dime store owner and a stay-at-home mom, expected him to become a doctor. As a result, he says, "medical school was the place where I felt the most comfortable." He grew up in downtown Philadelphia, where he was exposed primarily to community physicians. At the time, Horwitz expected he would one day have a small local practice of his own:

> My only role models in medicine were the physicians that practiced in our community. When I was growing up, the general physician had an office in the neighborhood and lived in a house attached to the office, and I thought of myself as doing that kind of work. I didn't understand the depths of opportunity that were available in academic medicine.

Once in school, however, he found himself drawn to academic medicine because he "loved the intellectual content of it." Academic medicine required the practitioner to be versatile, and Horwitz was especially attracted to the challenges of translating research into clinical practice:

> Academic medicine is so wonderfully challenging—those who practice it have an extraordinary depth of knowledge and understanding about human physiology and the way that knowledge applies to patients' illnesses. They move so comfortably from research to practice. The combination of knowledge that seemed relevant to patient care and the facility to research and practice attracted me.

THE BEGINNING OF A PASSION

While Horwitz was an intern, he experienced first-hand how clinical practice could be affected by clinical research. A controversial research paper had claimed that Reserpine, a prescription drug used to treat high blood pressure, was associated with the risk of breast cancer in women. Reserpine was popular because it was effective and had a more favorable side-effect profile than many of its pharmaceutical rivals, such as Aldomet and guanethidine. When the drug was linked with breast cancer, Horwitz spent long hours on the phone with patients. He was forced to substitute more complicated alternative prescriptions, often with difficult side-effects. Nine months later "two articles appeared back to back in the *New England Journal [of Medicine]* contradicting the original findings." Horwitz was very upset:

> Reserpine was a very easy medication, though it did have some side effects of depression, but the alternatives were not easy to take. I was so upset because I realized that I wasn't able to critically assess whether those original articles or the ones that came later were really accurate assessments of the relationship between Reserpine and breast cancer. So I wanted to learn how to do clinical research and how to evaluate it, because I thought it would make me a better doctor.

Driven by this experience, Horwitz approached Alvan Feinstein, a Yale professor renowned for his critical evaluation of clinical research. At the time,

Feinstein was also directing the Robert Wood Johnson Clinical Scholars program, a program that Horwitz quickly joined. Horwitz planned to complete the two-year program and subsequently pursue a residency in nephrology. Instead, he found himself intrigued by the process of doing research: "I was so excited by research that I didn't want it to be limited to any single specialty." Horwitz decided to pursue broader training, and completed his internal medicine residency at Massachusetts General Hospital. He subsequently returned to Yale and remained there, moving up the academic ladder for over 25 years.

THROUGH THE RANKS OF ACADEMIA

While Horwitz was both successful and independent in his early career as a researcher, he only later realized the benefits working more closely with colleagues:

> I isolated myself too much early in my career—I worked with few collaborators. There was a value to that: I became much more self-sufficient and self-reliant in methods of research. But later I found that working collaboratively was enormously satisfying and also increased the scope and impact of what one was doing.

Working collaboratively enabled Horwitz to expand his influence at Yale. He was eventually promoted to the chair of Medicine, and in that position created a premier program of clinical research, established the United States' first Ph.D. program for physicians devoted to careers in biomedical science, and expanded the department's clinical programs in the community and beyond.

The position he names as his greatest challenge, however, put him at the head of the program that had led him to Yale in the first place. In 1978, Horwitz was named co-director of the Robert Wood Johnson Clinical Scholars Program, in which he had been a fellow from 1975 to 1977. As co-director, he enjoyed working closely and intensively with a select group of clinical scholars.

Horwitz made some unconventional reforms at Yale. He invited playwright and actress Anna Deavere Smith to create a performance about the shared experience of doctors and patients in the midst of health crisis. Smith produced *Rounding it Out*, which has been performed at medical schools around the country and continues to be performed at Yale. Smith eventually developed *Rounding it Out* into a full-length play, *Let Me Down Easy*, which won widespread critical acclaim and was broadcast on PBS. Horwitz also started a writing group for medical residents to give narrative form to the doctor-patient relationships they experience.

Horwitz's decision to stay at Yale, motivated largely by personal factors, also meant that he had "to give up a lot of things that would make one visible on the national scene." Yet this was a sacrifice that seemed worthwhile:

> I did not spend a lot of time on the road trying to make myself as "seen" as I could have. It took me away from what mattered, so I was happy to let my work become known through applications rather than being a visiting professor at every institution that would invite me, and giving talks at every meeting that was available.

Still, he made this decision quite consciously. Horwitz's wife is also an academic with "an important and successful career of her own," and Yale provided both of them with an opportunity to thrive.

THE MOVE TO CASE WESTERN

Horwitz would have continued to grow and become still more inventive at Yale, he says, but he left his longtime academic home in 2003 to take a position as dean of Case Western Reserve University School of Medicine:

> I have always very much wanted an opportunity to shape not just a department of medicine, but a medical school, and to do so in a way that would be an example of what I believed great academic medical scholars and a medical school should be like nationally.

He hopes the move to Case Western will furnish him with an opportunity to put his beliefs about medical schools into practice. By unifying the university's many affiliated hospitals, he intends to provide a national model for integrating clinical programs. Cleveland, where Case Western is located, is unusual for a large city in that it has only a single medical school with several strong clinical affiliates. As a result, Horwitz sees it as a unique opportunity:

> I hope this school will be the central unifying force for the integration of clinical programs throughout the city, and I hope to create an academic medical center that is the best in the country—to reshape medical schools so they achieve a full seamless integration of clinical medicine and public health.

Horwitz's objectives for his move to Case Western reflect the same ideals that informed his original decision to go into academic medicine:

> I want students to understand both the biology of the disease and the social and behavioral context of illness. They need to link the practice of medicine to professional responsibility, understand what it means to care for individual patients, and yet to have a sense of responsibility for the health of the community.

Horwitz is also working with colleagues at the Cleveland Clinic to help integrate a distinctive new medical program within the Case School of Medicine. This program, The Lerner College of Medicine, will enroll approximately 30 students annually in a five-year course of instruction with a strong emphasis on preparing students for careers in clinical investigation. Horwitz believes that the Lerner College program complements the research activities of the larger medical school.

AFTERWORD: STANFORD AND BEYOND

In 2006, Horwitz moved on from Case Western to accept the position of chair of the Department of Medicine at Stanford. At this point, Horwitz had accomplished many of his goals for Case Western: the Lerner College had been successfully established, Case Western's affiliation with Cleveland and regional hospitals and clinics had been strengthened, and a new medical school curriculum had been put into practice. With Case Western transitioning from the development of new programs into their consolidation, Horwitz was attracted by the opportunity to oversee Stanford's medicine department at the beginning of its own period of new development. "Both the school and hospital," Horwitz remarked shortly after accepting his new position, "have committed to expanding and strengthening [their research, education, and clinical care]programs so that the Department of Medicine will be intellectually dominant nationally and clinically dominant regionally."[1]

Under Horwitz's leadership, the department expanded its faculty and increased its productivity in research, most notably in the area of patient and population studies, areas in which Stanford's department had not been as traditionally strong as in basic laboratory research. This new emphasis on patient and population research helped strengthen the Medicine Department's ability to translate its basic research into clinical applications.

Characteristically, though, Horwitz identified his greatest satisfaction at Stanford not in terms of an increase in research expenditures or depth of faculty, but rather in terms of the opportunity to help colleagues and students: "Contributing to the success of all of you," Horwitz wrote in a letter to the department in 2010, "has been the major source of my own satisfaction since coming to Stanford in 2006."[2]

In 2011, Horwitz moved on to yet another new role as a Senior Vice President for Clinical Evaluation Sciences at the pharmeceutical company GlaxoSmithKline. He also remains affiliated with the Yale School of Medicine, where he holds the title of Harold H. Hines, Jr. Professor Emeritus of Medicine and Epidemiology.

LOOKING BACK ON A LIFE IN ACADEMIA

Reflecting on his career, Horwitz says that the people he has worked with are the key to his own accomplishments. Although his success could be quantified by the increase in research dollars secured by his department or by his significant impact on observational research, Horwitz resists such measures:

> Just because it's easy to measure doesn't mean it's the most important measure. It is the careers of the individuals impacted that hopefully will turn out to be the most important marker of my success. As I became more involved in the Department of Internal Medicine at Yale, it was interacting with the residents and students that magnified my own interests and values. In many respects, therefore, my research accomplishments are amplified by the work of people that I've had an impact on. This most important aspect of my work is probably also the most enduring, the most lasting, and the most satisfying.

Horwitz, like many of his colleagues, says that it has been difficult to make compromises in his family life for the sake of his career; he believes that family commitments and relationships are the most important part of his life. He has been striving for a balance since he began working, and suggests that there is no single right solution: "People need to find their own answers, their own accommodations, because the problem is an intensely personal one."

Unlike some of his colleagues, Horwitz feels that many medical schools place too much focus on management and business coursework. He is concerned that too much didactic preparation is driving the creative spark out of the current generation of medical students, and he does not regret missing that coursework himself. He is also concerned that the current pressure on medical students to be well rounded and multidisciplinary is keeping them from developing a focused skill set: "I think that's a great tragedy, because continuing to acquire and develop your skills in research is important if you want to grow as an investigator and be successful at it." Instead of pursuing breadth, Horwitz advises physicians to pursue a passion:

> Do what you're passionate about. The most ennobling aspect of medicine is the practice of it—if that's what you're passionate about, there's no reason not to pursue it with enormous force and vigor. But if you get satisfaction and enjoyment out of research, and you're well prepared for a career in clinical investigation, you shouldn't shy away from teaching medicine in an academic setting. It's our fundamental duty to teach the next generation.

Notes

1. Ralph Horwitz, quoted in: Michelle L. Brandt, "New Chair to Lead Department of Medicine," *Stanford Report*, Aug. 23, 2006, http://news.stanford.edu/news/2006/august23/med-horwitz-082306.html.

2. "Message from Dr. Ralph Horwitz, Chair of the Department of Medicine," quoted in: Phil Pizzo, "The Dean's Newsletter," Aug. 30, 2010, http://deansnewsletter.stanford.edu/archive/08_30_10.html.

John K. Iglehart

Founding Editor, *Health Affairs*
Former National Correspondent, *New England Journal of Medicine*

John Iglehart is perhaps the most influential health policy journalist of our times. In 1981, he founded *Health Affairs*, which has since become the nation's premier journal for health services research and debate. He has also written more than a hundred health policy reports for the *New England Journal of Medicine*, where he translates and analyzes health policy issues for a largely clinical readership. In this profile, he discusses his career path and his role as a translator of ideas between communities. He also discusses the impact that health care journalism can have in facilitating open debate on important issues and proposals for reform.

EDUCATION & TRAINING

1957–61	B.A., University of Wisconsin-Milwaukee (Journalism)

CAREER

1962–1968	Correspondent, Associated Press
1968–1969	Congressional Fellow, U.S. House of Representatives
1969–1979	Writer, *The National Journal*
1975–1976	Editor-in-Chief, *The National Journal*
1977–	Elected Member, Institute of Medicine of the National Academy of Sciences; served on its Governing Council (1985–1991)
1979–1981	Vice President, Kaiser Permanente Medical Care Program
1981–2007	Founding Editor, *Health Affairs*
1981–	National Correspondent, *New England Journal of Medicine*
2013–	Founding Editor, *Health Affairs*

SELECTED PUBLICATIONS

Policy Reports, *New England Journal of Medicine* (more than 100 articles since 1981)

Health Affairs (www.healthaffairs.org)

My impact is explaining complex issues to people who are in some way invested in health care, whether they are doctors, members of Congress or Wall Street analysts.

—*John K. Iglehart*

With a readership of more than 30,000 people, *Health Affairs* is widely considered to be the preeminent forum for debating and evaluating research, ideas, and proposals in health policy. Filled with writing by academics, government executives, and private industry leaders, the journal is read by opinion-makers throughout the health care sector, and it is the most cited and arguably the most influential peer-reviewed journal in health policy. For over 25 years, at its helm sat founding editor John Iglehart. Soft-spoken and unassuming, Iglehart calls himself a "'just-the-facts' man." While Iglehart says that he does not seek to steer public discourse, his work influences many throughout the health care world, from legislators on Capitol Hill and pharmaceutical executives to practicing physicians.

In addition to his long-time role as editor of *Health Affairs*, Iglehart also has served as national correspondent for the *New England Journal of Medicine* since 1981, in which he has written more than one hundred essays in his regular "Health Policy Report" column. His career path has been shaped by his deep love of policy, his passion for explaining complex issues, and his ongoing commitment to objectivity. At the core of this commitment lies a firm belief that thoughtful and informed debate about ideas can play a central role in allowing the health care system to overcome great obstacles.

A RUDDERLESS YOUTH

Iglehart describes himself as a "rudderless youth" who began on the path toward journalism at age sixteen, when he met a former reporter turned public relations executive who contacted him looking for a tennis game. Iglehart was the Wisconsin state high school tennis champion in 1957. The PR executive helped Iglehart secure his first job, as a copyboy at the *Milwaukee Sentinel*. Iglehart later obtained a journalism degree from the University of

Wisconsin while working full-time at the Sentinel and went on to work as a reporter at the Associated Press, where he covered political events in the Wisconsin legislature and the governor's office.

After six years at the AP, Iglehart moved to Washington, D.C., with the goal of becoming a political writer. He was awarded a Congressional Fellowship to work for a member of the Senate Subcommittee on Employment, Manpower, and Poverty; this role provided Iglehart with his first exposure to social welfare issues at the federal level. While brief, this fellowship led to his first policy beat in journalism. Iglehart wrote for the *National Journal*, a policy analysis journal launched in 1969:

> All careers are somewhat fluky in terms of the directions you take, but journalism is *really* fluky. I went to the *National Journal* to apply for a job, and they were looking for a social welfare expert. I had spent half of my year on Capitol Hill working for the Senate Subcommittee on Employment, Manpower and Poverty, and that seemed to qualify me as a social welfare expert. So I was their man.

A year and a half after Iglehart started work at the *National Journal*, their health reporter left. Iglehart recalls management telling him: "You're now covering health and social welfare. Welcome to the real world." Until then, Iglehart had not been particularly interested in health policy, but his new beat gave him broad exposure to its complexities and importance, and before long he became quite fascinated with it:

> I wasn't there very long before I could see that while social welfare issues were very interesting, they dealt almost exclusively with the public sector. Health care, however, had a much more diverse set of interests, across both the public and private sectors. It's a much more interesting set of issues…that engages all of society.

Becoming a Health Care Journalist

To Iglehart, health policy's importance stems from two key factors: the enormous amount of money involved in the health care system, and the fact that health care affects everyone in a very immediate way:

> I think health policy is more important [than social welfare policy] in the sense that it involves *everyone*. You could make the case that social welfare involves everyone as well, because anyone who pays taxes has some of their taxes go to support folks who can't make their own way. But health is just a much richer canvas.

Health care journalism provided a venue where Iglehart could generate productive debate by bringing together different perspectives. One of the constant goals across his career has been facilitating open and informed discussion of complex issues, all while maintaining objectivity.

In 1975, six years after joining the *National Journal*, Iglehart was asked to serve as editor-in-chief, an honor which he accepted. About a year and a half into the job, he realized that he found his new position much less satisfying: "I decided I really enjoyed writing more than I enjoyed managing other people's problems." So he relinquished his position and returned to writing for the journal full time.

Iglehart's growing impact on the health care policy sphere was reflected by his 1977 election into the Institute of Medicine. The IOM charter stipulates that at least one-quarter of its members be selected from "professions other than those primarily concerned with medicine and health." "By 1977, I had done enough health care writing that Paul Ellwood and Alain Enthoven sponsored my application to the IOM," Iglehart explains. "It was the writing I had done from 1971 to 1977 that really was my ticket to membership."

In 1979, Iglehart wanted a change of scene and accepted a position as a vice president and director of the Washington office of the Kaiser Permanente Medical Care Program. Iglehart lobbied on behalf of the program, which the Nixon administration promoted as a model health maintenance organization in the early 1970s. For the first time Iglehart found himself actively taking sides in the health care debate, a move that helped him realize why he had become a journalist:

> The two years I spent with the Kaiser Permanente Medical Care Program was an important period in my career. It taught me that I really enjoy writing, and enjoy journalism—and I think I can do it reasonably well. I had been at it long enough that I developed my own mind and opinions about it, and I wasn't very effective at advocating on behalf of an interest. I have enormous respect for Kaiser Permanente, but the role I was playing did not suit my instincts or interests very well. I wanted to go back to the general role I started my career in, and had been in from 1962 to 1979. My realization at Kaiser Permanente that writing and reflecting were what I enjoyed most of all was very helpful, because, ever since, I have never had the feeling that the pastures are greener somewhere else.

This realization—his preference for objectivity and informed debate, and his distaste for taking sides—lay at the heart of the rest of Iglehart's career.

CREATING A FORUM FOR INFORMED DEBATE

Iglehart wanted to return to journalism but needed to find a way back in. For several years Daniel Greenberg had been writing a policy column in the *New England Journal of Medicine* entitled "The Washington Report," which Iglehart regularly read. Noticing that the column had not been published for several months, Iglehart contacted the editor, who told him that they were looking for a new writer for the column and that he was actually on their short list of candidates: "I went to see him and interviewed. And he said, why don't you try a piece for us, and see how we like it, and how you like us." He did, and the piece was accepted. The article, "Drawing the Lines for the Debate on Competition," published on July 30, 1981, was well-received, and the regular policy column was reborn under the title "Health Policy Report." Since then, Iglehart has published more than a hundred essays under this title, analyzing everything from health care costs, the evolution of new payment models, the 2010 Health Care Reform to prescription drug coverage, the quality improvement movement, physician workforce policy, and specialty hospitals.

His position at the *New England Journal*, while professionally quite satisfying, was, as he eloquently states, "high prestige, but low pay." Thus, as the father of two young children, Iglehart began to search for other opportunities. Around that time, William Walsh, a socially entrepreneurial cardiologist and the founder of Project HOPE, had been talking to Iglehart about the possibility of starting a health policy journal comparable to *Foreign Affairs*, which was the leading international relations journal at the time. Iglehart remembers initially thinking that the world was "littered with policy journals" and didn't need another one. Realizing he needed a more regular job, Iglehart gave it some more thought, and decided to accept Walsh's offer.

BUILDING A NEW JOURNAL

Project HOPE was founded in 1958 with the purpose of "expanding the health horizons of other nations by exporting the skills and services of American medicine." But after more than two decades of almost exclusively overseas work, its leadership realized that the American health care system could learn from the heath care systems of other nations. The project's board felt that by "transporting some of the lessons learned abroad, we could play a constructive role in the United States through discussion, research, data collection, and information dissemination." Accordingly, in 1979, HOPE developed its Institute for Health Policy, and in 1981, its Center for Health Science Information, Analysis, and Research. *Health Affairs* was created in part as a vehicle for the dissemination of the work of these two new programs.

Walsh's grander vision for the journal—and Iglehart's own beliefs about the advancement of policy—are evident from the inaugural issue in the winter of 1981. Walsh announced in the first Publisher's Letter that the journal would reflect the complexity of interests and views involved in health care and that it would cover "the concerns of private health interests, the several levels of government, academia, and the consumer of medical care."[1]

Doing this required remaining strictly non-partisan and open to all points of view. As the first issue stated: "*Health Affairs* will not be a political instrument dedicated to one approach, but rather will publish views reflective of the broader body politic." The journal was based in the belief that, "only through a relentless pursuit of the issues will answers be found and consensus emerge that is distinctly American, for the shaping of our future health care system." These commitments were as much a part of Iglehart's beliefs as Walsh's vision, and from the beginning Iglehart led the journal and its production. It would later become the most respected journal in its field. Iglehart continued to lead the journal for 27 years until he stepped down in 2007.

THE ROLE OF *HEALTH AFFAIRS* IN HEALTH POLICY

Under Iglehart's leadership for almost three decades, *Health Affairs* evolved to include a regular mix of feature articles, commentary, interviews, and narratives, alongside brief regular reports of health care trends, markets, recently awarded foundation grants, timely health policy news, and book reviews. The feature articles, which focus on new proposals, original research, and analysis of timely health policy issues, typically set the stage for the commentaries, which provide guest editorials on related issues. The interviews, which Iglehart frequently conducted himself, have spanned a wide range, from members of Congress to government and private-sector executives. Finally, *Health Affairs* features personal stories about the health care system that highlight policy issues of concern. For example, in 2005 *Health Affairs* published the widely read narrative by Jerald Winakur entitled "What Are We Going to Do With Dad?"[2] The essay is a poignant description of a physician's experience taking care of his aging father, and led to several newspaper and radio pieces on the issue of caring for the elderly.

Health Affairs is able to provide something that other journals do not. Before Iglehart founded *Health Affairs*, health policy articles were most often published in the *New England Journal of Medicine* (*NEJM*) and the *Journal of the American Medical Association* (*JAMA*):

> When I started, there wasn't a journal that was trying to translate analysis and information and make it accessible to broader communities and serious readers and the like. There just wasn't one, and today there is.

Considered "the bible of health policy,"[3] *Health Affairs* today is regularly read by government health care leaders, health policy analysts, hospital and insurance executives, and researchers and academics in subjects ranging from economics and health services research to law, public health, and political science. It is the most cited journal in the categories of health policy and health care science and services, and the national media frequently quote it, including the *Washington Post, New York Times, Wall Street Journal,* CNN, network television and radio, and National Public Radio.[4] In 2004 the *Washington Post* wrote:

> For more than twenty years, *Health Affairs* has been a must-read for anyone with a serious interest in medicine, health care, and health care policy. Its articles are rigorously researched, timely, original and thought-provoking, and easily understood by those of us without an advanced degree. Although it is hard to detect any consistent political slant to this bimonthly journal, the articles reflect a range of ideological bias that makes for a lively debate.[5]

Health Affairs is highly valued by readers in all parts of the health care sector for its depth and perceived lack of bias. *JAMA* and *NEJM* are published by and for the medical communities, and are therefore not seen as politically neutral. Iglehart recognizes that the evenhandedness *Health Affairs* maintains is in many ways a reflection of his own character:

> One of my strengths that is reflected in the journal is that people don't see me as highly invested in the right or the left, or in a market system or a regulated system, and we really play it pretty straight in terms of the content. We'll publish quality content that is relevant and passes review whether it reflects views on the left or the right, and that's one of the reasons *Health Affairs* has a lot of credibility.

Objectivity, Iglehart explains, has been a large part of his work throughout his career:

> My whole career, if you look at it, from the AP until now, I've been a "just-the-facts" man. The *National Journal* was that way too—more so when I was there than today—and *Health Affairs* is run the same way. We let the chips fall without taking a strong editorial stand. We don't have an editorial policy other than a widely-held belief that all Americans should have some form of insurance coverage.

Another reason that *Health Affairs* has been so successful is because it is accessible. Iglehart believes *Health Affairs* serves as a translator. He emphasizes that, in the current health policy environment, translation is critical because health care professionals need a common vocabulary to facilitate discussions and initiate change. Moreover, health care is an issue that affects everyone, and journalists are in a unique position to bring experts and readers from different backgrounds together, educate them about the modern health care system, and empower them to make the system better. Iglehart explains:

> I've had the most impact on transmitting understandable information between different sectors of health services research, health policy, media and other elites. The niche that *Health Affairs* fills—which didn't become clear

until after we had built it for a number of years—was that the very smart people in health services research and health policy need to translate their work into understandable English, language that resonates with people who are not trained in economics or other academic disciplines—elected officials, staff, and other policy leaders.

Iglehart's translations rest on a few basic principles. Articles in *Health Affairs* assume no technical expertise; when they involve technical statistical or economic analyses, or clinical details, the necessary information is artfully worked into the text, so as to make it accessible to all while not insulting anyone's intelligence.

Health Affairs' final distinctive feature is the depth of its coverage—something for which *JAMA* and *NEJM* are not designed. With an average of almost three hundred pages in each of its six issues per year, *Health Affairs* is, Iglehart points out, "about three times larger than anything that you could consider a competitor." As a result, Iglehart notes, the journal no longer really competes with *JAMA* or *NEJM*. He sees its primary challenge as maintaining a hold on its readership's time and attention:

> I have felt for many years that our major competitor is time, and how people spend it. It's whether someone is going to go to a movie, or take a walk with his family or read a journal. Ours is a very dense journal, not one that you pick up for a bit of light reading.

Impact and Change: Thoughts from a Long-Term Observer of Health Care

Iglehart is humble when discussing the impact of his work on the evolution of the health care system: "I assume my impact is explaining complex issues to people who care about them because they are in some way invested in health care....But I don't pretend that if I weren't here the world would be different."

One example of his impact was when he was able to summarize the complicated political drama of the Clinton Health Plan in 1994. In an essay titled "Health Care Reform. The Role of Physicians," Iglehart reviewed the key parties, agendas, and past actions involved in the plan, and came to the following conclusion:

> Clinton's proposal is simply too vast in scope and too disruptive of the current system to win the approval of Congress. The legislative branch is a fragmented institution with too many members who are worried chiefly about their own reelection for the administration to muster the necessary political backing for its original proposal.[6]

His prediction turned out to be largely correct.

Iglehart believes that the impact of his work is limited, though, partly due to the slow process of change in policy—and in health policy in particular:

> Change comes awfully slowly and painfully. There are many instances, particularly in recent years in health care, where the money has become so large, and the interests so invested in keeping what they have, that people are very entrenched.

The slow pace of change makes intervening at the crucial moments when change is most possible all the more important. In the political world, issues have their brief moments of debate in Washington—and important articles do not always appear at the right time.

The point is illustrated by one of the few times Iglehart believes his writing did have a direct impact on policy. In an extended Health Policy Report in the *New England Journal of Medicine* on support for academic medical centers in 1999, Iglehart included a detailed analysis of Health Care Finance Administration data demonstrating that there was up to a seven-fold variation in the amount of graduate medical education funding received per resident across the country.[7] The piece was released just as teaching hospitals in New York were experiencing big problems with the impact of the 1997 Balanced Budget Act on Medicare reimbursement for their residents. Two days later, the *New York Times* ran a front-page article about Iglehart's findings:

> Federal health officials have known for some time that Medicare payments for such training varied from hospital to hospital. But a study published this week in the *New England Journal of Medicine* highlights the disparities and provides more detail than had ever been publicly available.[8]

The media attention eventually prompted major change in the legislation surrounding Medicare reimbursement for residents, which was worked into the Medicare, Medicaid, and SCHIP Balanced Budget Refinement Act of 1999. To Iglehart, the heightened publicity was nice, but the real satisfaction came from having effectively translated the issues.

BELIEF IN THE POSSIBILITY OF PROGRESS

Through his role at *Health Affairs*, and continuing on today through his articles, Iglehart connects researchers, policy makers, practitioners, the media, and other interested parties. He helps his readers appreciate one another's perspectives on and approaches to dealing with a common set of issues, guiding them in turning abstract ideas into useable, practical knowledge.

Despite his record of non-partisanship, Iglehart is not a completely dispassionate observer—even if he assumes this stance in his writing. If his actual political convictions remain hidden from public view, his work evinces a deep hopefulness about the American health care system. In his heart,

Iglehart remains optimistic that problems in health care can be solved in a democratic fashion, through informed dialogue between educated and concerned parties. Health policy may be a difficult subject requiring intense debate, but eventually, Iglehart believes, the best answers will emerge. As he explained in opening remarks for a policy conference five years before the Obama health care reform legislation was enacted, he believes this even about some of the largest and most pressing issues faced by the health care system.

> As you know, *Health Affairs* has published more than its share of health reform proposals over the years, and we will undoubtedly continue to do that, not because it's going to happen tomorrow, but one of these days—one of these years—it will happen, because any country as wealthy as ours that has fully fifteen percent of its people without insurance will one day act.[9]

AFTERWORD

After leading the journal for 25 years, in 2007 Iglehart stepped down. He continued to be a frequent speaker and commentator on health care policy and continued his policy and perspective pieces for the *New England Journal*; when the Obama Healthcare plan passed in 2010 it was Iglehart who wrote the editorial.[10] In 2013, Iglehart returned to *Health Affairs* to once again lead the journal as well as lead the search for a new editor-in-chief after Susan Dentzer stepped down from that position.

Notes

1   Publisher's Letter, *Health Affairs* 1, no. 1 (1981).

2   Jerald Winakur, "What Are We Going to Do With Dad?" *Health Affairs* 24 (2005): 1064-72.

3   S. Pearlstein, "Consolidation: Health Care's Empty Promise," *Washington Post*, January 12, 2005.

4   As reported in both the Science Edition and Social Science Edition of the Institute for Scientific Information's journal impact factor.

5   "Readings," *Washington Post*, January 11, 2004.

6   John K. Iglehart, "Health Care Reform. The Role of Physicians," *NEJM* 331 (1994): 551-2.

7   Graduate medical education (GME) payments are the way in which the federal government reimburses teaching hospitals for the cost of training residents.

8   Robert Pear, "Study Highlights Disparities in Aid to Train Doctors," *New York Times*, July 25, 1999.

9   "Progressive Prescriptions for a Healthy America," Center for American Progress, March 23, 2005.

10 John K. Iglehart, "Historic Passage—Reform at Last," *NEJM* 362 (2010): e48.

Anula K. Jayasuriya

Health Care Private Equity Investor

Originally trained as a physician and a laboratory researcher in molecular genetics, Anula Jayasuriya has spent most of her career in the business world, particularly in venture capital and private equity. In this profile, Jayasuriya discusses the role of a physician in business, and why she believes she is able to have a greater impact through her current work than she would through patient care. She also discusses the complicated relationship between private equity and business, and the power of private equity to help achieve important goals such as enabling the development of new treatments, screening diagnostics and preventing disease. Lastly, she addresses her work with non-profits focused on bringing greater diversity to the workplace and providing access to medical care and education to the underserved, and describes how she has been able to channel her business experience into benefiting her non-profit endeavors.

EDUCATION & TRAINING

1980	A.B., Harvard College
1983	M. Phil., Cambridge University (Pharmacology)
1989	M.D., Ph.D., Harvard University
1989	Resident, Pediatric Medicine, Children's Hospital (Boston)
1993	M.B.A., Harvard Business School (HBS)

CAREER PATH

1993–1995	Director, Outcomes Research, Syntex Laboratories
1995–1997	Vice President, Roche Global Development
1999–2000	Vice President, Corporate Development and Strategy, Genomics Collaborative
2001	Principal, Techno Venture Management
2002	Partner, Skyline Ventures
2003	Venture Partner, ATP Capital, L.P.
2006–	Co-founder and Managing Director, Evolvence India Life Sciences Fund I (and Evolvence India Life Sciences Fund II in 2014)
2014–	Co-founder, eXXclaim Capital

NON-PROFIT BOARD MEMBERSHIPS

Interplast (former)
Astia
Level Playing Field (former)
HBS Health Care Alumni Association
Gruter Institute
EPPIC

As an undergraduate, I was a strong science student, and I firmly believed that most bright people pursued careers related to the sciences. I had equally firmly held preconceived and pejorative misperceptions about business and the people who went into business.

—*Anula Jayasuriya*

Anula Jayasuriya spent her early years growing up in Sri Lanka in the shadow of her brother, who was twelve years her senior and renowned for his intelligence and accomplishments. Of herself, Jayasuriya says: "I was smart, but I was sort of normally smart." After graduating as the top student of both the nation's universities, her brother won a scholarship to Oxford. On his way to sign the documents for his scholarship, his Jeep, a present from his mother for his achievements, skidded and overturned, leaving him with permanent brain injuries.

Jayasuriya recalls how they spent much of the next two years, when she was twelve and thirteen: "We lived in the hospital, and hung on every word of the doctors—just begging them to make him better, to tell us something optimistic." The accident left her brother significantly impaired and caused major personality changes. For a year, while suffering from amnesia, he even insisted that Jayasuriya was not his sister, which she found profoundly disorienting. Jayasuriya's interest in medicine and research was born from this painful experience:

> It was my understanding of the limitations, but also of the power, of medicine. That was when I first thought you had to couple medicine with research: you practiced what you knew, and then you researched what you didn't.

This interest in medicine has sustained itself throughout Jayasuriya's career, but has taken on forms that, as a teenager, she never would have foreseen. Trained as a physician and research scientist, Jayasuriya changed course in mid-career to enter the world of business and, eventually, to become a leading health care venture capitalist. Jayasuriya's profession has allowed her to integrate ethical and professional goals: she has been able to play a pivotal role in the funding and development of new medical technologies, to advance the cause of diversity in the business world, and to devote her significant talents and resources to non-profit organizations focused on access to health care, education and fairness in the workplace.

BEFRIENDING THE BIZARRE: FROM MEDICAL SCIENCE TO AN M.B.A.

In the years following her brother's accident, Jayasuriya formed the goal of becoming a physician and a medical researcher. To achieve this goal, she went against her mother's wishes and moved to the United States for college in 1976. Jayasuriya graduated from Harvard in 1980, and continued her training to become a clinical scientist by earning a master's degree in pharmacology at Cambridge University, followed by an M.D. and Ph.D., both from Harvard Medical School.

In 1987, while working on her Ph.D. at HMS, Jayasuriya struck up a conversation with a young man named David Gilmour at a small gathering of fellow Harvard alumni. The two had never met, despite having graduated from Harvard College the same year. Gilmour was working in business at the Lotus Corporation, and Jayasuriya found herself intrigued by Gilmour and his work—by what he did, what different roles and titles in business entailed, and what all the jargon meant. Her curiosity about the business world was spurred in part by a certain suspicion of it: "My expectation was that it was all going to be completely bizarre and dull," she recalls. Much to her surprise, however, neither Gilmour nor all their discussions about business were unappealing. Far from it, in fact a year later, the two were married.

Over the next few years, Jayasuriya began to have doubts about the academic career upon which she had embarked. She was in a prominent lab, yet all of the post-docs around her were having trouble getting faculty positions at prestigious institutions. Moreover, managed care was permeating U.S. medicine and many physicians were vocal about their displeasure. As she questioned her future as a physician-scientist, she found herself increasingly thinking about the business world. Her husband had enrolled at Harvard Business School in 1982, giving Jayasuriya the opportunity to meet many of his fellow students and colleagues:

> I met all these people, and I realized to my chagrin that my caricature of those who chose business school and what they did with their lives—or at least who I had thought they were—was very far from reality. I was transported into a whole different world, and I really had to rethink my (mis)conceptions. These were very smart, really talented, really creative and entrepreneurial people. They were neither driven purely by money nor morally inferior, as I had suspected. In fact, many of them were making significant contributions to society. I was also struck that, in general, they seemed to be happier with their careers than the newly minted scientists and doctors by whom I was surrounded during my residency training.

As Jayasuriya revised her preconceptions, she began exploring the possibilities of a career in business herself. Business and finance were having a profound effect on the practice of medicine and at the same time, the business of biotechnology was yielding some very compelling new treatments. Arriving at the conclusion that medicine and science were increasingly interfacing with business, after her internship in pediatrics at Children's Hospital in Boston, she took the then unorthodox step of applying to Harvard Business School in and was accepted. However, at the time Jayasuriya was deeply criticized and shunned by many of her medical and science colleagues who felt she was going to the "dark side."

A PHYSICIAN-SCIENTIST IN THE BUSINESS WORLD

At HBS, Jayasuriya found that the cultural differences between the business school and the world of medical research were profound and, at that moment in her training, "quite liberating":

> It was amazing to me that in business you could just present smart ideas— you could say things that weren't supported by ten experiments. I could just develop a logical and plausible set of arguments, and because it was rational and reasonable, people would pay attention.

In the summer between her first and second year of business school, Jayasuriya interned at the Boston Consulting Group, where she worked on strategic planning for an HMO. She enjoyed her work, and was offered a full-time position upon graduating, but declined because she wanted to experience a traditional product industry firsthand:

> BCG was a fabulous experience, but it was so far away from making actual "widgets." I felt that since I had made this huge transition from medicine into business, I had to work someplace where there was a real product and sales focus—e.g., where they were making and selling medicines. Strategic consulting is more academic, and I thought I would never feel like I had really been in business if I weren't in a pharmaceutical company.

Eager to gain some hands-on operational experience, Jayasuriya accepted a position in 1993 as director of outcomes research for the Syntex Corporation, the only pharmaceutical company in California at the time. Jayasuriya had followed her husband, an IT entrepreneur, to Silicon Valley, along with their baby daughter, who was born while she was a student at HBS.

BRINGING BUSINESS SCHOOL CASE STUDIES TO LIFE

Syntex offered Jayasuriya much of the operational experience she had sought. A year after she joined, the firm was acquired by Roche, providing her with some particularly significant exposure to real-world business problems:

It was exactly what I had learned in business school about mergers and acquisitions and the attendant cultural upheavals. Except this time it was not an HBS case study but real life. It was really very exciting for me. While it was heart-wrenching for the people who had been at Syntex for years, and were seeing their careers ripped out from under them and being given pink slips, I had the opportunity to live through an HBS case firsthand. We had McKinsey consultants coming in and giving presentations on the integration of the two companies. It was fascinating for me, and I wanted to stay through it.

The acquisition also provided her with some unexpected early career opportunities. At HBS, Jayasuriya had learned that change brings opportunity, and she now found herself in the midst of just such a change: "If I stick around," Jayasuriya found herself thinking, "I am going to get a job that I would never have gotten had this change not occurred. Because people are taking their parachutes and leaving in droves there are going to many senior positions open."

She was right, and just two years out of business school, she was made a vice president and asked to run a team of over one hundred people in charge of developing Cytovene, a drug used to treat viral infections in AIDS and liver transplant patients. The team included physicians writing clinical protocols and monitoring trials, clinical research associates running the trials, statisticians analyzing the data, chemistry, manufacturing, and control specialists producing the drug, business people developing the strategy, and regulatory experts filing FDA requirements. Acquiring this challenging role so shortly after completing her M.B.A. provided Jayasuriya with invaluable experience:

> I had a large number of people reporting to me. It was a job I didn't already know how to do, but I was a quick learner. It would have taken me ten years to get a job like that by working my way up at another pharmaceutical firm.

From the start, Jayasuriya's plan had been to stay in pharmaceuticals for five years, during which time she intended to learn as many different functions as possible. By 1997, once the integration of Syntex and Roche was complete, she felt it was time to move on:

> I had gotten exactly what I wanted—actually, much more than I had thought I was going to get. Once I felt that I had learned what I wanted to know—marketing and drug development—I was ready for something much more entrepreneurial.

Fascinated by entrepreneurship (and married to an entrepreneur), Jayasuriya began consulting for several venture capital (VC) firms focused on the health care and biotechnology sectors. VCs provide funding to entrepreneurs and early-stage companies in exchange for an equity stake in the company. Through her VC network, Jayasuriya found her next job as vice president of business development for Genomics Collaborative Inc. (GCI), a venture-backed biotechnology start-up based in Cambridge, Massachusetts, which at the time had only nine employees.

Her work in business development involved traveling extensively to meet with the company's customers and potential partners around the globe. Many of GCI's partners were in Asia: Vietnam, Singapore and India. Jayasuriya had lived in India as a child and had a longstanding connection to India that was revitalized in the course of setting up a partnership for GCI with a hospital in Pune. This was the beginning of her exposure to, and interest in, the nascent and emerging health care opportunities in India. In the course of the following years Jayasuriya began to increase her involvement in the Indian life science sector. She joined the board of an Indian genomics company and set about establishing a network in India. An idea began germinating in her mind about investing in India in the future.

The next step in Jayasuriya's career was to become a venture capitalist herself. She first joined the German-U.S. VC firm, TVM Capital, which was opening up an office in San Francisco. In 2001, after the technology bubble burst, TVM closed its San Francisco office, and Jayasuriya joined Skyline, another VC firm; in 2003 she became a venture partner at ATP Capital. In 2006, with a partner, Jayasuriya founded the Evolvence Life Sciences Fund, a venture capital firm investing in health care and pharmaceutical companies in India; successful exits in this first Evolvence fund enabled the creation of a second. Most recently, in 2014 Jayasuriya launched eXXclaim Capital, a VC fund investing exclusively in women's health care start-ups.

A New Fund for an Emerging Market in India

In 2005, Jayasuriya came to some important conclusions for her future path:

> I needed to form a new fund in order to make the investments I believed in, and often bucked the conventional wisdom in the "valley" and also changed aspects of the culture that I found less appealing. I also wanted to look at emerging economies, especially India. My peers saw India only as a location for technology and business process outsourcing—not opportunities in health care or life science.

Jayasuriya began spending time in India learning about the market and began searching beyond the bounds of Silicon Valley for like-minded partners to launch an exciting and entrepreneurial new fund.

In May of 2006, together with two Indian partners, Jayasuriya co-founded the Evolvence India Life Sciences Fund (EILSF), based in Hyderabad, India. EILSF is the first life science-focused fund investing in India. The investment focus of EILSF is broad, encompassing pharmaceuticals, generics, diagnostics, medical devices, medical services, and research and development services.

By January 2008, EILSF had raised $85 million, and had chosen as its first investment, a network of oncology treatment clinics, meeting a greatly underserved need in India. This investment resulted from Jayasuriya's relationship with Indian entrepreneurs, and drew on the full range of her medical and scientific knowledge. The new company, Health Care Global (HCG), not only treats cancer patients, but also provides sophisticated genetic testing for targeted treatment and performs clinical trials for new treatments being developed by global pharmaceutical and biotech companies.

The umbrella term "private equity" encompasses a spectrum of funds that invest in private companies. While VC firms generally invest smaller amounts of money in young, rapidly growing companies with high potential and high risk, traditional PE firms typically invest larger sums in more mature companies with lower risk. As Jayasuriya explains, most of the opportunities in India involve providing capital for growth and expansion to existing companies. EILSF is therefore more a traditional private equity fund rather than a specific VC fund.

THE THRILL OF PRIVATE EQUITY, VENTURE CAPITAL, AND THE QUEST FOR ROI

Jayasuriya's life, work, and background have made her passionately committed to several causes, three of which stand out among the rest: the advancement of medical technology to help patients; greater diversity in business leadership; and charitable medical care in less developed nations. The business world has provided her with a powerful set of means to further these causes. VC firms can have a huge impact on which entrepreneurs end up succeeding: the combination of much-needed funding, expertise, and credentials that a VC firm's investment provides is often the difference between success and failure, especially for a young business.

The stakes are nearly as high for the VC investors as they are for the entrepreneurs. Because the businesses that VC firms invest in are not yet proven, they are high-risk investments: a significant number will never become profitable. The higher the perceived risk, the higher the anticipated profits (or bottom line) must be to offset this risk. The ratio of the future profits to the initial investment is called "return on investment" or ROI, and it serves as the primary compass for VC firms navigating through numerous investment opportunities. PE funds follow similar economics.

The partners who manage private equity funds—like Jayasuriya—typically invest not only the fund's money but also a large proportion of their professional energy in portfolio companies. They take a seat on the board and often function as strategic consultants, perform business development, help with hiring and sometimes even take on senior management roles in the companies in which they invest. Most of the time entrepreneurs and investors work as a team, building value in their companies. However, sometimes tensions develop when incentives are misaligned. "I live with an entrepreneur, so I have deep empathy for the other side" says Jayasuriya; many of her husband's projects have been backed by VC firms.

Because of the exceptionally diverse roles people in VC can play, as well as the high potential financial rewards and relative independence, VC is among the most highly sought fields in the business world. These are, without doubt, among the attributes that drew Jayasuriya to VC. But for her, the most exciting aspect of her work is the role it lets her play in influencing patient care and the realization of future technologies:

> For me, a large part of the thrill is looking at the vast array of medical/research technologies—I have always loved being at the leading edge of technical advance. A lot of people can look at technology and be enamored of it. The skill—and the thrill—is being able to do the thought experiment of predicting which technology can actually be made into a product, and actually both make returns for the investors and be valuable, in people's hands, in a timeframe that matches an investment fund's lifecycle. That is the trick.

Much emphasis here falls on the timeframe. Unlike a scientist engaged in pure research funded by non-profit or government institutions, who might be able to engage in projects whose real-world applications lie decades in the future, a private equity investor must work within a timeframe realistic and relevant for investors. Being able to judge which developing technologies can be implemented successfully within such a timeframe is Jayasuriya's challenge:

> Every day I see really cool technologies, but I know that they are not going to be reducible to practice in a timeframe that I can fund—because it is my fiduciary responsibility to the people whose money I have taken that I strive to get returns in a five- to ten-year timeframe.

Since Jayasuriya invests exclusively in health care, the investment decisions she makes are one way in which she can impact people's lives: products that hold the greatest promise to help people also often hold the greatest promise of future profits. In this respect, her ethical ideals and her professional responsibilities are largely aligned. It is frustrating to her that this is not always the case, however. Some pressing human health concerns—substandard medical care in third-world countries or the treatment of certain rare diseases, for example—cannot be profitably addressed by biotechnology companies: "You really have to go where there is a market. It can't just be an unmet clinical need. It has to be an unmet clinical need that can be reimbursed." If fulfilling a medical necessity cannot promise profit to would-be investors, then the need will continue to go unmet, at least by profit-driven sectors. This can be frustrating, but Jayasuriya is encouraged by the steps taken by non-profit foundations to remedy this situation. She also sees ways to surmount these traditional barriers by investing in countries like India where low-cost solutions can be developed for diseases of underserved populations.

THE LIMITATIONS OF ROI, MULTIPLE BOTTOM LINES, AND THE LARGER IMPACT OF PRIVATE EQUITY

Jayasuriya accepts that some of these limitations are intrinsic to the business world, but she is particularly interested in investments where this is not the case—interested, that is, in investing with what is known as a double or triple bottom line, when financial and social objectives can be met simultaneously.[1] "I believe that you can have above-market, top-quartile financial performance, and also facilitate social change," she explains. Her second cause—greater diversity in business leadership—is something she strives for in her investments and in her non-profit endeavors.

Early in her career in VC, Jayasuriya realized how unbalanced the field was with respect to women:

> It had never occurred to me previously, but once I began working in venture capital I realized it's a very male-dominated field, more so than medicine, pharmaceuticals or biotechnology. Biotech has many more women—maybe not as many CEOs as I would like—but still a lot of women in the upper ranks. But venture capital has very few, especially in health care, and especially at the senior or founding partner level.

This realization led to a career-long interest in increasing diversity in business. Jayasuriya and many others feel that the ethnic and gender imbalance of VC firms contributes to a lack of funding for female and minority entrepreneurs and propagates an unrepresentative culture among business leaders:[2]

> I believe VC and entrepreneurship are yin and yang—it doesn't help to have a thousand women entrepreneurs if they don't get funded. Just increasing the number of women entrepreneurs is not going to be sufficient. That presumes that the funders are going to be equally comfortable funding a male or a female. The same applies to ethnicity. I think we can get to a point where gender and ethnicity do not become issues and that is where I want us to get to.

The culture of VC and the gender and ethnic ratios in its senior ranks influence each other reciprocally—the culture can propagate gender and ethnic imbalances, while the gender and ethnic imbalances can also propagate the culture:

> Even though people used to call medicine the ultimate "old boys' club," private equity is the quintessential club dominated by men. Venture is not a scalable industry; it's a cottage industry kind of business where you work with small groups of people. In this type of environment it is easy to favor some and exclude others based on long-established affinities rather than merits. I dare say that the prevailing deal-making culture typically reflects traditionally male traits and embodies unconscious biases.[3]

To change this culture, Jayasuriya believes that it is not enough for women to simply work their way up through the ranks. Women must become active at the level at which business culture is formed and can thus be profoundly changed—for example, in the founding of new companies and in the founding of new VC firms:

> In my mind, what matters is more than being a partner—it is being a founder of the first fund. When one becomes a partner in a fund that has been established by a group of men then one inevitably conforms to the culture and ethos that is already there—in fact, it becomes part of the partner selection process. But a fund that is founded by a more balanced team—a mixture of men and women—will build a more diverse culture from the outset.

Jayasuriya has put her beliefs into practice by co-founding a new firm that embodies her values.

In discussing the current state of the business culture in VC firms, Jayasuriya calls to mind by way of comparison the transformation that has taken place in medicine:

> I witnessed the gender and ethnic transformation in medicine. When I started medical school in 1980, the entering class was one quarter women. Today entering classes are half women or greater. In the early 1980s patients still said "I go to a lady doctor." Today I am delighted that people simply say "my doctor" and don't bother to specify whether it's a man or a woman. This is an important experience for me—I've lived through this in medicine, and I want to see the same happen in VC and entrepreneurship

Jayasuriya believes that the timing is ripe for a similar transition in VC. She also takes this into account when making investments:

> In addition to the financial metrics, I am interested in the culture of the companies that I fund, and their hiring practices. Not to mandate policy or to make companies un-entrepreneurial, but I am interested in recruiting talent from all possible pools. It is implicit that you would look at women and minority talent, because they constitute under-tapped resources.

Jayasuriya makes it clear that she does not want women to be treated as a special interest group, or to be given special privileges or advantages over men. Her goal, rather, is for women in VC to become mainstream, for them to simply become the norm.

Although she does not feel she has suffered from blatant sexism, Jayasuriya believes that long-standing, tacit prejudices probably do exist in the workplace. "You just have to prove yourself more," she explains, noting that her multiple degrees from prestigious educational institutions may have insulated her from more direct discrimination in her career.

Non-Profits and the Scope of Impact

Jayasuriya's non-profit work focuses on several aspects of social change. Since 2006 she has served on the board of trustees of Astria, an organization that promotes women entrepreneurs by providing mentorship, access to capital, and networking. She has also served on the board of the Level Playing Field Institute, which provides access to education for young people belonging to under-represented minorities and also promotes workplace fairness and the removal of hidden barriers and unconscious bias. For four years, Jayasuriya served on the board of Interplast, an organization that performs free reconstructive surgery to indigent people in developing countries. Jayasuriya was instrumental in setting up Interplast's program in her native land, Sri Lanka, where many victims of the long-standing civil strife, as well as children with congenital malformations, receive reconstructive surgeries that restore or improve functionality.

In her role on the boards of several non-profits, Jayasuriya contributes her business skills and also helps with fundraising. While Jayasuriya does not see herself leaving private equity in the near term, her goal is to become sufficiently financially successful that she will be able to devote increasing amounts of her time to the non-profit world:

> Ideally, if I could wave a wand, I would be successful investor, as defined by having chosen, backed, and contributed to the success of several companies that have significant impact on human health. And then I would like to focus on the non-profit sector.

Physicians in Business and the Value of Breadth

What draws Jayasuriya intellectually to the life science industry is its position between the rapidly evolving biomedical research sphere and the commercial world. She has always found interdisciplinary studies appealing. Inevitably, her preference for breadth has prevented her from delving deeply into any single area of science, but she does relish the scientific aspects of her career: "Right now, I'm not a world's expert in anything; however, I am involved in a wide range of different fields—from nanotechnology, to drug discovery, to generic pharmaceuticals, to oncology treatment and research tools."

Jayasuriya is quick to praise the value of a medical degree: "I'm very glad I trained in medicine. It has given me the deeply gratifying experience and understanding that uniquely come from caring for the sick. In addition, it signals to the world a widely recognized accomplishment." The degree has also proven highly useful in her work, giving her firsthand knowledge of how medicines and devices are used in patient care and how the health care industry functions. Jayasuriya necessarily relies on the medical expertise of others as well as on her own; she rarely completes due diligence on potential portfolio companies without consulting experts in the fields most relevant to each project. "I look at so many different interventions that there's no way I could have been a specialist in every one of those particular areas," she points out. But when she speaks with area specialists, she knows exactly what they're talking about:

> I think what's important is to be able to understand the basics of how medicine is practiced, and to have a network and the credibility to talk to medical practitioners as a peer. A doctor is more likely to be able to ask the right questions.

Jayasuriya, who often expounds the virtues of breadth rather than depth in her work, is less certain about the value of her Ph.D. Of her highly specialized graduate work, she observes: "If you think of my field of research as a pond, I was an important fish in that pond, but I didn't really know about the ocean or lakes or anything else. It also consumed a large chunk of my youth. In private equity, one becomes a generalist, but a pretty competent generalist within a given sector." She adds that, with regard to both her M.D. and her Ph.D., what matters most in her current field is the knowledge and practical experience they provided her with, not the degrees themselves: "What matters in business is what you actually produce and successfully do, rather than one's academic credentials," she explains. And these credentials, while invaluable in some respects, come at a certain cost:

> One of the things that is difficult about entering industry after extensive academic training is that you are older than your professional peers. It's a little disheartening. The other thing that's a negative is that you start at the bottom of the ladder several times in succession. Medicine is a hierarchy—you go through it, and then you step off and start again at zero in another field. As they teach us in business school, there is an opportunity cost.

REFLECTIONS ON LEAVING CLINICAL PRACTICE

As opportunities for clinicians in business have expanded rapidly due to the growth of technology and health care-related businesses, partially or completely left clinical care to take on roles in business. Increasing numbers of physicians have partially or completely left clinical care to take on roles in business. Having seen her colleagues on both sides of this divide, Jayasuriya notes that "people in 'industry' generally seem to be much happier with their work environment."

The move from clinical medicine into business and industry presents physicians with a complicated set of new and lost opportunities. Like most physicians in the business world, Jaysuriya has stopped practicing altogether—she believes practicing medicine would be irresponsible at this point, since she does not have the time required to stay current in the field.

She has not left behind this part of her career without regret, however: "I do miss clinical care—I really looked forward to the Interplast trips for that reason. I still very much love medicine. I still keep my licenses current and have a plan to practice *pro bono* in a primary care setting in a place where access to medical care is scarce." Though convinced that clinical medicine was not the best fit for her, Jayasuriya has strong feelings about the importance of the profession:

> What I think is wonderful about medicine is that you can give, and you give directly to people. In most other professions you are at least once removed. It is an important part of my identity and I am privileged to have had the training—I would never wish it otherwise. And I have enormous respect for my colleagues who stayed in medicine despite the challenges.

Notes

1   The "double bottom line" refers to measuring both a company's financial return (profits) and social impact, both direct (e.g. through its products) and indirect (e.g. through its hiring practices). The "triple bottom line" factors in the environmental impact of the company's actions as well.

2   Male dominance in the VC industry has been well documented, perhaps most notably in the Kauffman Foundation's Diana Project. This study is a multi-university, multi-year project dedicated to the study of female business owners. Its first report targets the relationship between women business owners and equity capital, analyzing issues such as the myths about women and equity capital, and the steps taken by successful women entrepreneurs. A copy of the report is available at the Kauffman Foundation website, *www.kauffman.org.*

3   "Unconscious bias" has been studied scientifically by, for example, Harvard psychologist Mahzarin Banaji. See for example M.R. Banaji and R. Bhaskar, "Implicit stereotypes and memory: The Bounded Rationality of Social Belief," in *Memory, Brain, and Belief,* ed. D.L. Schacter and E. Scarry (Cambridge, MA: Harvard University Press, 2000), 139–175.

Arthur L. Kellermann

Dean, F. Edward Hébert School of Medicine, Uniformed Services University of the Health Sciences; Former Professor of Emergency Medicine and Associate Dean for Health Policy, Emory University Medical School

Arthur Kellermann was perhaps the first researcher to address the problem of firearm injuries as a public health issue, and has also done groundbreaking work on the problem of public insurance and the access-to-care crisis in the United States. He is a prolific researcher and public health advocate. In this profile, he discusses the events which led him to combine public health and emergency care—a combination which, he says, is finally gaining the regard it has long deserved—as well as the role of physicians as managers in the health care system.

Education & Training

1972–1976	B.S., Rhodes College
1976–1980	M.D., Emory University School of Medicine
1983–1985	M.P.H., University of Washington School of Public Health

Career Path

1982–1983	Chief Resident, Department of Medicine, University of Washington
1983–1985	Acting Instructor, Department of Medicine, University of Washington
1986–1993	Assistant and Associate Professor, Departments of Internal Medicine and Preventive Medicine, University of Tennessee
1993–1999	Associate Professor (1993–1996) and Professor (1996–1999), Department of Surgery, Emory University Medical School
1993–2010	Associate Professor (1993–1996) and Professor (1996–2010), Department of Environmental and Occupational Health, Rollins School of Public Health
1993–2006	Director, Center for Injury Control, Rollins School of Public Health
1999–2010	Founding Chairman (1999–2006) and Professor, Department of Emergency Medicine, Emory University Medical School
2007	RWJ Fellow and Legislative Staff, Committee on Oversight and Government Reform, U.S. House of Representatives
2008–2010	Associate Dean for Health Policy, Emory University Medical School
2010–2013	Paul O'Neill-Alcoa Chair in Policy Analysis, the RAND Corporation
2013–	Dean, F. Edward Hébert School of Medicine, Uniformed Services University of the Health Sciences

One of my basic philosophies is that happenstance conversations often play very pivotal roles in people's lives. I've been lucky enough to meet truly great people in medicine over the course of my career, people who pass by and leave me nuggets of wisdom. Sometimes I feel like Forrest Gump. What you'll find with a lot of careers is, it's not navigating across the lake, it's shooting the rapids. Chance encounters with exceptional patients and exceptional people have bumped me in one direction or another as I have gone down this stream—I only half comprehend where it's taking me or what I'll do when I get there.

—*Arthur Kellermann*

Halfway through work on his M.P.H. thesis about the clinical management of drug overdose, Arthur Kellermann found himself alone in a room explaining his work to a senior scholar in the field, just the kind of expert who should have been interested in the work. Instead, Kellermann found himself watching as his interlocutor literally fell asleep. Desperate to say something interesting, he mentioned a project he had been developing on the side, a study approaching gun deaths among homeowners in the surrounding county as a public health problem: "Suddenly," Kellermann recalls, "his head whips back, and his pupils dilate—I could see them dilate—and he goes: 'You're doing what?!'"

Kellermann's research has been waking people up ever since. His career has taken shape at the intersection of emergency medicine and public health, exploring issues ranging from firearm injuries to emergency cardiac care to the problem of private hospitals "dumping" emergency patients into the already strained ERs of their public counterparts. The founding chair of the Department of Emergency Medicine at Emory University and a professor at Emory's Rollins School of Public Health, Kellermann has held numerous lectureships, seminars, and visiting professorships, and published scores of articles, books and teaching aids. He served as director of Emory's Center for Injury Control from its establishment in 1993 through 2006. In addition to working as an educator and a researcher in the fields of public health and emergency medicine, Kellermann has been a tireless advocate for the uninsured. He was instrumental in the passage of legislation ensuring that no patient would be turned away because he or she cannot pay for emergency care.

From a Career Aspiration to a "Calling"

Kellermann grew up in South Pittsburg, a small town in rural eastern Tennessee. His family ran a small manufacturing business, and had no connection with the medical professions. He credits his father with teaching him a commitment to community service, and his mother, a "brilliant, frustrated high school graduate who had no chance to go to college," with teaching him to "fight the bad guys." Both influences would shape his future career.

Kellermann, who considers his primary education to be poor, coasted through his high school and enrolled at Rhodes University in Tennessee. He knew he wanted to be a doctor, but his reasons for choosing the career were underdeveloped. After a difficult freshman year spent catching up with better educated classmates, he found himself reevaluating his career goals: he had worked harder than he had ever worked in his life, but he only earned a 2.8 GPA. His father suggested that he talk to Dr. Hiram Moore, his father's best friend since childhood. Moore was a solo general practitioner and a leading citizen in his segregated hometown's African-American community:

> I went by his house the night before I went back to college for my sophomore year, and confessed that I didn't have what it takes, and he said, "Well, I don't know why you want to be a doctor, but I'll tell you why I became a doctor." And three hours later, I walked out of his house about ten feet off the ground, convinced that this was what I was supposed to do. I mean, it was really like a tent revival experience: I was "called" to this role.

College: "Phi Beta Kappa, and Yadda Yadda Yadda"

When Kellermann returned to college, it was with a new sense of purpose. He began studying not to make grades, but to gain the skills and knowledge he would need to become a good doctor.

He also found an unusual opportunity to get hands-on experience as an undergraduate. During two of his summers at Rhodes, Kellermann worked as a gopher at a small-town hospital doing what he describes in hindsight as "incredibly illegal things." As a college student with no formal medical training or certifications, he was taught to take and develop X-rays, run lab work, run simple lab tests, give injections, and help around the hospital: "I was the emergency room orderly, and it was literally an emergency 'room.' I got incredible clinical training before I ever did one day of medical school. I also got an opportunity to watch good and bad examples of physician interaction with patients and low-level staff before I became a doctor." This kind of unorthodox but ultimately useful experience has also been a hallmark of Kellermann's career.

When he returned to Rhodes for his senior year, he found that his new approach to studying had earned an impressive return. He graduated with an array of distinctions which he summarizes as "Phi Beta Kappa and yadda yadda yadda": membership in two honors societies and recognition for several non-academic leadership roles in the student body.

MEDICAL SCHOOL AND A MASTER'S IN PUBLIC HEALTH

In accordance with his original goals, Kellermann went immediately from Rhodes to medical school at Emory. He "slugged through" two years of basic science and then began working on the wards, where he felt more at home because of his undergraduate stint as a *de facto* orderly. He recalls with fondness the medical school faculty's strong commitment to student education, but he was struck by the disdain many of Emory's medical and surgical specialists and subspecialists expressed for the young specialty of emergency medicine. "In academic medical centers," Kellermann explains, "generalists are often regarded as less capable or competent than specialists. This is ironic, because emergency medicine is one of the most intellectually, technically, and physically demanding specialties in medicine."

At the end of a summer clerkship at the Atlanta-based Centers for Disease Control and Prevention (CDC), he had another one of his career-changing encounters. He had the temerity to call the office of the CDC director and ask for an appointment. To his amazement, the answer was yes. Later that week, he spent an hour talking to Bill Foege, one of the world's leading figures in public health. "I didn't realize it at the time" Kellermann explains, "but this meeting later proved to be as pivotal in kindling my interest in public health as Hiram Moore was in inspiring me to become a doctor."

By the time Kellermann finished medical school he was firmly committed to emergency medicine, but he also knew that he wanted to go into academic medicine, so he developed a strategy to meet both goals. First, he would go to the University of Washington and complete a residency in the excellent internal medicine department there. Then, he would return to Atlanta to pursue training in emergency medicine at Grady Memorial Hospital, a residency program which Kellermann believed trained good clinicians but was "politically weak."

Initially, everything proceeded according to plan. After medical school he began his residency at the University of Washington, and sought out every opportunity to maximize his exposure to the Harborview Emergency Trauma Center, the major emergency department for the City of Seattle. Harborview also serves as the base hospital for Medic One, the City's acclaimed EMS (ambulance) system.

Michael Copass, head of the Harborview ER and medical director of Medic One, was a dedicated teacher and a demanding taskmaster. When

Kellermann approached him for a letter of recommendation to support his pursuit of a second residency in emergency medicine, Copass growled back in response: "Why don't you stay in Seattle and learn how to run an emergency department and EMS system instead of repeating your internship?" Kellermann took the counteroffer as a challenge that he could not refuse.

At about the same time, Kellermann learned that the University of Washington's Clinical Scholars Program, a unique clinical research and policy fellowship sponsored by the Robert Wood Johnson Foundation, was accepting applications. The combination of clinical experience and management training at Harborview and formal training in health services research with the Clinical Scholars Program proved to be irresistible:

> I knew that I would never be as well trained clinically as a residency-trained emergency physician, but I knew this was a unique opportunity that I couldn't pass up. I quickly calculated that over the next six years, I could log enough clinical hours in emergency medicine to qualify for board certification under the specialty's expiring "practice track." It would be close, but I knew I could do it.

Just as Kellermann took on the role of emergency room orderly while still a college undergraduate, he ended up practicing emergency medicine without doing a formal residency in the field. He is quick to point out, however, that what made sense for him then does not make sense for a young trainee today. "As it matured as a specialty, emergency medicine wisely terminated the 'practice track' to board certification, just as other specialties did before it," Kellermann notes. "A medical student who wishes to pursue a satisfying career in emergency medicine today must seek residency training in emergency medicine, and become board-certified in the specialty."

A NEW ENCOUNTER WITH PUBLIC HEALTH

With his acceptance into the UW Clinical Scholars Program, Kellermann realized that his happenstance meeting with Foege at the CDC had been more influential than he had realized: "Here I was at the University of Washington, and damned if I wasn't in an M.P.H. program without a clear idea that I was going to pursue a career in public health." Shortly thereafter, Kellermann's career took on greater focus—this time, because of the death of a celebrity.

Kellermann was studying epidemiology one afternoon when he heard over the radio that Marvin Gaye had been shot and killed by Gaye's father. The news deeply affected him. Kellermann realized that, while many homeowners bought guns to protect their families, he had "never seen a bad guy shot by a homeowner" in all his time working in the Harborview ER. "However, I saw plenty of homeowners shot by accident, in suicide attempts, or in domestic disputes." Having grown up in a gun-owning family, Kellermann thought it should be possible to apply classic public health research methods to study the relationship between firearm ownership and violent death, just as earlier researchers had used public health methods to explore the relationship between cigarette smoking and lung cancer.

At the time of this epiphany, Kellermann was completing a somewhat uninspired master's thesis on the impact of drug screens on the clinical management of drug overdose. Because he found his thesis work "very boring, very ponderous," he was drawn to the case files of gunshot victims in the Office of the King County Medical Examiner. Not everyone shared his enthusiasm for this work. His program director, James LoGerfo, wondered why he was spending so much time on this "bizarre look at gunshot deaths" and feared that he would never finish his thesis.

Fortunately, encouragement came from an improbable direction. John Eisenberg, a giant in health services research, had come to the UW Clinical Scholars program as a visiting professor, and it was his duty to meet with each scholar to discuss their work one-on-one:

> So I'm explaining to John Eisenberg my drug screen study, and as I'm talking to him, he nods off. We're in a private room, one-on-one, and he falls asleep as I'm describing to him my Masters work. I'm dumbfounded. As he began to snore, I mumbled, "Well, Dr. Eisenberg, there's one other study that I'm doing, it's kind of a hobby, it's a little thing on the side." And he kind of mutters in a semiconscious state, "Oh, yeah, what's that?" I said, "I'm doing a study of gunshot deaths in homes in King County."

> Suddenly his head whips back, and his pupils dilate—I could see them dilate—and he goes: "You're doing what?!" John Eisenberg gave me the affirmation I needed to push ahead. He was the one who said "Follow your heart, do the stuff that really matters, and don't let anybody talk you out of it." And so when that first study ended up as a special article in the New England Journal of Medicine, my research career headed off in a new and fascinating direction.

PATIENT "DUMPING" IN MEMPHIS, TENNESSEE

After he finished his fellowship and M.P.H., Kellermann accepted a position in his home state at the University of Tennessee, Memphis. The firearm injury research he had published in the New England Journal of Medicine was highly regarded and widely influential, but he still considered himself an emergency physician first and foremost, with no sustained interest in health policy. All of that changed as the result of an encounter with an emergency room patient. During one of Kellermann's first shifts in Memphis, a young man was transferred to the emergency department in profound, life-threatening diabetic ketoacidosis (DKA). "This guy rolls in, he's a bad DKA-er; and he's obviously on death's door," Kellermann recalls. When Kellermann reached to check the victim's pulse, he found that the patient was wearing the bright yellow wrist band of a private hospital a few blocks up the street:

> I look at the paramedic and say, "What the hell's this?" and he goes, "Doc, he's a transfer." I say, "What do you mean he's a transfer?" He goes, "Doc, he's an indigent, and that's why he was transferred; they don't do indigent care."

Kellermann was furious. Although he understood that public hospitals like the Regional Medical Center at Memphis (known as "The Med") have a special mission to care for the poor, he did not believe that this gave private hospitals the "right to precipitously transfer unstable patients for purely economic reasons," as he thought was the case with this patient.

To get a handle on the magnitude of patient "dumping" in Memphis, Kellermann and some colleagues conducted a 90-day descriptive study of inter-facility transfers to the emergency department of The Med. In the course of this work, they recorded phone calls from doctors at wealthy private hospitals, explaining, in bold terms, that patients were being transferred because they were indigent or uninsured: "The doctors knew that they were being recorded, but they didn't care—this was simply the way things were done. The practice of dumping was so common and so institutionalized that the doctors were wholly unself-conscious about it." Kellermann also compiled financial data on the private hospitals, many of which were "very profitable non-profits," and contrasted it to the financial status of The Med, which was struggling. Lastly, he asked his nurses to clip the wrist bracelets of transferred patients, offering dinner for two at the best restaurant in Memphis to the nurse who collected the most bracelets over the study period.

Armed with this compelling evidence, Kellermann went before the Tennessee state legislature, and later the House Intergovernmental Affairs Committee of the U.S. Congress. At both hearings, he presented his figures and played the recorded phone conversations. At the end of his testimony, he pulled up a plastic bag, and dumped his collection of wristbands on the hearing table. The impact, he says, was palpable.

Kellermann acknowledges that he has a gift for this kind of high-impact presentation. But he insists that knowing how to present data in an accessible and compelling way, and how to mix it with illustrative stories of real people, is an essential skill for those interested in promoting public health. Accordingly, he recommends that medicine, nursing and public health students seek out courses or seminars on media and legislative advocacy.

The 90-day study of inter-facility transfers gave rise to Kellermann's long-term interest in the public insurance crisis in the United States, and his passion for insurance reform finally left him with an undeniable and sustained interest in public health research. Kellermann's work was influential in the subsequent development of the 1986 Emergency Medical Treatment and Active Labor Act (EMTALA), which requires hospitals to provide emergency care regardless of a patient's citizenship or financial status.

The law, which has been criticized for requiring care while not making adequate provisions for funding, is a legacy that he acknowledges with conflicted feelings. He jokes about being Dr. Frankenstein, creating legislation with the best of intentions that has turned into a tremendous, unfunded legislative monster: "I have mixed feelings about EMTALA, because the law has had a lot of unintended consequences, including financially destabilizing many emergency departments. But I stand behind the principle of the original legislation: that patient dumping is a dangerous and unethical practice."

Kellermann insists that the crisis of "uninsurance" is creating a tremendous access-to-care problem for all demographic groups, insured and uninsured alike: "We have real capacity and access issues across the board." He believes strongly that the only way to successfully address the problem is to appeal to the self-interest of the American population, and convince them that the best course of action is to insure everyone.

RETURNING TO EMORY

Kellermann worked his way up to the position of chief of the Division of Emergency Medicine at the University of Tennessee. He put all his effort behind developing a residency program which, he felt, was not only crucial to the future of his program, but essential to provide qualified emergency physicians for the state. Unfortunately, he was opposed by the chief of the trauma service, who was not interested in the program. As Kellermann worked his way up the hierarchy of the medical school and ultimately of the university, he was taken aback by what he considered to be unreasonable disinterest in the program. When his concerns were summarily dismissed by the chancellor of UT Memphis, he felt it was time to leave.

Declaring that he was "sick and tired of medical school politics," he eagerly accepted a primary appointment at Emory's Rollins School of Public Health as the founding director of the school's Center for Injury Control. The CIC's mission is to study injuries from a public health standpoint, as statistically measurable and avoidable problems rather than as mere accidents; the CIC has focused on firearm injuries, domestic violence, child abuse, and motor vehicle injuries, among others, and has developed several highly successful programs to reduce such problems.

While Kellermann's work with the CIC was absorbing, his hiatus from "medical school politics" did not last for long. After he had been at Emory for just two years, the division of emergency medicine and its historic residency program underwent a crisis. With great reluctance, he agreed to become acting chief of emergency medicine "for eighteen months and not a day longer." Yet short-term involvement inexorably turned into long-term commitment, and four years later, Kellermann says, "I ended up chairman of a new academic department of EM, and as they say—the rest is history."

One of Kellermann's goals in the department has been to foster diversity. Recalling the hardships faced by his mentor, Hiram Moore, who built a successful solo practice in a racially polarized southern community, he has been a lifelong supporter of affirmative action. His department has been nationally recognized for its commitment to equal opportunity and for the accomplishments of its faculty. Kellermann proudly cites two African-American faculty members in his department who were included in the annual list of the state's "Top forty under 40" in the magazine *Georgia Trend*.

While Kellermann has accomplished much as the department's chair, his ultimate goal has been to build an academic department that was not "personality-dependent": a department in which the commitment to key values is so institutionalized, and the talent pool so deep, that he himself would become "irrelevant to its ongoing success."

A LIFE IN EMERGENCY MEDICINE

When reflecting on his career, Kellermann explains that the reasons he originally entered emergency medicine are different from the reasons he stayed:

> I went into emergency medicine, like most students and residents, because it's exciting and tense and rewarding and dramatic—you can make a difference, and make it in a hurry. I stayed in emergency medicine because it is the frontline of our health care system in its interface with the public: it's where people go when public health fails.

Throughout his career, Kellermann has placed a premium on doing what he thinks is the right thing rather than sticking with accepted but ineffective norms. His description of the typical ER physician—"very outcomes-oriented, programmed to make decisions, and programmed to be collaborative"—characterizes his own approach to both clinical practice and research. It also describes his approach to teaching and supervision. Kellermann recognizes that his tendency to act with decisiveness rather than textbook correctness rubs some people the wrong way, but he considers it a major strength of his administrative style:

What career attributes do you want in a manager? You want somebody who is thinking strategically, who is results-oriented; who is going to get it done now, and not three or four years from now; but who can also play on a team. You want a manager who is not afraid to make a decision with incomplete information when a decision must be made. We emergency physicians do that all the time.

Because emergency medicine develops such a valuable and flexible set of skills, Kellermann sees a bright future for physicians in the specialty:

As American health care continues to evolve, I think you're going to see emergency physicians go beyond the roles of department chair, practice group manager, and clinical entrepreneur: A growing number will become deans, health system CEOs, and heads of major federal agencies.

Kellermann has experienced, and to some extent helped to create, these expanding possibilities in the field of emergency medicine during his own career. He is especially pleased that people now accept that combining the fields of emergency medicine and public health is a logical choice:

For years I heard people ask, "Why does an ER doc have an M.P.H.? You are the resuscitation doctors. You're totally focused on an individual patient, pouring tons of resources into him, right when they are at death's door. That's the exact opposite of public health." I'm pleased I no longer have to explain as much why public health is relevant to emergency medicine, or why emergency physicians have a lot to say about public health. Our engagement in that arena is not only legitimate, it's expected.

Given the possibility of such combinations, Kellermann believes that young physicians interested in public health can find many different and fulfilling career paths. Academic research, government work, and professional associations such as the American College of Emergency Physicians and the American Public Health Association can all provide opportunities to bring together medicine and public health. Whatever path a doctor chooses, Kellermann emphasizes that he or she must be willing to develop the formal skills necessary for success.

STAYING AHEAD OF THE CURVE

In his own research, Kellermann has tried to stay a step ahead of policy debates, investigating what he believes will be future areas of concern. "If there's a theme to my research and to the stuff I publish," he says, "it's big effects and issues that matter":

I do my best to devise studies that are rigorous and unbiased, but others are probably more elegant methodologists than I am. To compensate, I try to come up with novel approaches to important social problems that have not been previously researched—generally they involve very big effects. By being the first to address an issue, or the second, I help push people to look at the problem in a new way and hopefully identify solutions.

These efforts have earned Kellermann numerous honors and awards over the course of his career. The one that means the most to him is the joint resolution "to honor and commend Dr. Arthur Kellermann for meritorious service to the citizens of Tennessee" that was adopted by the Tennessee State Senate when he returned to Emory in 1993. In 1999, Kellermann was elected to the Institute of Medicine. The following year, he was asked to co-chair the IOM's Committee on the Consequences of Uninsurance. Over a three-year period, this committee systematically analyzed the consequences of being uninsured for individuals, families, entire communities, and the country as a whole. The committee's work culminated in the 2004 report *Insuring America's Health: Principles and Recommendations*.

In 2006, Kellermann won a prestigious Robert Wood Johnson Health Policy Fellowship, allowing him a year of leave from Emory to work on health policy issues in the federal government. Kellermann joined the staff of the House Committee on Government Oversight and Reform in 2007. Kellermann returned to Emory in 2008 to resume his work as a professor of emergency medicine, and with the new administrative role of associate dean for health policy. In 2010 Kellermann was appointed the Paul O'Neill-Alcoa chair in policy analysis at the RAND Corporation, a nonprofit institution headquartered in Santa Monica, California. A year later, in 2011, Kellermann served for a time as vice president and director of RAND Health, where he oversaw the research of the nation's largest independent health policy research program. However, he missed directly working on health policy, and, at his request, transferred back to RAND's Washington, D.C. office in the fall of 2012. In 2013, Kellermann was named dean of the F. Edward Hébert School of Medicine at the Uniformed Services University of the Health Sciences in Bethesda. The school's mission includes educating specially trained physicians to serve in the armed forces, and it places a strong emphasis on public health as well as traditional medical training. Kellermann sees the school's mission as continuous with his previous experiences. "I am humbled and excited by the opportunity," he said in a press release at the time of his appointment. "In many regards, USU is America's medical school."

THE ETHOS OF EMERGENCY MEDICINE

While Kellermann is proud of his accomplishments, he acknowledges that involvement with persistent public health problems and with the agonizingly slow process of policy change leads to occasional doubts. Calling to mind the still horrific number of gun deaths each year and the millions of

Americans who continue to go without health insurance, he says:

> I don't know that I've really made a difference in anything. What would have happened if I hadn't spent the last twenty years tilting at those windmills? I don't know. In fairness, I can't say: "This antibiotic is there because I invented it."

Kellermann's accomplishments have also come at some personal cost, and he worries that the sacrifices have too often been his wife's rather than his own. To maintain a balance, Kellermann has passed up professional opportunities that would require long-distance moves in order to allow his wife's legal practice to flourish. "One thing I'm determined to do," he says, "is to only get married once."

In the face of challenges both personal and professional, one thing that Kellermann credits with continuing to drive his work is the ethos that he believes to be an intrinsic part of emergency medicine: "I am proud of my specialty's professional and ethical commitment to patients over profits. I don't regret that I fought for the fact that sick and injured patients shouldn't be dumped." That ethos brings with it a sense of obligation that, Kellermann says, it has often been difficult to put limits on—and this for reasons that go back to his childhood:

> It can be tough to make choices, and my biggest struggle I think—personally and professionally—is not taking on every cause. I have a real, real problem with that. It's my mom in the back of my head, saying, "You're not going to let them get away with that, are you?"

Note

1   The article is "Protection or Peril? An analysis of firearm related deaths in the home," *New England Journal of Medicine* 314 (1986): 1557–60.

Arthur M. Kleinman

Former Chair, Department of Anthropology, Harvard University
Professor of Psychiatry and Social Medicine, Harvard Medical School

Kleinman, one of the pioneers of medical anthropology, has built his career at the intersection of psychiatry and anthropology. His work, much of which has focused on Chinese society, has included such diverse topics as patterns of healing, depression, suicide, violence, the structure of health care systems, and global mental health. In this profile, he traces the origins of his interdisciplinary career from his childhood to the present. He also discusses his shift in focus away from medicine, with its emphasis on individual cases, and towards anthropology and broader questions about entire cultures and societies.

Education & Training

1960–1962	A.B., Stanford University
1962–1967	M.D., Stanford University
1967–1968	Intern, Yale-New Haven Hospital, New Haven, CT
1968–1970	Research Fellow, Geographic Medicine Branch, National Institutes of Health
1969–1970	Research Fellow, U.S. Naval Medical Research Unit #2, Taipei, Taiwan
1970–1972	Research Fellow, Department of History of Science, Harvard University
1972–1974	M.A., Social Anthropology, Harvard University
1972–1975	Resident, Department of Psychiatry, Harvard Medical School (HMS) & Massachusetts General Hospital

Career Path

1968–1970	Surgeon, U.S. Public Health Service
1975–1976	Lecturer in Anthropology and Clinical Instructor in Psychiatry, Harvard
1976–1982	Positions culminating in Professor of Psychiatry and Behavioral Science and Adjunct Professor of Anthropology, University of Washington
1982–	Positions culminating in Chair (2004–2007) and Esther and Sidney Rabb Professor of Anthropology (2002–), Department of Anthropology, Harvard University
1982–	Professor of Medical Anthropology and Psychiatry (1982–) and Chair (1991–2000), Department of Social Medicine, HMS
2008–	Victor and William Fung Director, Harvard University Asia Center

Selected Publications

A selection of Kleinman's books and articles can be found at the end of this profile.

A person comes in with a pain in his chest. You do an EKG, and it's not a heart attack. What kind of pain is it? You better know that person, what's going on in their life. That's how you figure that one out. And in my life, that's basically what drove me, the interest in experience.

—*Arthur Kleinman*

As a child growing up in the years after World War II in the complex Jewish community of New York City, Arthur Kleinman was dimly but intimately aware of the complex experience being lived through, often painfully, by different parts of this community in the wake of the Holocaust. Only after a brilliant undergraduate career at Stanford and the first years of medical school would Kleinman, on a trip to Europe, begin coming to terms with the context of his own childhood, discovering as if for the first time a history through which he had lived. Kleinman has dedicated his career as a medical anthropologist focusing on China to understanding, as faithfully as possible, the implication of any experience of suffering in a social and cultural context. His work has explored how even the most apparently personal experiences of suffering, such as depression, need to be grasped in relation to contexts ranging from family history to large-scale events such as China's Cultural Revolution. The truth of such experiences lies at the intersection of the individual and her culture; the possibility of successfully healing the sufferer—and not merely the disease—lies in the physician's ability to recognize the importance of this intersection. Kleinman's work has helped to reorient medical and especially psychiatric training towards recognizing and treating a patient's culturally specific experience of illness. His later work has increasingly sought to use societal experiences of suffering as a way to understand the meaning of moral experience.

EARLY CONTEXTS: NEW YORK, STANFORD, ALSACE

Kleinman's love of the academic life developed early in his education. While he was a teenager, his family moved from New York City to Long Island. Kleinman began his sophomore year in a small public high school known for turning out high-achieving academics: economist Marty Feldstein and research psychiatrist Dave Kupfer graduated from the school within a few classes of Kleinman. "It was a very high-level high school," Kleinman says, "but a public high school with a tremendous interest in history and how history informed policy, and I would say that that issue carried into my career."

It was there that Kleinman first developed his interest in history, and with it the respect for the importance of context that would motivate his later research: "The argument that you could not answer any question practically unless you understood its context—this was the key idea I got out of high school."

After high school, Kleinman, who first attended Tufts, decided to move across the country to attend Stanford University—in part, he later realized, in order to change his own context:

> The reason I went to Stanford was that it was the greatest distance from where I grew up, which was New York City. I didn't know about Hawaii—I might have gone to Hawaii if I'd known. And Stanford was a great place for me because unlike Harvard—perhaps more like Princeton and Yale—it was kind of a protected environment.

At Stanford, where he chose to major in history, Kleinman again found himself part of an attentive academic community. Stanford in the 1960s was more undergraduate-oriented than many of the Ivy League schools closer to his home, and even compared to other students there Kleinman had an exceptional experience: he was one of a select group of students admitted to an interdisciplinary humanities program that paired them with senior professors for one-on-one study.

Kleinman describes his first semester in the program, during his junior year, as "probably the greatest single intellectual experience" of his life:

> We focused on studying Europe from 1900 to 1905—just those five years. We did the social history, the art, the music, the physics and other science…and it was just astonishing. This brought to fruition what I had learned in high school—that context was critical, that if you were to know anything about Europe from 1900 to 1905, whether it was the art, the music, or the science, you had to put it in historical context. What had led up to Europe at that stage—the great movements of colonialism, the huge developments in racialism and eugenics—all these key things played a role not just in the politics, but in the art, the music, and the science.

This confirmation of his earlier interest convinced Kleinman that his own career would be interdisciplinary. Since long before Stanford or even high school, Kleinman had aspired to a career in medicine. His stepfather was an attorney who, frustrated with his work in law, had expressed enthusiasm for his son's wish to become a physician; Kleinman's mother had often volunteered in medical settings, and he had grown up with great respect for his own family doctor. His work at Stanford had now complicated his aspirations in a good way:

> I knew, as I was going through this program, that my career was always going to have two sides to it. It was going to have a humanities-social science side—I wasn't sure if it was going to be history or anthropology or what exactly—and the medical side, but I didn't know how it would come together.

This uncertainty played itself out as Kleinman applied to graduate and professional schools after graduating from Stanford with high honors. He applied to Stanford Medical School—and Stanford Law School, and to Stanford's graduate school for a further degree in history: "I was accepted to all three...and I told all three I was coming." His final decision, depending on what you believe, was either completely random or completely predetermined:

> The day classes began, as I was driving up Palm Drive, I made my decision to go to medical school. I actually made it in a funny way: it's the first right turn you make as you get on Palm Drive, and a car actually swerved in front of me, and I had to go to the right. I said to myself, "Well, it feels right, it was natural to happen, so I might as well go there."

He admits, however, that the car had swerved in the direction of his own inclinations: "I probably wouldn't have gone to law school, and history I could always combine with medicine."

Stanford, unlike other medical schools at the time, had a five-year program. The opportunity this provided to do research, take extra classes, and travel fit in perfectly with Kleinman's desire to combine medicine with his other interests. At first he was quite happy with the mix, even enrolling in graduate history classes during his pre-clinical years, but before long he found himself losing interest in the coursework that demanded the majority of his time:

> Basic science seemed to be too distant. At that stage medical school did not let you go into the clinics for your first couple of years, so I didn't have any feelings for the clinical side, and the basic research side, the basic biological research, just didn't excite me.

Craving time away from a frustrating academic period, Kleinman sought refuge in Europe, from which earlier generations of his family had emigrated to America. The trip proved to be a pivotal experience in the evolution of his thinking.

DISCOVERING "LIVED EXPERIENCE"

To understand the significance of Kleinman's experience in Europe, one has to understand his own context—the ethnic origins and history of his family, and his own complex relationship to that history. Both of his parents' families were Jewish, but they were of different national backgrounds. His mother's family was Russian and had come to the U.S. in 1880, just before the first great pogrom in Europe. His biological father's family was German and had come to America before the Civil War. In New York in the 1940s, he explains, these two communities did not mix well:

> The German Jews dominated New York economically in the 1940s, and they were not interested in the Russian Jews, who they saw as *nouveau riche*—or really as just new arrivals. There was a tension between those communities which I could see in my own parents' families.

Kleinman grew up in the home of his maternal grandparents, who were very wealthy and, as an anecdote from Kleinman's childhood attests, very secular:

> We lived in Brooklyn, where I grew up, and Menachem Schneersen, the Lubavitch *Rebbe*,[1] moved into the house next to us. The first Saturday he was there, he saw me playing basketball, and he ran out and he took my basketball away. He told me it was the Sabbath, and I shouldn't be playing basketball.

Kleinman, who was five or six years old at the time, went home crying to his grandfather, who in turn went back across the street and "had it out with *Rav* Schneersen. He came back with the basketball and he said to me, 'Arthur, I really don't care what you do about playing basketball—but I want you to promise me you will play every Saturday.'"

Kleinman's relationship to his Jewish heritage was thus, from the beginning, extraordinarily complex, and this was perhaps still more true of his understanding of the Holocaust or *Shoah* (the Hebrew word now commonly used for the Holocaust). As a child growing up in the 1940s and '50s, Kleinman did not know exactly what the Holocaust was: "In the 1950s," he explains, "there was almost no literature on the Shoah and no attention paid to it":

> People did not have the full understanding of what the Holocaust was about. It was an industrial destruction of a people, but that was not known widely at the time. And there was also a lot of guilt in the Jewish community that they had been so spectacularly ineffective at doing anything. Even in the late 1940s, when I was not even ten, I understood this.

Complicating matters still further were different attitudes to the Holocaust even within the Jewish community. American Jews, Kleinman explains, were uneasy in their relation to those who had been closer to events in Europe:

> People who came from the so-called remnant community were looked down upon by American Jews at that stage, especially on the East Coast. Something

terrible had happened to them, and it was like a stigma, especially because there were whispers and rumors that they had participated in their own catastrophe by not resisting and getting out in time.

While Kleinman had acquired what was in many ways an intimate understanding of the aftermath of the Holocaust while growing up, there were still large gaps in his knowledge of the history involved when he went to Europe as a young medical student. His travels there dramatically changed his understanding of that history and of his own relation to it.

Since Kleinman spoke German, he spent much of his time that summer in Germany—"but never once," he says, "did I think about asking about the Holocaust or the war." At the end of the summer, Kleinman crossed the French-German border into the Alsace region, and stayed in a village near the town of Colmar on the French side of the Rhine.

Alsace has been a crossroads of French and German culture for centuries and, particularly in the nineteenth and twentieth centuries, a site of repeated conflict and territorial dispute: it has changed nationality four times since the newly formed German nation took it over in 1871 during the Franco-Prussian War. In June of 1940, the German army invaded the region and annexed it, establishing concentration camps and forcing 140,000 men to fight for the German army, the majority of whom did not return. Kleinman knew few of these details during his first journey there, and almost literally stumbled into an awareness of them:

> It started to rain, and so I ran to a clump of trees, and suddenly I was smack in the middle of a Jewish cemetery. I was huddling from this summer shower under a monument which was to a family called Rubin, and you could see there were about eleven members in this family, and they all had the same day of death, which kind of astonished me.

When the rain subsided, Kleinman returned to the small pension where he was staying and, knowing little French, addressed the innkeeper in German:

> And so here a guy comes in, with blond hair and blue eyes, speaking German, and asks them, "What about this family Rubin? How come they all died the same day?" And the woman just looked at me and said: "You fucking German! You don't know what happened in 1940 when the Nazis crossed over here?"

Kleinman now understands this episode as a tangle of misapprehended contexts: the innkeeper had placed Kleinman in the wrong context, assuming he was a German; Kleinman's lack of knowledge about the region's history had led him to ask the question; more personally, Kleinman, who had grown up hearing the Holocaust spoken about in hushed voices and veiled by a sense of shame, had now experienced a result of it in his own life. This event affected Kleinman profoundly, crystallizing his long-standing interest in context and in understanding what he calls lived experience:

> For the first time I really had, in my lived experience, the Holocaust. And so what came together for me were a few things. One, I had been blind to the context of my own life while studying other contexts. Also, how critical it is to go under things, to look deeper, to go beyond the surface. And I think that clearly ties into the Jewish cultural interests—Freud, touched by happenstance, developed an understanding of the depth of this. I became interested in experience, in lived experience, and how it's different from book-learning, from intellectualized experience.

Upon returning to medical school, Kleinman began concentrating on the experience in front of him—that of human illness. This new focus led Kleinman in two related directions. On the one hand, he chose to focus his energies on the study of anthropology, which he describes as "fundamentally about lived experience, what everyday experience is in different societies, in different cultures." In the context of his medical training, Kleinman wanted to choose a specialty that would harmonize with his interest in anthropology. He found this in psychiatry: not only did it emphasize experience, but it was closely related to anthropology because of what Kleinman began to understand as the inherently subjective and contextual—social, cultural, even political—components of psychiatric illness. While a heart attack, in general, remains clinically similar from one society to another, psychiatric illnesses—their prevalence, form, diagnosis, treatment, and impact on society—differ greatly among societies.

In these two disciplines, anthropology and psychiatry, Kleinman had found the combination that would determine his subsequent path. His new focus on illness experience likewise stayed with him in the long term, forming the basis of his research for the next fifteen years and an overarching framework for his entire career.

Anthropology as a Tool for Understanding the Illness Experience

Kleinman's initial approach to combining medicine and anthropology was to use anthropology as a lens through which to understand human illness. He felt that the individual illness experience—the patient's understanding and experience of her medical condition, as opposed to the biomedically defined disease—was a concept that could be expanded to address cultural and societal contexts, and that likewise, an understanding of the individual illness experience could be inferred from cultural and societal context.

In the nine years after medical school, Kleinman prepared himself for this interdisciplinary work by completing both a medical residency in psychiatry and academic post-doctoral work. He first completed an internship at the Yale-New Haven Hospital, after which he took a hiatus from his clinical training to take on a series of post-doctoral fellowships, first with the Geographic Medicine Branch at the National Institutes of Health, and then with the U.S. Naval Medical Research Unit. This latter fellowship took him to Taipei, Taiwan, and thus introduced him to Chinese society and culture, which Kleinman would continue to study over the coming decades. In Taiwan, where Kleinman focused on leprosy, tuberculosis, and stigma, he discovered a complex medical landscape, rich in overlapping and sometimes conflicting traditions, and intricate in its levels of meaning to patients.

Following these two fellowships, Kleinman spent an additional two years, from 1970 to 1972, as a research fellow in a program on the comparative study of medicine; the program was anthropological in focus though housed in Harvard's history of science department. During those two years and the two that followed, Kleinman completed all of the training of a social anthropologist, including fieldwork for a dissertation, though because he never officially completed the dissertation he now holds a master's degree, but not a doctorate, in anthropology.

Kleinman recalls spending these years at Harvard "reading [his] way through all the literature [he] could find concerned with medicine and psychiatry in different cultures." He was at once intrigued and disturbed by the breadth of this literature and by its lack of "discriminating theoretical frameworks and systematic methods." It was an "unorganized, but extremely fascinating field," he says.

Kleinman published prolifically during this period, authoring papers on immunology, bio-ethics, the formation of the illness experience, and on the cross-cultural anthropological and ethnographic components of medicine. Such extraordinary range and productivity was startling for so young an academic, and helped Kleinman to win respect as a researcher, physician, and anthropologist from colleagues and contemporaries years his senior. "I was on the fast track," he explains. By the time he returned to his residency in 1972, he had more articles accepted for publication than many assistant professors. In 1973, as a second-year psychiatry resident at Massachusetts General Hospital (MGH), Kleinman published a cluster of four papers: "Medicine's Symbolic Reality," "Toward a Comparative Study of Medical Systems," "Some Issues for a Comparative Study of Medical Healing," and "The Background and Development of Public Health in China." This body of work, he later realized, provided a conceptual framework for much of the next fifteen years of his career.

During his residency at MGH, Kleinman also began what would be one of the most important academic relationships of his career with Leon Eisenberg, chair of the social medicine department at Harvard Medical School and formerly chair of psychiatry at MGH. Supervising Kleinman in his residency, Eisenberg was quick to see his student's potential as an academic. The two formed a close bond that helped Kleinman steer through his complicated multi-disciplinary career.

After completing his residency in 1975, Kleinman received a post-doctoral fellowship to conduct more research on the medical system in Taiwan. Upon his return to the U.S., he had two job offers. The first was to serve as an assistant professor at the Harvard School of Public Health, as well as chair of its department of health and human behavior. It was rare for an assistant professor to be made chair of a department, and so it surprised many of his colleagues that he turned this position down, opting instead to take a position as an associate professor of psychiatry and an adjunct professor of anthropology at the University of Washington in Seattle. The position was tenured, and it gave Kleinman the opportunity to build his own program in social and cultural psychiatry. During this time he also founded the journal *Culture, Medicine and Psychiatry*, which he edited for a decade.

PATIENTS AND HEALERS IN THE CONTEXT OF CULTURE

In his early years at UW, Kleinman wrote his first book, *Patients and Healers in the Context of Culture* (1980), which is based on his research in Taiwan from 1975 to 1976. The book's larger goal is to provide a "theoretical framework for studying the relationship between medicine, psychiatry, and culture."[2] To do so, Kleinman begins his analysis using the example of the complicated medical landscape in the Lung-Shan district of Taipei. In the few city blocks around the Lung Shan Temple, he explains, patients could seek care from a startling array of medical practitioners: Western-style and Chinese-style physicians and pharmacists, eye specialists and bone-setters licensed to practice neither Western nor Chinese medicine, a fortune-teller, and merchants selling religious paraphernalia such as amulets to protect a child's health or guard a pregnant mother. Kleinman then uses this complicated landscape to develop a theoretical framework for understanding a health care system in its own context.

Patients and Healers became a cornerstone of the burgeoning field of medical anthropology. As Kleinman later wrote of the book: "Widely reviewed and commented upon, the book seemed to take on a life of its own. A generation of graduate students, it seems, was trained in medical anthropology in criticizing its contents."[3] This book and the works that followed firmly positioned Kleinman as one of the founders of medical anthropology.

RETHINKING ILLNESS, DISEASE, AND PSYCHIATRY

In 1978, Kleinman had begun to shift the geographic focus of his work from Taiwan to the People's Republic of China; conceptually, he began thinking about the experience of illness in terms of "social suffering," which would remain a theme of his research for many years to come. From 1980 to 1983, Kleinman conducted a study of Chinese patients with neurasthenia, pain and depression, seeking to understand these illnesses in the context of China's culture and recent history. The resulting book, *Social Origins of Distress and Disease: Neurasthenia, Depression and Pain in Modern China* (1986), was the first systematic study of survivors of China's Cultural Revolution.

Throughout this work and others from this period, Kleinman makes a clear distinction between "illness" and "disease." Illness relates to the patient's perception, experience, expression, and pattern of coping with symptoms; disease refers to the way practitioners recast illness in terms of their theoretical models of pathology. While it is tempting to summarize "illness" as subjective and "disease" as objective, Kleinman's point is precisely to challenge such a schema. He seeks to show how a patient's experience of illness is conditioned by cultural and social factors not reducible to a merely personal or idiosyncratic interpretation of physical ailments. Conversely, he argues that diagnostic categories, especially in psychiatry, are themselves culturally specific: "A psychiatric diagnosis is an *interpretation* of a person's experience."[4] This interpretation depends on the cultural background, including the professional training, of the clinician.

A central example from *Social Origins of Distress and Disease* involves the diagnosis of neurasthenia in China. Kleinman discusses patients whose symptoms and circumstances would lead most Western psychiatrists to diagnose depression. In China, though, a diagnosis of mental illness traditionally carried with it an intense stigma that extended from the patient to the patient's family; the diagnosis could thus reinforce the feelings of shame and isolation that the psychiatrist intended to heal. Chinese psychiatrists tended to diagnose such cases as neurasthenia, a syndrome of exhaustion and diffuse bodily complaints believed to be caused by insufficient energy in the central nervous system. Though no longer recognized as a valid diagnosis by the American Psychiatric Association, neurasthenia was preferred as a diagnosis by Chinese doctors and patients because its quasi-physiological nature allowed patients to acknowledge illness and pursue treatment without incurring the stigma of mental illness. A diagnosis of depression that ignored this culturally determined stigma would be, Kleinman argues, not at all a case of more advanced Western psychiatry correcting an antiquated Chinese diagnosis; it would be therapeutically counterproductive and thus medically wrong.

In *Rethinking Psychiatry: From Cultural Category to Personal Experience* (1988), Kleinman expanded upon the case for cross-cultural studies in psychiatry implicit in his work on neurasthenia and depression in China. Noting that psychiatry, with its almost exclusively Western origins, has largely dismissed the clinical importance of cultural differences as "soft," he argues that the discipline needs cross-cultural studies in order to be relevant to the 80 percent of the world's people who live in non-Western societies (*RP* xii).

To illustrate the kind of problem that needs to be solved, Kleinman describes a scene that has lingered in his mind, a composite of his own experience with immigrant patients. The scene, in which an assimilated translator fails to overcome an immigrant's shame about experience felt to be incommunicable, also resonates with Kleinman's experience of the Jewish community in America in the years following the Holocaust.

An elderly patient who speaks no English is thought to have a psychiatric disorder in addition to the non-psychiatric cause of his hospitalization. A young professional woman, a thoroughly Americanized immigrant from the patient's own country, serves as a translator during the psychiatrist's interview. But the patient is deeply humiliated by having to discuss his personal thoughts with strangers, and particularly uncomfortable with being interviewed by a young woman. Based on his extensive experience with such patients, Kleinman reconstructs the man's thoughts about his interaction with the translator:

> How to respond to her prying questions? How to tell her of his sadness for the homeland? How to explain the meaning of giving up the land? The shame of having left the ancestral graves unattended.... She would laugh at him, he knows from experience, if he told her that he must find a spirit-medium to propitiate the ancestral shades and learn which one is attacking him. (*RP* 176)

The translator partially confirms the old man's fears. Asked by the psychiatrists if the man is hearing voices, a symptom commonly associated with schizophrenia in Western psychiatry, she responds: "I don't think he hears voices....He told me that he sometimes hears the ancestors weeping....I have told him not to speak such superstitious stuff, because he is in America now" (*RP* 176). Kleinman points out that this well-meaning translator has made it unlikely that the man will now share anything that really matters to him and that could thus aid in his treatment. The psychiatric team's failure to provide meaningful therapy for him could, Kleinman suggests, be remedied by a more culturally astute, "anthropologically-informed" mode of practice. What might very well be diagnosed as symptoms of a disease in one society may be understood as an integral part of the culture in another.

Whereas *Rethinking Psychiatry* argues for the importance of cross-cultural study to psychiatry, Kleinman's best-known book, *The Illness Narratives* (1988), argues that not just psychiatry but all medical disciplines should attend to and treat the patient's experience of illness, and not just the biomedical mechanisms of disease. To make this argument, Kleinman focuses on cases of chronic illness, most of which are drawn from his own clinical experience and interview notes: he tells the stories of patients living with diabetes, severe burn damage, and cancer, among other illnesses, and includes as much as possible the patient's own account of the illness. In cases of chronic illness, the patient's experience of an illness—his ability to adapt to new physical or social limitations, his willingness to seek out help and participate in his own care, his degree of hope or despair—inevitably makes a profound difference to the success or failure of treatment. In such cases, Kleinman argues,

> neither the interpretation of illness nor the handling of deeply felt emotions within intimate personal relationships can be dismissed as peripheral tasks. They constitute, rather, the point of medicine…The failure to address these issues is a fundamental flaw in the work of doctoring.

SHIFTING FROM MEDICINE TO ANTHROPOLOGY

While Kleinman's position at UW had offered him considerable autonomy, much of his work there had remained quite clinical; this emphasis was reflected by the higher level of his appointment in the psychiatry department, where he became a full professor in 1979, as compared with his adjunct status in the department of anthropology. As his interests increasingly steered towards anthropology, this situation began to frustrate Kleinman.

Back at Harvard, his mentor, Leon Eisenberg, kept making offers to bring Kleinman back, and in 1982 he succeeded. Kleinman accepted on the condition that his appointment would be divided between the medical school and the anthropology department: "I think it was the critical thing for me, bureaucratically," he explains. "I could never have built the medical anthropology program unless I was in the anthropology department. I was the first medical anthropologist in the department." With an appointment committing one third of his time to the anthropology department and two thirds to the medical school, Kleinman returned to Harvard as the leading voice in medical anthropology in the social medicine department, which he later chaired from 1991 to 2000.

The shift from medicine to anthropology was again reflected in Kleinman's decision to change the balance of his departmental commitments. In 1999, Stanford actively recruited Kleinman to a high-ranking professorship; Harvard, intent on keeping him, responded by allowing him to redesign his appointment. Kleinman chose to reverse its proportions, now committing two thirds of his time to anthropology and one third to the medical school. In 2004, Kleinman became chair of Harvard's anthropology department, making him one of only a handful of professors who have chaired departments in two completely separate faculties at Harvard. This appointment was particularly significant in that Kleinman does not hold a Ph.D. in anthropology.

Behind these changing departmental commitments lay a shift in the nature of Kleinman's research. Over the years, Kleinman's focus had shifted from understanding the individual in the context of a culture to understanding the culture itself. This shift in emphasis drove his academic move from psychiatry and social medicine to anthropology:

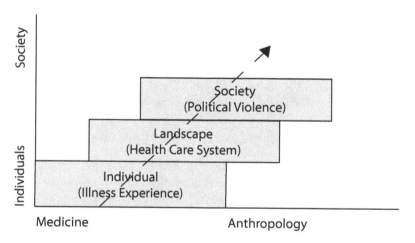

Kleinman has increasingly used the individual's experience of illness and suffering as a lens through which to understand a society, rather than the reverse. This approach has led to substantial results. Kleinman's examinations of suicide in China, to take just one instance, reveal several interesting insights into Chinese society. One of Kleinman's basic questions was why statistics showed a higher rate of suicide among women than among men in China—in the U.S., the case is the opposite. Kleinman's answer was grounded in an understanding of social change in contemporary China. There, men from the rural areas are migrating to find work in the more rapidly developing economies of large cities, often leaving their wives behind to care for children and elderly relatives. This burden borne in isolation is thought to be a primary driver of suicide, which is most common among rural women in China. The methods of suicide most prevalent in each country also fit in with this picture of societal change: while in the U.S., most men kill themselves with firearms, in China the most prevalent method is taking the agricultural poisons kept in rural homes.

RETHINKING PAST THEORIES

Along with his shift in disciplinary focus, Kleinman's beliefs and theories have also evolved significantly over the course of his career. In the early 1990s, while chair of Harvard's department of social medicine, Kleinman wrote a series of essays re-examining some of his theories. These works, collectively published in *Writing at the Margin* (1995), explain how his thinking evolved over the first fifteen years of his career.

One major shift Kleinman identifies is a turn away from thinking about societies in terms of structures and models, which "imply too much formalism, specificity, and authorial certainty." As a means of avoiding such excesses and more faithfully describing the cultures he studies, Kleinman has come to focus on narratives, on "the lived experience of suffering" and on "medical practice as a historicized mode of social being-in-the-world."

Some of his initial beliefs remained unchanged, however, such as the strong social constructionist position espoused in *Patients and Healers*. Closely related to this is Kleinman's sustained belief in the importance of context:

> Context has stayed with me my whole career. It's also fed on the interdisciplinary nature of my work...and in anything I do now, you see that. I developed a theory on experience: What is experience? How do we understand it? Where is it localized? I argued that it is always localized, always in a local world. It doesn't have to be a neighborhood, or a village, or a street; it could be a network that is transatlantic, or transcontinental, but it's always localized by the intrinsic relations between people. It is about what is at stake for you, what really matters to you at any given point.

A BROADENING DEFINITION OF SUFFERING

Closely related to Kleinman's shift from medicine to anthropology is the expanding scope of his interest in suffering: "Illness experience carried me through the first fifteen years of my career and then it broadened to suffering more generally...all kinds of forms of suffering: displaced people, political violence, and so forth." Similarly, while his primary focus for many years was applying his knowledge of depression and suffering to different illnesses and disorders, the non-medical aspects of societies have become important to him as well. "Increasingly, as I've studied depression," he notes, "the economics, the morals, and even the political dimensions of depression have become increasingly interesting to me."

Kleinman's more recent work, in broad terms, focuses on what the challenges faced by a population can explain about its social life; it uses indicators of personal crisis, such as depression, suicide, and violence, to gain insight into the structural changes undergone by a society, and increasingly examines what Kleinman calls the moral code of societies. "In situations of suffering, you see elements of everyday social life that you don't otherwise see in the everyday social domain," he explains. "Everyday social life is much more dangerous than any of us let on. Our efforts are designed to deflect attention from that danger." Kleinman explains that the primary sources of this thinly veiled danger are disease, poverty, powerlessness, and political unrest, and he believes that examining such danger from an anthropological standpoint is essential for understanding the moral life of a society: "Revealed in people's responses to danger is the moral core of social life."

While Kleinman's later work on Chinese society explores many forms of suffering, he still often focuses on health care-related issues. For instance, Kleinman has studied how the Chinese elderly spend their final days in Shanghai as a way to understand the changes taking place in urban family life. As urban families increasingly have two people who work outside the home, the elderly are more often spending their last months and years in institutions, instead of dying at home as had long been the tradition. Members of the younger generation, Kleinman has found, often feel quite guilty for "shirking their responsibility." This culturally-specific sense of responsibility, which resonates with the immigrant hospital patient's shame for abandoning his ancestors' graves, is an example of what Kleinman is examining with his work on the moral codes of different societies. Many of these ideas are discussed in his 2006 book, *What Really Matters: Living the Moral Life Amidst Danger and Uncertainty.*

Kleinman has also studied epidemics in China, particularly AIDS and SARS. His interest in the 2003 outbreak of SARS included not only the experience of the patients and the health care system, but also the social stigma that developed around the disease. He was particularly interested in the transference of SARS fears from SARS itself to Chinese people across the world, which closely mirrored his own experience of the Jewish community's sense of shame during the immediate post-Holocaust era.

SOCIAL IMPACT BEYOND ACADEMIA

Kleinman is, at his core, a dedicated academic and intellectual, driven above all else by an insatiable desire to understand experience. While this kind of intellectual interest leads some academics to work with relatively little concern for the immediate applications of their research, Kleinman has managed to strike a balance in this regard. With AIDS, for instance, Kleinman has realized that one of the primary ways in which HIV is spread in China is through the rural practice of peasants selling their blood to blood-dealers, who in turn supply it to physicians and clinics. The unsterile practices of these blood-dealers have transmitted HIV to countless donors. Kleinman believes that this practice, most common in the Henan province, may account for hundreds of thousands of unreported AIDS cases in China, in addition to the million officially reported there.

Kleinman's work on mental health has also led to his involvement in numerous organizations committed to understanding mental illness, and to understanding and preventing suicide in particular. From 1993 to 1995 he directed the World Mental Health Report, which culminated with the publication of *World Mental Health*, the leading authoritative report on the subject. He also authored the 2002 Institute of Medicine report on reducing suicide in the U.S. Kleinman sits on the board of advisors of the Beijing Municipal Suicide Prevention Center, and in 1999 he served as the main consultant to the director general of the World Health Organization for the development of China's first national conference on suicide, depression, and schizophrenia. He has led conferences on the economic, political, and social consequences of both SARS and AIDS in China.

Kleinman has also had considerable impact through his teaching and his close relationship with clinical practitioners. In addition to having advised more than two hundred graduate students and post-doctoral fellows, he has directed a medical fellowship program designed to train Chinese and Southeast Asian psychiatrists. While Kleinman no longer maintains a psychiatric practice, he is frequently asked to consult on Chinese patients in Boston whose cultural and linguistic background stands in the way of their treatment.

AN ANTHROPOLOGIST WHO IS A PHYSICIAN: CAREER THOUGHTS AND REFLECTIONS

Though Kleinman's focus over the years has shifted away from clinical psychiatry and towards anthropology, he has by no means left medical questions behind, and says that the best label for him is simply "medical anthropologist": "I am an anthropologist who studies medicine—not just any anthropologist. I think there is something special about an anthropologist who is a physician." This conviction stems in part from what Kleinman regards as the unique insight into others' experience made possible by medical training. The practice of medicine is, for the physician attentive to context, anthropological from the outset:

> I've always been astonished what a privileged opportunity medicine provides for the doctor to enter the life-world of the patient, and the lived experience of suffering. To make sense of that lived experience, you really have to know the context of the person. A person comes in with a pain in their chest. You do an EKG, but it's not a heart attack. What kind of pain is it? You better know

that person, what's going on in their life. That's how you figure that one out.

Kleinman believes that, as he sought to integrate his psychiatric training with an anthropological approach to his research, finding an extraordinary mentor—in his case, Leon Eisenberg—was a pivotal and enabling experience. No less important, he says, was the eventual need to work independently of Eisenberg's influence:

> When you are young, you can't fully be on your own terms. You may not be exactly intellectually in sync with your mentor—you may have something different you want to play out. So at some point you need to establish yourself independently. For me, going to Seattle provided that critical break.

Yet Kleinman feels that many of the turns his career has taken were motivated from within, simply by the search for answers to the questions he found most pressing and the resulting need to cross disciplinary boundaries: "The form to my career was basically having, intrinsic to my own lived world, come up with a topic and then playing that topic out." His success, however, he attributes to being "pathologically obsessed" with his learning and research: "I put in hundred-hour weeks. I used to fall asleep at two o'clock in the morning routinely while I was working, and my wife would find me slumped in the chair."

However, this obsession with his work is not without cost; it is essential that he leaves other things out: "I don't watch television, I don't read people's magazines, and I don't go to the movies." And, he adds, this frame of mind might conflict with mainstream views about working life:

> I think in the younger generation there are many exceptions—there's such a commitment to going to the gym, making sure you're healthy, watching what you eat, paying a lot of attention to things that were irrelevant in my background. In my time it was, "Who cares what you smoked and what you ate and what you drank—so long as you got your work done!" And you really did get your work done.

Even Kleinman's attempts to prevent himself from being entirely absorbed by his work have been ambitious. He tells of promising himself, when he chose to give up the humanities for medicine and social science, that he would read a book a day outside of his field—a promise he kept for twenty years. He also manages occasionally to go to the opera or theater; he is, he says, very much a "standard intellectual of the European mode."

Kleinman does make time for his family. His late wife, Joan Kleinman, also studied China as a sinologist at Harvard; she died of Alzheimer's in 2011. Their daughter, Anne Kleinman, holds a Ph.D. from Yale in Chinese politics. The Kleinmans lived in Chinese societies for a total of six years; each year they traveled to China for research and teaching.

Kleinman insists that, taxing as his career may have been at times, he has "not a single regret" about how it has unfolded, and he acknowledges with a laugh that though his career path might not be for everyone, it has been perfect for him:

> I knew I was interested in both anthropology and psychiatry as early as 1970, when I went to the American Anthropological Association meeting in New York City. And as I left the building the doorman was saying to an elderly woman, "If you thought the anthropologists were bad, you should have seen the psychiatrists."

It was at this moment, Kleinman recalls, that he figured he was "going in the right direction."

Notes

1   The spiritual leader of the Lubavitch sect of Orthodox Jews, commonly known as Chabad.

2   *Patients and Healers in the Context of Culture: An Exploration of the Borderland between Anthropology, Medicine, and Psychiatry* (Berkeley: University of California Press, 1980), ix.

3   *Writing at the Margin: Discourse between Anthropology and Medicine* (Berkeley: University of California Press, 1995), 6.

4   *Rethinking Psychiatry: From Cultural Category to Personal Experience* (New York: Free Press, 1988), 7. Cited internally hereafter as *RP*.

Parts of this profile are drawn from the article "Personal Pain, National Character: Kleinman shows how individual travails reveal a society" by Alvin Powell, Harvard News Office.

Selected Books and Articles

What Really Matters: Living a Moral Life Amidst Uncertainty and Danger. New York: Oxford University Press, 2006.

Ji, Jianlin, Arthur Kleinman and Anne Becker. "Suicide in Contemporary China: A Review of China's Distinctive Suicide Demographics in their Sociocultural Context." *Harvard Review of Psychiatry* 9 (2001): 1–12.

Writing at the Margin: Discourse between Anthropology and Medicine. Berkeley: University of California Press, 1995.

Rethinking Psychiatry: From Cultural Category to Personal Experience. New York: Free Press, 1988.

The Illness Narratives: Suffering. Healing and the Human Condition. New York: Basic Books, 1988.

Social Origins of Distress and Disease: Neurasthenia, Depression and Pain in Modern China. New Haven: Yale University Press, 1984.

Patients and Healers in the Context of Culture. Berkeley: University of California Press, 1980.

"Medicine's Symbolic Reality: A Central Problem in the Philosophy of Medicine." *Inquiry* 16 (1973): 206–213.

"Toward a Comparative Study of Medical Systems." *Science, Medicine and Man* 1 (1973): 55–65.

"Some Issues for a Comparative Study of Medical Healing." *International Journal of Social Psychiatry* 19 (1973): 159–165.

"The Background and Development of Public Health in China." In *Public Health in the People's Republic of China,* edited by M.E. Wegman, T.Y. Lin, and E.F. Purcell, 1–23. New York: Josiah Macy, Jr. Foundation, 1973.

Howard K. Koh

Former Assistant Secretary for Health, U.S. Department of Health and Human Services; Former Commissioner of Public Health, Commonwealth of Massachusetts; Professor, Practice of Public Health Leadership, Harvard University

A board-certified physician in internal medicine, hematology, medical oncology and dermatology, Howard Koh has devoted his career to the integration of medical practice and public health policy. Koh has focused much of his public health work on cancer prevention and tobacco policy. In this profile, he discusses how caring for cancer patients led him to a broader commitment to public health, the struggle to fund the Tobacco Control Program in Massachusetts, and the rewards and frustrations of working at the intersection of health care and politics.

EDUCATION & TRAINING

1969–1973	B.A., Yale College
1973–1977	M.D., Yale University School of Medicine
1977–1980	Intern and Resident, Internal Medicine, Boston City Hospital
1980–1981	Fellow, Hematology-Oncology, Massachusetts General Hospital (MGH)
1981–1982	Chief Resident in Medicine, Boston City Hospital
1982–1985	Fellow in Hematology-Oncology, Chief Resident in Dermatology, MGH
1992–1995	M.P.H., Boston University School of Public Health

CAREER PATH

1985–1997	Faculty positions culminating in Professor of Dermatology, Medicine and Public Health, Boston University Schools of Medicine & Public Health
1992–1997	Director, Cancer Prevention and Control Center, BU Medical Center
1997–2003	Commissioner of Public Health, Commonwealth of Massachusetts
2004–2009	Associate Dean for Public Health Practice and Director of the Division of Public Health Practice, Harvard School of Public Health (HSPH)
2004–	Professor of the Practice of Public Health, HSPH
2009–	Assistant Secretary for Health, U.S. Dept. of Health and Human Services

SELECTED PUBLICATIONS

A selection of Koh's publications can be found at the end of this profile.

My motivations have been constant throughout my career: How can we ease and prevent human suffering? How can human beings reach their highest attainable standard of health? Good health is such a gift. The joy of public health is helping each person reach his or her full potential for health, whatever that potential may be.

—Howard Koh

It was not just a love for science and a desire to cure disease that attracted Howard Koh to medicine and public health, but rather a broader commitment to the challenge of helping people stay healthy. This motivation has led Koh into a variety of academic and governmental roles: he has served as a professor at Boston University and the Harvard School of Public Health; volunteered as a public advocate in a landmark struggle to fund Massachusetts's Tobacco Control Program with a tax on tobacco; served as the Massachusetts commissioner of public health from 1997 to 2003; and in 2009 was unanimously confirmed by the Senate as the assistant secretary for health in the U.S. Department of Health and Human Services. In this role, Koh is the top advisor on public health issues to Secretary Kathleen Sebelius and oversees the public health agencies within HHS.

Koh, a Korean-American, is the eldest son of an immigrant family. His decision to go to medical school was in part a reflection of his family's cultural values: "Becoming a physician is considered by many to be a marker that an immigrant family has become fully established in American society." Koh also sees connections between his parents' passion for democracy and human rights and his own desire to prevent human suffering:

My late father was the former ambassador to the United States from South Korea. He and my mother journeyed to this country in search of the American dream. Their passions focused on democracy, education, family and human rights. So in hindsight I developed my passion for public health and justice from my parents, even though neither of them was oriented toward medicine or science.

Koh's family's values were not the only factor motivating him during the challenging years of medical school and residency. Koh also attributes his drive to become a physician to an interest in working with people and a strong personal desire to have a broad impact on society.

A PUBLIC HEALTH EDUCATION

Koh attended Yale College, where he was president of the Yale Glee Club: "Singing lifts the human soul and creates harmony in a magical way—it's great for public health!" After college, he enrolled in Yale Medical School. It was not until his internship and residency at Boston City Hospital, however, that his education in public health began. After medical school Koh was eager to gain exposure to what he considered the real world by training in a major urban hospital. He believed that Boston would be a good place to do this, and relocated there to start his residency. At Boston City Hospital he was exposed to the impoverished, the uninsured, and those wrestling with substance abuse and tobacco addictions. Koh found himself in a veritable crash course in public health, and he recalls learning far more than just the medicine behind patient care: "I saw that problems existed in a social context, that there was an array of forces impacting people's health well beyond the biology of their disease."

During his medical training, Koh achieved board certification in four fields: internal medicine, hematology, medical oncology, and dermatology. His experience in oncology had an especially strong impact on his understanding of the relationship between medicine and society. The main approach to cancer at the time was to place patients in clinical trials to test new treatment methods, while less attention was given to preventive care that could change the behaviors and conditions causing cancer in the first place. As Koh treated more and more cancer patients, he became deeply frustrated: "Patient after patient died under my care from cancer that could have been prevented. I was alternately outraged and overwhelmingly anguished. I was convinced that there were better ways to keep people healthy." Koh began to view medical problems, especially diseases such as lung cancer and melanoma, a form of skin cancer, within the context of broader societal problems.

Motivated by this experience to integrate public health policy more closely with medical practice, Koh joined Boston University's faculty in 1985 to co-instruct a course called "Cancer Prevention as a Public Health Problem":

> I had the wonderful opportunity of serving as a faculty member in both the medical school and the public health school. A colleague of mine invited me to teach a cancer prevention course, and help develop a cancer prevention agenda for the school. That was a tremendous opportunity because at the time cancer prevention was not a well recognized field. Cynics said such a field didn't even exist. My colleague's invitation to join her at BU allowed me

to contribute to an evolving field and develop the area. That was a very crucial part of my public health evolution.

Initially, the cancer prevention curriculum primarily addressed issues such as tobacco control. Koh helped to make melanoma detection, prevention, and education a part of the field as well, and it has since grown to include chemoprevention, nutrition and many other areas.

During Koh's tenure at Boston University, he established the Cancer Prevention and Control Center at Boston University Medical Center. He worked in multiple fields, serving as professor of dermatology, medicine, and public health: "The work was interdisciplinary, while overlapping two schools and a number of departments. I've always enjoyed staying very broad and interdisciplinary in my perspective. So it was invigorating and exciting."

Developing the field of cancer prevention was not without its difficulties. Koh's initiatives involved joint efforts by the school of public health and the medical school, and required broad acceptance by diverse groups:

> Interdisciplinary work is also often difficult because one attempts to forge consensus in collaboration with multiple parties. What was ultimately exhilarating though was the feeling of working toward a common goal and sharing a common mission.

Although Koh enjoyed working at the school of public health, he found it disconcerting that he was teaching students who were working toward a degree that he himself had not received. Koh therefore became a student in the very program he had been helping to teach, and began working towards a Masters of Public Health:

> That education granted me a broader foundation in public health—it was fascinating. It provided me with a more formal, multi-disciplinary way of viewing health issues because the medical model is usually very specialized. In the medical model, one studies diseases or organs or very narrow parts of the medical universe. In public health, one considers issues in their entirety and looks at the impact of policy, sociocultural factors, education and behavior as well as biology.

INTRODUCTION TO THE PUBLIC ARENA

Koh entered the public arena in 1992 when he became involved in efforts to support a special cigarette tax ballot initiative that would fund a new Massachusetts Tobacco Control Program. As a volunteer with the American Cancer Society, Koh became a public advocate for the initiative, acting as part of a coalition that ultimately succeeded. Massachusetts became the second state in the country to implement a tobacco tax for the purpose of establishing a statewide tobacco control program. It was an eye-opening experience for Koh:

> I was living the political process. Passing the initiative petition was a huge challenge because we were fighting the powerful tobacco industry. To actually work in the trenches through this historic chapter was my first experience living public health in the public arena.

Two years after completing his M.P.H., Koh was appointed commissioner of public health for the state of Massachusetts. The appointment came as a complete surprise:

> I didn't know Governor Weld personally. I'd never thought of the possibility of being commissioner before being notified that my name had joined a list of twenty candidates. Then, after several months, the list was narrowed down to three or four candidates. Governor Weld interviewed all of the finalists. He and I shared a certain chemistry in that interview. He was very interested in not only health and government, but also in my background as a son in an immigrant family. He asked many questions about my parents, especially my late father. So we ended up talking about the immigrant experience and my parents' journey to this country.

During the selection process Koh became increasingly excited about the possibility of serving as commissioner: "I understood that these opportunities don't come about very often." When the time came, Koh accepted the appointment without hesitation.

As commissioner of public health, Koh was directly responsible for the oversight of three thousand employees at the Department of Public Health, and through them for the health issues affecting the entire state: "I was honored and also extremely humbled to be asked to uphold the public health of six million people." For Koh, the challenges of medical school, residency, a career in academia, and public health training paled in comparison to the massive responsibilities of serving as commissioner. These responsibilities included planning for and responding to threats such as HIV, cancer, substance abuse, bio-terrorism and outbreaks of infectious disease, as well as handling requests from the media, elected officials, advocates, patients and providers.

Koh's focus as commissioner spanned a wide range of diseases and populations. He developed initiatives to increase organ donation and newborn screenings, decrease emergency room overcrowding and homeless deaths, and improve interpreter services in emergency rooms. He supervised the implementation of programs for suicide prevention, AIDS treatment and prevention, and substance abuse services. He placed renewed emphasis on minority populations, the homeless, the disabled, and uninsured youths as a means to eliminate health disparities. Under his guidance, the Massachusetts Tobacco Control Program gained national recognition as a model for reducing cigarette consumption and preventing addiction. After September 11th and the threat of anthrax that followed, bioterrorism preparedness became a key issue on his agenda as well.

Serving as commissioner gave Koh a new perspective on many fundamental issues:

> I now have the privilege to reflect on what I've experienced. Public service helped me think about the purpose of society, and our collective responsibility to people in need. I look at the world differently now. It was never easy, but still a great honor and an extraordinary life experience.

By the end of Koh's tenure, the state had risen in public health rankings to the third healthiest in the nation. The national ranking evaluated statewide health outcomes by indicators such as smoking prevalence, infant mortality, immunizations, and teen births: "It was thrilling to see data indicating that outcomes were improved and suffering was being prevented. That's what it's all about." He attributes the rise in rankings to the tremendous efforts and commitment of the public health community in the state.

Although Koh enjoyed his work as commissioner it was not without its frustrations. The position involved a constant battle for funding, which he attributes to the low priority given to disease prevention on the political agenda. As the fiscal climate changed and Massachusetts faced a massive budget deficit, commitment to public health waned even further. After his departure, competing issues gained priority in the new administration's agenda, and funding of disease prevention and health promotion initiatives was curtailed. In 2003, Massachusetts fell to fifth in the nation—its first decline in over a decade. Many attributed Massachusetts's change in score primarily to decreased support for public health care, measured as a ratio of public expenditure to low-income population. To Koh's disappointment, many of the groundbreaking health initiatives developed during his tenure lost their funding. But he remains resolute about the future: "We will and we must rebuild public health—there is simply no other option."

RETURNING TO ACADEMIA

Koh remained in his position as commissioner through the administrations of Governor Weld and his two successors, Governor Paul Cellucci and Governor Jane Swift. After six years in the position Koh stepped down, shortly after the start of the Mitt Romney administration. At the time of his departure, U.S. Senator Edward Kennedy noted that he had been a "tireless advocate for improving our public health care system and increasing public health research."

After leaving the Massachusetts Department of Public Health, Koh joined the Harvard School of Public Health as associate dean for public health practice and professor of health policy and management and was subsequently named the Harvey V. Fineberg Professor of the Practice of Public Health, a position created in honor of Harvey Fineberg, the previous dean of HSPH.[1] While at Harvard Koh served as the principal investigator of multiple research grants related to community-based participatory research, cancer disparities affecting underserved and minority populations, tobacco control and emergency preparedness. He was also director of the Harvard School of Public Health Center for Public Health Preparedness, which promotes education about bioterrorism, pandemic influenza, and other emerging health threats. In these positions, Koh brought his real-world experience to Harvard students and faculty, and set his sights on finding new ways to educate aspiring public health leaders.

While at Harvard, in addition to performing his academic and administrative duties, Koh continued to care for patients directly. In fact, Koh has cared for patients throughout his career. During his years as public health commissioner, state regulations did not permit him to see patients during typical work hours, so instead he did so during evening clinics. He believes this experience has been extremely valuable for his work in health care policy:

> First of all, many patients still depend on me to care for them. Also, I had trained for many years to develop subspecialty expertise, and want to retain these medical skills. It is also a way to ground me—I had the incredible opportunity to think about public health issues not only from the broadest perspective as a health commissioner, but also from my individual perspective as a doctor taking care of patients. I never forget that while caring for patients, I am also committed to doing all that I can so that people won't become patients in the first place.

JOINING THE OBAMA ADMINISTRATION

In 2009, President Obama asked Koh to join his administration as assistant secretary for health in the department of health and human services (just a few days after his brother, Harold Koh, was invited to join the Obama administration as the top lawyer at the State Department). Koh was subsequently unanimously confirmed by the Senate in June, 2009. In this position, Koh serves as the top advisor on public health issues to the secretary of health and human services and oversees the twelve public health agencies of HHS, including the National Institutes of Health, the Food and Drug Administration, and the Center for Medicare and Medicaid Services. In this role, Koh has continued to work on a wide range of public health issues, perhaps most notably on tobacco control: Koh chairs HHS's Tobacco Control Implementation Steering Committee, newly established in 2011. He has also worked to communicate with the public about HHS's programs and goals, publishing in both professional journals and mass media outlets like the *Huffington Post*.

Note

1   A profile of Harvey Fineberg can be found on page 186.

SELECTED PUBLICATIONS

"The End of The 'Tobacco and Cancer' Century." *Journal of the National Cancer Institute*. 1999 Apr 21; 91(8): 660–661.

Koh HK, Walker DK. "The Role of State Health Agencies in Cancer Prevention and Control: Lessons Learned from Massachusetts." *Cancer Epidemiology, Biomarkers and Prevention*. 2003 Mar; 12(3):261s–268s.

Alpert HR, Koh HK, Connolly GN. "After the Master Settlement Agreement: Targeting and Exposure of Youth to Magazine Tobacco Advertising." *Health Affairs*. 2008 Nov–Dec; 27(6):503–12.

Koh HK, Sebelius K. "Ending the Tobacco Epidemic." *Journal of the American Medical Association*. 2012 Aug 22/29; 308(8):767–768.

Paul F. Levy

Former President and Chief Executive Officer, Beth Israel Deaconess Medical Center

As the CEO of a large academic medical center for almost a decade Paul Levy became widely known for his "Running a Hospital" blog, in which he openly shared many of the trials and tribulations faced by his institution. In this profile Levy describes how he was motivated to pursue widely varied positions across his career, and how his non-clinical background gives him unique insight into how he can manage his staff and resources with creativity and determination. Levy also tells of the challenges faced by a leader entering the industry from the outside—and of the advantages that perspective can provide.

EDUCATION & TRAINING

1974	B.S., MIT (Economics and Urban Studies & Planning) and M.S., MIT (City Planning)

CAREER PATH

1974–1978	Deputy Director, Massachusetts Energy Policy Office
1978–1979	Commissioner and Chairman, Massachusetts Department of Public Utilities
1979–1981	Director, Arkansas Department of Energy
1981–1983	Senior Consultant, Economics and Technology, Inc.
1983–1987	Chairman, Massachusetts Department of Public Utilities
1987–1992	Executive Director, Massachusetts Water Resources Authority
1992–1995	Visiting Lecturer, MIT, Department of Urban Studies and Planning
1995–1998	Adjunct Professor of Environmental Policy, MIT
1998–2002	Executive Dean for Administration, Harvard Medical School
2002–2011	President & Chief Executive Officer, Beth Israel Deaconess Medical Center
2013–	Senior Advisor, Lax Sebenius LLC

FURTHER INFORMATION

Not Running a Hospital: www.runningahospital.blogspot.com

Beth Israel Deaconess Medical Center: www.bidmc.harvard.edu

SELECTED PUBLICATIONS:

Goal Play!: Leadership Lessons from the Soccer Field (2012)

How a Blog Held Off the Most Powerful Union in America (2013)

I don't plan ahead. I really don't—if you want to be someone who does interesting things in interesting fields, you have to be opportunistic about what comes along. I have three criteria: it has to be a place where I'm providing a public service, it has to be a place where I'm learning something new, and it has to be a place where I can have fun, which has a lot to do with the personal interactions. Beyond that, I don't care.

—*Paul Levy*

For Paul Levy, being an outsider has often just been a way to plunge into the thick of things. When he was offered the position of CEO of a financially struggling Beth Israel Deaconess Medical Center, he was given the chance to defer his appointment until a report on restructuring the hospital's management had been released. Instead, he chose to start the job early in order to see that report from the staff's point of view. After guiding the hospital through its financial crisis, he remained CEO for almost a decade, overseeing the activities of its 4,800-person staff. During this time he became widely known for his blog, "Running a Hospital," in which he regularly shared his thoughts and insights into the issues he and his hospital were facing.

FIRST MOTIVATIONS

Levy has always been interested in systems that provide basic infrastructure or social services on at least the regional level. This general interest is the principle underlying what may at first glance seem a disjointed career path, embracing sectors as different as energy and health care. In moving between such disparate sectors, Levy has successfully adapted to the technological and organizational challenges specific to each.

Levy has always had a bent towards public service: "I would not have been interested in a company that made cruise missiles, for example," he points out. This influence, he believes, most likely originated during his teen years in the 1960s:

> Basic social services, basic human services—I care about them. This goes back to Jack Kennedy. When you grow up listening to him giving speeches saying, "What are you going to do for the world and your country?" you frame your life around what you are going to do for the world and your country.

Infused with this sense of responsibility, Levy was first captivated during his undergraduate education at the Massachusetts Institute of Technology by systems involving energy and water management and distribution. He spent his first years of undergraduate work as a double major in economics and urban studies & planning, studying the intricate workings of these systems. Towards the end of his studies, though, he shifted his primary focus to energy—just when, in 1973, the OPEC oil embargo was going into effect: "I was interested in a nice mix of engineering and economics and societal issues, and, with the oil embargo, there it was."

Before finishing his undergraduate coursework, Levy went straight into MIT's master's program in city planning, and wrote a thesis on electricity demand in the New England area. At the same time, he served as a research assistant in the MIT Energy Laboratory, where he did research about the economic implications of energy and transportation policy. He also worked on the governor's Energy Task Force, helping to prepare a plan to counter the effects of the oil embargo.

EARLY CAREER CHOICES

Immediately after completing his master's degree, Levy accepted a position as deputy director of the Massachusetts Energy Policy Office. He also spent a year as commissioner and chairman of the Massachusetts Department of Public Utilities, and then moved to Arkansas for two years to take a position as the director of the Arkansas Department of Energy. This was followed by time spent as a consultant at a private firm that did work on telecommunications regulation and management, and a four-year stint as chairman of the Department of Public Utilities back in Massachusetts.

In 1987, Levy accepted an offer to become the executive director of the Massachusetts Water Resources Authority. In this position, he managed a staff of over 1,500 people and an annual budget of over $270 million. He also organized such projects as a ten-year wastewater and water system construction program, a demand-management program that ultimately reduced water consumption by fifteen percent over the three years he oversaw it, and the well-known Boston Harbor Cleanup project, now hailed by many as a remarkable success in pollution control. The harbor cleanup is, to date, one of the largest projects of its kind in the world.

Speaking about his time spent in this and other energy-related fields, Levy points to the attitude that has made it possible for him to make such sweeping career changes:

> At MIT I took engineering courses, so I know the difference between amps and volts, but my view is that you don't have to be a technical expert in the field in order to choose to get involved in it, particularly in the managerial

capacity. You have to be curious about it to learn what you need to know, but ultimately you don't want to do the job of the specialists. In fact, you want to retain a bit of a point of view of the generalist because you're trying to bring in insights from other places.

He also notes that the ability to change an industry often requires a different outlook and a different set of skills than working within it during times of stability:

It's hard not to get embedded in the culture if you stay in one industry for years, and that's a serious problem, particularly in an industry that's going through structural changes. Those who succeeded when an industry was going through a structural change were those who were comfortable with ambiguity and who were willing to take risks—both personal risks in terms of their career and institutional risks with regard to the direction of their organization.

After more then ten years of dealing with the often tumultuous field of energy and utilities, Levy had come to expect, and to thrive upon, the unexpected. This flexibility would, in the end, help him to navigate the even larger transitions on the horizon.

BIG TRANSITIONS: ENERGY TO HEALTH CARE

After spending five years at the Water Resources Authority, Levy worked as an independent consultant advising on energy, telecommunications and water industry concerns. He was also a professor of environmental policy at MIT, where he drew on his expertise to help prepare the next generation of professionals and scientists for their own careers. Levy remembers the time he spent as a professor at MIT as one of the most rewarding experiences of his career to date:

Teaching gave me the greatest satisfaction. I love it. You have these really bright kids and you work with them, and mentor them, and create long-lasting relationships. I'm still in touch with a lot of the kids from there. I remember when I was at MIT teaching—I literally remember walking into 77 Mass Ave., looking up at the columns thinking, "I can't believe they're letting me do this." It was such a kick and such a privilege.

Then, in 1998, he was offered the opportunity to make his biggest transition yet. His friend and colleague Martha Wineberg introduced him to Joseph Martin, the dean of Harvard Medical School. Wineberg decided to connect the two because Levy had voiced his fascination with health care:

Dean Martin and I hit it off, and he said, "Why don't you come join me as dean for administration?" and I said, "How about because I don't know anything about medicine?" He said, "Well that's perfect, because I want someone with a fresh perspective."

This would be an almost unheard of transition—Levy, in contrast with almost all of the other administrators in well-known medical schools, had no medical training whatsoever when he was offered the job. Yet his desire to explore new challenges, increase his knowledge of different systems, and bring fresh perspective to enduring problems convinced him he could make the transition work for both him and his employer. In fact, Levy believes that physician-managers are not always the best choice for a medical school or health care organization:

> I think it's the unusual physician who can manage an organization in this kind of environment. It's not that they should be excluded, it's just that if you look at the profile of a successful academic medical person and what they've been rewarded for professionally through their lives, they've not been rewarded for teamwork or interpersonal skills. It's just not valued by their profession.

Another factor that made Levy feel capable of managing the organizational aspects of his new position was Harvard Medical School's unique relationship to the hospitals:

> Harvard Medical School doesn't own any hospitals, unlike most medical schools, and its relationship with its affiliates is collegiate. My job as dean of administration was to be chief operating officer of the medical school, but also to be this liaison with the hospital on business matters. In that capacity, I got to know a lot of people at Partners, CareGroup, Mass Eye and Ear, Children's, and all the other affiliates.

Levy found that many of the business aspects of the job were already familiar to him, and working at the Harvard Medical School was an excellent opportunity to try his hand at the medical side of business that he was interested in. As executive dean for administration at the medical school, Levy's responsibilities included making decisions about everything from facilities management to information systems needs, organizing joint programs with affiliated Boston-area hospitals, and allocating an annual budget of $300 million to the hospitals' teaching and research programs.

Always anxious to expand his knowledge in an environment where he could contribute to societal goals, Levy found that he learned quickly and enjoyed the work. He found his new field so compelling that in 2002, when the opportunity arose for him to serve as CEO of Beth Israel Deaconess Medical Center (BIDMC)—one of Harvard's three major academic medical centers—he decided to accept the position.

A NEW PERSPECTIVE ON HEALTH CARE: BETH ISRAEL

Having proven his abilities at Harvard Medical School, Levy found his colleagues were quite willing to overlook the fact that he had no medical or health care background. With his first few years in health care behind him, Levy offers some perspective on how challenging it may or may not be to work in an industry where one has little background:

> The medical knowledge could, of course, be valuable—just like in the phone business it helped that I knew how switches work. That being said, so far nothing's come up of a medical matter that has been so complex that after a few minutes I don't understand it. We all took biology; we all live in the world and read. If someone is trying to slip something by and you ask the question "Explain to me how it works," you'll know pretty soon if they're really not doing anything.

In situations requiring a technical knowledge of medicine, Levy appreciatively depends on the hospital's chief operating officer, a physician, to ask the right questions: "Just give me someone in a position of high authority who really understands how blood works. I can read the medical evidence as well as anybody, but there's some value in that medical knowledge. My COO brings a lot to the table in those discussions."

It is fortunate for both BIDMC and Levy that he was not apprehensive about his transition, for it would bring challenges apart from those involved in a large-scale career change. When Levy came to BIDMC in 2002, the hospital was undergoing an intense financial and management crisis. Not unaccustomed to this type of rescue operation—"I'm attracted to institutions in crisis," he says—Levy was not put off by the fact that the Hunter Group, a consulting firm that restructures hospital management, had been brought in to BIDMC. In fact, one of Levy's first demands to BIDMC's board of directors was that he begin work before the Hunter report came out. This was an unusual request from a person taking over a failing organization, since he could have taken the position after the report had been submitted, which would have shielded him from any blame:

> I told them I needed to be there by the first week of January, before the report came out, or I didn't want the job. And they said, "Why? Don't you want the report to come out first?" And I said, "No, we need to frame it so people in the organization understand its purpose and so that we can use that report to properly motivate folks to make changes, to draw value from what the consultant says." I said to them that the reason for that is that in six months, after this is all over and things are working again, we want the staff to be invested in the solutions so that they own the place.

After being offered the position of CEO, Levy found out that, without the BIDMC board's knowledge, the Massachusetts Attorney General, Tom Reilly, was pushing for the hospital to be sold as a private organization. This would have ended the non-profit hospital's affiliation with Harvard Medical

School, and put it at a major risk for a number of structural and management changes:

> So imagine this: the BIDMC search committee goes ahead and picks me in late December. They say, "We think you should go talk to the chairman of the CareGroup board [the head of the health system that owns BIDMC] because he needs to tell you some things." So I go and see John Hammill and he says, "You need to understand that the AG wants to sell this place." First time I had heard it! Imagine going through the search process, and no one's mentioned this! So I said to him, "Look, I don't want the job under those conditions. I want the job to save the hospital, not so sell it." And he said that I had to go talk to the attorney general.

Levy did just that, and he and Reilly decided they were willing to take a chance on Levy's management skills. With a plan in place and frequent, periodic reports to the attorney general, the agreement was set, all within several days of Levy's start as chief executive.

Shortly after taking control of the hospital Levy made yet another unorthodox move, one that testifies to his democratic style of leadership: he released the Hunter report on BIDMC's internal website:

> Someone on the staff asked how they could see the report, and I said, "Oh, we'll just put it up on the website." I figured that if one person wants to see it, maybe several hundred others do, too. One of the things I needed to do was engage people in understanding the nature of the problem and the potential solutions. We had just spent a lot of money on this consulting report which did that analysis. Why wouldn't I share that?

Levy believes that much of what enabled the hospital to succeed under his management was his status as an outsider: he was not "entrenched as the top management" at the hospital during the time the report was being made, and "didn't have the problem of it reflecting poorly on him." Levy had no preexisting obligations or loyalties to any one party or perspective, nor did he have "favorite" methods for fulfilling his obligations to the hospital. Levy notes that in his earliest months at BIDMC, his flexibility and willingness to try every good idea that came along helped him to discover lasting solutions for the organization's financial problems:

> I would say that to people: "We're going to try twenty things and if nineteen work and one doesn't we're going to throw out the one. If nineteen don't work and one does, we'll throw out the nineteen and we'll start over again." I was agnostic as far as what would work and what wouldn't work. I had certain gut feelings, but until you try, you don't know.

BIDMC achieved much under Levy's management. In addition to avoiding receivership and becoming profitable again, the hospital embarked upon a series of quality and safety initiatives as well as expansion of several of its departments and services. Levy believes that BIDMC remains the "friendliest of all the Harvard hospitals," and that the hospital's culture is felt by all who interact with it. Still, he laments that Massachusetts General Hospital is sometimes seen as the premier hospital in Boston:

> We see Harvard medical students who come here for clerkships and love it, but who choose to match for their residencies at MGH because they're told that, professionally, that will be better for them in their life. It's not true, but it's part of the mystique. But there is a warmth and friendliness to the place that's really palpable. It's the old joke: A guy flies into Logan Airport and he's sick and needs to go to the hospital. He says to the cabdriver, "I need to go to a hospital, where should I go?" and the cabbie says, "Well, Mass General's the best hospital in the world." And the guy says, "Well take me there," and the cabbie says, "Nah, you don't want to go there. You want to go to the BIDMC; it's the best hospital in Boston."

ORGANIZATIONAL MISSION AND FINDING MEANING IN ONE'S WORK

Although a desire to be involved with an organization that provided a public service attracted him to BIDMC, Levy points out that the non-profit nature of the hospital was unimportant to him. He recalls an anecdote about Aaron Feuerstein, who continued to pay his employees despite the fact that his mill had burned down days before Christmas in 1995, as an example:

> The fact that something is for-profit doesn't mean that it is not good to society. For example, at Malden Mills, Aaron Feuerstein is making fabric. But if you ask him, he says, "I'm not just making fabric here. I'm providing a livelihood for so many thousands of people in Lawrence, Mass. Part of my job is to be a community servant for those people and I do it by making a profit selling Polartec." And I could do that, too, if I found it interesting as a field.

Levy believes that the primary responsibility he had as CEO was to the hospital's patients and their families. Although his daily responsibilities were largely administrative, he focused on making decisions with the ultimate goal of improving care. In this way, despite the fact that he had no medical training, he felt as if he had a direct impact on the patients in the hospital:

> I visit patients and I actually do clinical care—not as a doctor, but when the president of the hospital walks into your room, it makes people feel better. I hadn't realized the fringe benefit of the job. It's very nice. Truthfully, there are times when I'm talking to a surgeon and I say, "Gee, I wish I could do that," but I never could go to medical school at this point. I could have back in college, but then I wouldn't have had the chance to do other things.

For Levy, all the "other things" he has done came together in his job as a hospital CEO. For instance, he explains that he used the teaching skills he gained at MIT almost every day at BIDMC:

> The whole job here is teaching people who don't see themselves as students. That's the wonderful subtlety. I help the experts here solve the problems the hospital is facing, which means that I need to teach them a whole new construct for what they do. They're making day-to-day decisions that could be at odds with where we need to take the hospital. These are the most well-intentioned people in the world, but they are trained in a certain way. I'm not going to come in and tell them how to do heart surgery, but I am going to tell them that we're doing heart surgery in a certain way, and from a business point of view, it isn't very responsive to the marketplace, or it isn't making the best use of equipment or people. My job is to create an environment where I can teach them to solve that problem so that it works for them, works for the hospital and works for the patients.

BEING THE COACH

In the corner of Levy's large, neat and elegantly simple office sits a bright turquoise director's chair with the word "COACH" emblazoned on it in bold letters. The chair was given to him for his role coaching the girls' soccer team on which his daughter used to play, but its place in his office symbolizes the continuity of that role in his life inside and outside of his work. He explains, "People would probably call me a professional administrator or a professional manager or something like that…but I don't think of myself as that." In all of his many roles, Levy has viewed himself as the person responsible for assisting others to do the best work that they can.

Levy uses the definition to create commonality between the seemingly disparate stages of his working life. When asked whether he ever worried about not having a formal trade—like medicine or law—he reflects: "I used to worry about not having a trade when I was younger. I used to think, 'gee, shouldn't I have a trade?'" Levy then pauses, and his eyes inadvertently glance over at the chair: "And then I came to realize… my trade is being the coach."

AFTERWORD

In 2010, after eight years at the helm of BIDMC with the hospital firmly in the black, Levy stepped down and focused mostly on writing. His blog, which by then had become one of the most widely read in health care, was continued under the title "Not Running a Hospital." He engaged his wide readership in debates on subjects ranging from the quality improvement movement to the passage of Obamacare to the politics of the insurance market in Boston. He also wrote two books. The first, entitled *Goal Play! Leadership Lessons from the Soccer Field*, discussed the wide range of insights

Levy had gathered from his leadership experiences, ranging from coaching girls soccer to leading large institutions. The book won widespread praise for its inspirational ideas. The second, entitled *How a Blog Held Off the Most Powerful Union in America*, focused on the power of social media to help organizations communicate their message to the public.

James J. Mongan

Former President and Chief Executive Officer, Partners HealthCare System, Inc.

A trained physician, James Mongan assumed across his career a variety of roles within the health care industry, focusing his attention on policy and administration rather than clinical endeavors. He spent eleven years in Washington, working in both the legislative and executive branches, and then spent more than twenty years as a hospital executive. In this profile, he discusses how he balanced his interest in medicine with his passion for politics and policy, his decision to leave clinical practice, and how his positions across the public and private sectors have provided him with a platform for involvement in policy.

EDUCATION & TRAINING

1959–1962	A.B., University of California at Berkeley
1963–1967	M.D., Stanford Medical School
1967–1968	Rotating Internship, Kaiser Foundation Hospital, San Francisco, CA

CAREER PATH

1968–1970	Medical Officer, U.S. Public Health Service
1970–1977	Professional Staff member, U.S. Senate Finance Committee
1977–1979	Deputy Assistant Secretary for Health Policy, Department of Health, Education and Welfare
1979–1981	Assistant Surgeon General & Associate Director for Health and Human Resources, The White House
1981–1996	Executive Director, Truman Medical Center, Kansas City, MO
1987–1996	Dean, University of Missouri-Kansas City School of Medicine
1996–2009	Professor of Health Care Policy and of Social Medicine, Harvard Medical School
1996–2002	President, Massachusetts General Hospital
2002–2009	President and CEO, Partners HealthCare System, Inc.

ADDITIONAL INFORMATION

Partners HealthCare, Inc.: www.partners.org

Massachusetts General Hospital: www.mgh.harvard.edu

I spent endless hours thinking about what I wanted to do, and where I wanted to land and all that sort of stuff—planning careers. I think I learned as I went forward that it was this balance between preparation and chance. I think I got a little more relaxed about it, and went with the flow a bit more.

— *James Mongan*

As a young physician in the Public Health Service, James Mongan was on the verge of turning away from involvement with government and returning to private practice. A timely call from Washingon gave him the chance to influence Medicare policy in its formative stages, though, and Mongan couldn't turn down the opportunity. Similarly charged decisions about where he could most make a difference have guided his career ever since, leading him first into and then out of government. His career culminated in his 2002 appointment as president and CEO of Boston-based Partners HealthCare System, the parent organization of both Massachusetts General Hospital and Brigham and Women's Hospital. In this role, Mongan has shaped the policy of one of the nation's most prestigious health care organizations. Through this role, as well as through his role as chairman of Boston's chamber of commerce, he was instrumental in negotiating passage of the landmark Massachusetts universal health care coverage legislation. The Partners System includes primary and specialty care physicians, community care centers, six hospitals, a teaching affiliation with Harvard Medical School, as well as joint ventures with the Dana-Farber Cancer Institute and the Harvard Clinical Research Institute. Mongan retired from this role in 2009. When he died of cancer in 2011, he was warmly remembered by others in the profession as a brilliant colleague and a leader in the fight to cover the uninsured.

GOVERNMENT AND MEDICINE

"I started as an undifferentiated stem cell in college," Mongan explains, noting that it was political science and not medicine that he planned to pursue at the time. His attraction to medicine was developed when his father—a city official—said to him: "Well, you could be a doctor and then you could mess around a bit." Mongan considered the suggestion, realizing that medicine might be a pragmatic way to support himself while exploring his interest in politics. Concluding that medicine would provide a solid backup if his political aspirations withered, he enrolled in Stanford Medical School in 1963.

This choice would have long-term effects on Mongan's career. His interests in government were now defined in the context of medicine. As he worked his way through medical school, he became increasingly oriented towards making an impact through health care policy. This goal led him to choose to complete his medical internship at the Kaiser Foundation Hospital in San Francisco:

> I was hedging my bets right out of medical school. I went to Kaiser for my internship, because I needed an internship, but I wanted to stay involved in government. And I asked myself where I could learn something about how health systems work at the same time—a combination of the two.

Mongan's internship at Kaiser, from 1967 to 1968, took place during the early enactment of Medicare and Medicaid, which had been passed into law in 1965 and went into effect in 1966. Although he started his internship with a desire to learn more about health systems, the political climate steered his interest towards national health insurance for the poor and elderly. Since Mongan also had to fulfill his military obligation at this time, he pursued his interest by joining the Public Health Service (PHS) in Denver in 1968:

> I was looking for ways to be a doctor and also play around with politics—going into the PHS enabled me to do this. I had a hand in picking my assignment to Denver. I wanted to get a look at what government and medicine was. Those two years were another type of cut-point because they gave me a view that there was life in government and medicine.

Though Mongan's assignment from the PHS was to travel around the western mountain states and consult with hospitals on meeting the newly imposed Medicare standards, his role was hazily defined: "I didn't know what they wanted me to do, so I was basically doing what I wanted to do." Mongan therefore focused on migrant health programs, and ended up learning a lot about the relationship between government and medicine and medical politics—something he recalls feeling both attracted and repelled by. This disillusionment led him to decide to return to residency, "going down that traditional path of, 'oh, I'll be a doctor and then I'll fool around with government and medicine.'" Before he had the chance to act on this decision, however, a new opportunity presented itself.

A CROSSROADS ON THE HILL

After two years in Denver with the PHS, Mongan had what he calls his "first stroke of substantial luck." He was offered a position as a professional staff member on the Senate Finance Committee. His work in the PHS made him precisely what the committee was looking for: a physician who understood Medicare. Despite his belief at the time that the Senate Finance Committee was a "noted conservative bastion where everything was either killed or choked to death," Mongan still did not want to turn down the position. He was attracted by the idea of holding such a high position in Washington at his age, but more important was his interest in the committee's jurisdiction over Medicaid, Medicare and health insurance. The staff position gave him significant influence over issues that had become very important to him.

Mongan's background in the PHS and his experience with hospital standards and processes, like utilization review, allowed him to implement a very detailed set of changes to Medicare, the first major revisions since the law's passage in 1965. The legislation he worked on included Medicare policies on drugs, for which his medical knowledge proved important. The perspective offered by his experience as an M.D. working for PHS also led to the legislation that he considers to be among his most significant interventions in health care policy—the End-Stage Renal Disease (ESRD) Entitlement Provisions of 1972, which extended Medicare coverage to patients suffering from chronic renal failure and thus requiring dialysis. Mongan is humble about his accomplishments, but this is one piece of legislation that he feels particularly proud of: "The End-stage Renal Disease Act under Medicare is one I can almost say honestly wouldn't have happened if I wasn't there."

Choosing Between Policy and Clinical Practice

During Mongan's first year in Washington, he tried to stay involved with clinical work by attending rounds at George Washington Hospital. As the year went on, he found that important meetings on the Hill took place at the same time that he was supposed to be at rounds. "I couldn't do it all," Mongan concedes, and he decided that his involvement with national politics outweighed the rewards of clinical practice at the time: "I was wrapped up enough in the excitement of Capitol Hill and what was going on that I didn't have time to miss clinical work." Even after choosing to forgo clinical medicine for policy, Mongan still considered returning to clinical work for a number of years. Slowly this option faded away, until he realized that he had unwittingly passed the point where that was a possibility:

> I remember thinking in my second or third year in the Senate that that was my out—that when it stopped being fun I could either do something there or I could go back to the clinic. But by the time I was in Washington six or seven years, I realized that I was really into what I was doing—and I realized that I would not be able to move back towards the clinic.

Changing Administrations and Changing Jobs

After Mongan's seventh year in the Senate Finance Committee, Jimmy Carter took office as president. The Carter administration, intent on pushing forward a national health plan, was looking for people to join the Department of Health, Education, and Welfare (HEW) to research and develop potential options. "It was natural to turn to the Hill staff," Mongan explains, "and I was asked to become the HEW assistant secretary for health policy and special assistant to the secretary for national health insurance." After two years in this position, he was again a candidate for promotion. This time he moved to the White House, where he served as assistant surgeon general and associate director for health and human resources for the domestic policy staff. He acted as one of the major architects of the Carter Health Plan along with Karen Davis (page 152), transforming the president's ideas into legislative, regulatory and budgetary programs and then working with Congress to get the programs passed.

Since Mongan's position was a political appointment, it ended with the Carter administration when Ronald Reagan took office in 1981. He had little interest in his most apparently viable option—staying in Washington as a lobbyist. He considered returning to the PHS or getting involved with international health, but had no clear-cut path he wanted to follow.

Looking back on his years in Washington, Mongan believes that his time there was fairly unique: "My pathway was so very different in a sense from what one is likely to pursue, because I went from being a standard medical intern to a position right in the middle of the health policy world." However, he notes, experience and stature in the policy world does not guarantee expanding options: "Even though you're the White House health advisor, getting another job from that perch is a tricky thing." In 1981, unsure of where exactly he wanted to head next, he was offered the position of executive director of the Truman Medical Center, a large urban public hospital in Kansas City, Missouri. Mongan jumped at the opportunity.

From Policy Wonk to Executive

Despite his diverse prior experiences, running the Truman Medical Center landed Mongan in particularly unfamiliar territory:

> The man who had founded Truman called the people there and said, "Look, Mongan's never run anything before, but he's smart, and who the hell else are you going to get to run a public hospital in the middle of the country?" It allowed me to make that key transition from being just a policy person to actually running something. That took a huge amount of on-the-job training—I barely knew what a balance sheet was, much less receivables or accounts pay-

able. It took some good people who were willing to work with me to get me through that first year.

As much as Mongan enjoyed his time in Washington, the years he spent at Truman proved even more satisfying. He enjoyed the tangible results of his work at Truman and the chance it gave him to affect how the hospital was caring for its patients: "It seemed to be the perfect way to match my public policy interests and my medical goals." Mongan remained as executive director of Truman for fifteen years, from 1981 to 1996, taking on the additional role of dean of the University of Missouri-Kansas City Medical School in 1987.

MISSION, POLICY, AND MANAGEMENT

Mongan feels that he had much success during his fifteen-year tenure at Truman. Above all, he is proud that he was able to keep the hospital up and running, despite some particularly challenging times: "It's a tough world at a public hospital—just sustaining it over time. This achievement has its heights, but it is really more of a cumulative statement than any particular moment or accomplishment." Reflecting on this period, Mongan explains how important it was for him to believe in Truman's mission of public service:

> Would I have enjoyed being president of Procter and Gamble? I think I would have. I like managing. I like setting objectives and seeing them happen. I like working with people. But deep down, it's important for me to be strongly connected to the core mission of the organization I am running, and for me that meant keeping a hospital afloat that was providing care to the indigent.

When he considers the opportunities he may have had in Washington had he stayed there, he has few regrets about following a different path:

> Let's say Carter had been reelected in 1980, and I had stayed on at the White House, and then Walter Mondale had been elected in 1984. There is a possibility that I might have eventually been able to serve as an under-secretary or secretary of health and human services. From my current viewpoint at 60, being secretary doesn't look nearly as important as it did from the viewpoint at 30.

Mongan's departure from the health care policy world became a more active decision when in 1993, shortly after taking office, President Bill Clinton invited Mongan to work on his nascent health care plan. Mongan declined the invitation. His family was one factor in this decision—his children were starting college, and joining the administration would have involved a significant pay cut. But more important was the fact that the prospect of "endlessly running around in circles" on Capitol Hill no longer seemed as appealing after a decade of running an organization that was directly involved in delivering care. "I didn't want to see another train wreck," he later told the *Boston Globe* of his decision.

THE DECISION TO GO TO MGH

After fifteen years at Truman, Massachusetts General Hospital (MGH) offered Mongan the position of president and CEO. When considering whether or not to accept the offer, Mongan realized that he would have a limited number of opportunities to make large changes in his career: "I knew that I either was going to do one more thing or I was going to stay at Truman. I could have stayed, but I was ready to try something different." In addition, MGH held an allure for Mongan that preceded the hospital's offer. He even recalls joking a few years earlier with a recruit that he "wasn't going anywhere other than Truman unless Mass General called." Mongan wanted to be sure, though, that he was not sacrificing his ability to make a direct impact on the daily operations of a large health care institution:

> I always enjoyed being where you could see what was going on in and around the emergency room. Or when you open a new clinic, being able to go over and look at it. And when there's a standards problem, seeing it be fixed.

Ultimately he accepted the position, and moved to Boston to begin his new role at MGH: "By that time I'd done a fair amount on the policy side and the administrative side, and MGH gave me a good megaphone to stay involved." In 2003, Mongan was asked to step up into the role of president and CEO of MGH's parent organization, Partners HealthCare. Partners HealthCare had been founded amidst the first wave of managed care, in 1994, as a merger between MGH and Brigham and Women's Hospital. The position provided him with a platform to again become a national spokesperson for health-related issues while still actively influencing health care policy and institutions. At the same time, moving from MGH to Partners' corporate headquarters in Boston's Prudential Tower marked the first time in 22 years that Mongan had worked in a building that did not provide patient care.

During his tenure at the helm of Partners he oversaw the organization's transformation into a national model of an integrated academic health care delivery system. Among his most significant achievements was his "High Performance Medicine" initiative which included the near 100 percent adoption of electronic medical records by Partners' primary care physicians as well as reduction in medication errors with the adoption of computerized physician order entry systems. During this time he also played a central role in the Massachusetts health insurance reform law, which was enacted in 2006, and mandated that nearly every resident of the state have a minimum level of insurance coverage. He also served as chairman of the Commonwealth Fund's influential Commission on a High Performance Health System.[1]

Mongan retired from his position as the head of Partners in 2009. At that time, Partners' large and influential Institute for Health Policy was renamed the Mongan Institute for Health Policy, honoring his enormous contribution.[2]

LEGACY AND IMPACT

In 2011, at the age of 69, Mongan died after a battle with cancer, leaving behind his wife, son, daughter, and grandson, as well as a lasting legacy in the world of health policy.

Among Mongan's greatest legacies is his long-standing commitment and contribution to coverage of the uninsured, an issue which he felt passionate about throughout his career. He felt that the failure to cover the uninsured reflected a fundamental disconnect between what Americans felt they believed and what they were willing to pay for. In a 2005 editorial in the *New England Journal of Medicine,* Mongan and a colleague wrote:

> As a society, we don't want to see childbirth occur in the street or an obviously broken bone ignored. We are willing to pay enough to move the care indoors and out of sight. But we are not willing to provide coverage for the chronic conditions and preventive care that might enable the uninsured to lead more productive and happier lives.

> How can a country as idealistic and generous as the United States fail repeatedly to accomplish in health care coverage what every other industrialized nation has achieved? One explanation may be that we are not so idealistic or generous as we would like to believe we are.[3]

Mongan lived to see the first significant step towards the goal of covering the uninsured in the 2010 passage of national health care reform, an achievement for which his lifelong work had helped to prepare the way. As the Mongan Institute for Health Policy stated of him on the occasion of its renaming, "Every major effort to enact universal health care in the United States over the past three decades, including the current one, has carried his imprint." At the time of his death, Karen Davis, a long-time friend, commented on what made Mongan so effective in influencing change in health care:

> He just had an ability to synthesize what was really important, to crisply go to the heart of every matter and to lay out what the issues were, what the alternatives were and what the key arguments were...He was very effective at that, building consensus by helping people understand what the choices

were, what was at stake, what the implications were and coming together around a realistic way forward.[4]

While Mongan will likely be remembered best for his impact on health policy, in his later years he increasingly emphasized the interdependence of policy and clinical work. Neither, he felt, is necessarily of greater importance. Ultimately it is the balance of the two that enables change:

> In my younger days I would say, well you see twenty kids with sore throats and you help those twenty kids, but if you could really make the neighborhood a better place, they would be healthier. As I have gotten older, I'm a little more balanced about these differences in impact. I have more respect for the taking care of twenty sore throats, and I have less belief that there's one individual who makes the decisions that fix the neighborhood. Everything you do, you're part of thirty people working on one advancement.

Notes

1 For further discussion of the Commonwealth Fund please see the profile of its long-standing president, Karen Davis, on page 152.

2 The founder and long-time director of the Institute for Health Policy, David Blumenthal, is profiled on page 84. Blumenthal is now president of the Commonwealth Fund.

3 James Mongan and T.H. Lee, "Do We Really Want Broad Access to Health Care?" *New England Journal of Medicine* 352 (2005):1260–1263.

4 Quoted in Jaimy Lee, "Execs: Mongan's Legacy Lives On," *Modern Healthcare* (Digital Edition), May 9, 2011.

Fitzhugh S. M. Mullan

Murdock Head Professor of Medicine and Health Policy, George Washington University
Physician-Writer

Fitzhugh Mullan is a leading expert on and teacher of socially progressive health care policy and practice, notably community-oriented primary care. In this profile, Mullan discusses the continuities between his early involvement in the civil rights movement, his work in government and the Public Health Service, and his teaching and research as a professor of health policy. He also reflects on his return to the clinic as a pediatrician after two decades of administrative work had left him with little time to practice medicine.

EDUCATION & TRAINING

1960–1964	B.A., Harvard College (History)
1964–1968	M.D., University of Chicago Medical School
1968–1971	Intern and Resident, Einstein College of Medicine, NYC (Pediatrics)

CAREER PATH

1972–1975	Physician, National Health Service Corps, Public Health Service (PHS)
1975–1977	Chief Medical Officer, NHSC
1977–1981	Director, NHSC
1981–1982	Scholar-in-Residence, Institute of Medicine, National Academy of Sciences
1982–1984	Chief Medical Officer, Office for Medical Applications of Research, NIH
1984–1985	Secretary, Dept. of Health and Environment, State of New Mexico
1986–1988	Visiting Associate Professor, Dept. of Health Policy and Management, Johns Hopkins University School of Hygiene and Public Health
1988–1996	Positions in the PHS culminating in Director, Bureau of Health Professions (1990–1996) and Assistant Surgeon General (1991–1996)
1996–	Contributing Editor, *Health Affairs*
1996–	Appointments culminating in Murdock Head Professor of Medicine and Health Policy, and Professor of Pediatrics, George Washington University

SELECTED PUBLICATIONS

A selection of Fitzhugh Mullan's publications can be found at the end of this profile.

Public health and primary care are what added most of the 30 years to the American lifespan in the twentieth century, from 40-plus to 70-plus—not stents or bariatric surgery. This reality is often forgotten in today's rush to expensive medical technologies even as many of our citizens don't get basic services. We are not short on inventiveness or commercial capability. We are short on equity.

—Fitzhugh Mullan

Since participating in the civil rights movement during his medical student days at the University of Chicago, Fitzhugh Mullan has devoted his career to practicing medicine and reforming health care systems in the interest of social justice. In particular, Mullan has been a powerful advocate for the importance of community-based primary care in the U.S. health care system. He has also practiced the kind of medicine he advocates, serving in and then directing the Public Health Service's National Health Service Corps, which sends primary care health professionals to underserved areas of the United States. While Mullan was an Assistant Surgeon General and an advisor to President Clinton's Health Care Task Force, he is perhaps best known as a contributing editor of the journal *Health Affairs* and as the author of several books, including a history of the PHS, a collection of oral histories of primary care physicians, and two memoirs concerning his early training as a physician-activist and his later struggle with cancer. Mullan's teaching and publishing as a professor at George Washington University have increasingly focused on the health care workforce as a global issue. He served as lead editor of the Institute of Medicine's 2005 report on U.S. health care workers' efforts to combat to the worldwide HIV/AIDS epidemic.

GROWING UP IN A MEDICAL FAMILY

Mullan grew up in New York City as the son of a successful psychiatrist and the grandson of a doctor who spent his career in the U.S. Public Health Service. While this family tradition made Mullan curious about medicine from an early age, his curiosity took the form of a vocation relatively late and only after considerable inner conflict.

While fascinated as a child by his father's work, Mullan would only learn much later how atypical psychiatric practice was of most clinical medicine.

Meanwhile, he excelled at and enjoyed his high school classes in biology: "The fact that biology really turned out to be interesting, and that it was kind of on the road to what Dad was doing, which I sort of thought I wanted to do—that made a kind of familial sense."

It continued to make sense at Harvard, where Mullan fulfilled his basic premed requirements while majoring in history. After writing a thesis in history and graduating cum laude in 1964, Mullan appeared to be on a clear path into medical school at the University of Chicago. But he began to experience the pressures of medical school even before he officially started the program. Because he had completed only the required premed science courses, Chicago asked him to take an additional course in embryology before starting class in the fall. "I burned a summer," he recalls incredulously, "doing embry-God-help-us-ology." At the same time, Mullan learned that he had won a scholarship to go to France for the year and study history. Eager to go abroad, Mullan asked the head of the medical school to defer his admission: "He said, well, you can go to France if you like, but we're not going to defer your admission, and I certainly would not count on getting in again." Not wanting to risk his place in the program, Mullan gave up his plans for France and began classes in the fall.

His experience that first semester was an unpleasant surprise. Mullan had thrived at Harvard doing independent, intellectually stimulating writing and research. He felt that his introductory courses in medical school were just the opposite: "I didn't like the science courses, I didn't like the rote requirements. To go from writing a thesis at Harvard to memorizing every sinew of the body—medical school was boot camp."

At the end of his first semester, Mullan decided to leave medical school, going as far as getting a job teaching history in New York. Mullan's family had never forced him into a medical career, but had pressured him indirectly in other ways:

> There were lots of intra-family cues that this was a good thing to do: If you want to be the first son, you know, and be the pleaser you're supposed to be, you'll become a doc?

These cues erupted into open conflict when Mullan announced his decision, but his father's anger soon passed into more gentle persuasion and even a degree of understanding. A dean from the medical school and his father, Mullan says, "wooed me and cajoled me into staying." Mullan relented and continued study that spring. It was his escape from the classroom during the following summer, though, that renewed his sense of purpose as a medical student and motivated him to get through the remaining year of coursework.

TO MISSISSIPPI AND BACK: MEDICINE AND CIVIL RIGHTS

In the summer of 1965, Mullan went to work for an organization called the Medical Committee for Human Rights. He was assigned to work in Holmes County, Mississippi, as an advocate for the desegregation of health care. Excited to be a part of the growing civil rights movement, Mullan also found himself not wholly prepared for his work: "Here I was between first and second year, knowing very little of practical value. They called me the baby doctor—joked that I was in my conceptual phases, my early phases."

Nor was the work itself always clearly defined. While Mullan had signed on to do specifically medical civil rights work, he often found himself swept up in the larger movement and doing whatever was required—working on voter registration, registering African-American children in newly integrated schools, once even spending a night with a shotgun in his lap guarding an African-American church that had been the target of recent arson attempts.

Mullan had taken this job at a pivotal moment in the process of desegregation. The Civil Rights Act had been passed in 1964 and was gradually being implemented and enforced. More important still for health care was President Lyndon Johnson's Medicare legislation, passed during the very summer Mullan went to Mississippi. Crucially, Medicare linked funding for hospitals to their desegregation: "So a lot of hospitals had to swallow hard and desegregate, but I think it was '66 or '67 by the time that actually happened."

Meanwhile, Mullan was assigned to prepare the way for integration in health care by speaking, as a member of the medical community, to local physicians and health care officials about civil rights, usually with the expectation that he would not find a willing audience. Only two of the five local doctors, he recalls, would even agree to speak to him:

> The idea was to serve notice on racist institutions that the civil rights movement was here, and here to stay. And we [medical student volunteers] were used as sort of spear-carriers or front guard in that process, to let the hospitals know. I'm sure they thought, "What's this twirpy medical student from Chicago doing here?" But the idea was to get some credence.

Mullan would later re-evaluate at least some aspects of his experience that summer, questioning, for example, his tacit assumption that racism was primarily a southern, and not an American, problem. But his work with the community in Holmes County was, on the whole, an overwhelmingly positive turning point in his career:

> The summer simply gave me a vision—of why there were causes and people and populations and families for whom I would want to be a doc. It showed me situations where having the skills and putting them to work really made sense—in the context of the civil rights movement, or health equity, or pov-

erty, or the variety of ways in which you could define it.

Mullan had gone to medical school hoping, he explains, that he could do practical and useful work, and his experience with the community in Holmes County had let him do just that.

White Coat, Clenched Fist: Student, Resident, Activist

Mississippi was just the beginning of Mullan's student activism, which would include some battles that, while intense at the time, seem much less so in retrospect. A campaign to save a fellow medical student's beard from the faculty's demand that he shave even received its own acronym: operation SWAB, for "Save Waller's Beard."

Yet the epicenter of the civil rights movement seemed to travel along with Mullan during these years. More typical of his activism were the marches in which he participated for housing integration in Chicago, led by Martin Luther King, Jr. beginning in 1966. Mullan and other members of the Medical Committee for Human Rights served as a visible medical presence during these marches, reassuring demonstrators that if the threats of violence against them became a reality, care would be nearby.

Even operation SWAB was a symptom of a much weightier contest between activist medical students and what Mullan describes as "a very stodgy, very wooden medical school establishment." For Mullan, commitment to a career in medicine did not at all mean approval of the medical profession as it existed. He became a leader in the Student Health Organization, which sought to become a radical alternative to the more established Student American Medical Association (SAMA).

The SHO, explains Mullan, was successful in its early years in winning federal grants to support socially progressive community health projects; he recalls helping to coordinate a summer project pairing students in the health care professions with interested high school students to do community work in Chicago. Intentionally decentralized and increasingly absorbed in the antiwar movement, SHO proved to be short-lived, but nonetheless had a profound impact on medical student culture: "Its involvement in social activisms, the student instinct towards social justice—these were captured by SAMA," which cut its ties to the American Medical Association to become a fully independent student organization during these years. SAMA, now known as the American Medical Student Association, still bears the stamp of its transformation during the Vietnam War era.

Never reconciled to the felt disconnect between his vision of medicine as a public service and the often detached, alienating experience of the classroom and the clinic, Mullan continued to advocate for and participate in reform during his internship and residency in pediatrics. He chose to complete this stage of his training back home in New York City at Einstein Medical College, first at Jacobi Hospital and then at Lincoln Hospital, both in the Bronx. The return home was appealing to Mullan, but more important still was the opportunity to practice in what he saw as New York City's unique health care system:

> Where else could one go in the United States and be part of a medical system that was attempting to deal in some coherent way with the health problems of the poor and indigent?

After two years of rotations in the University of Chicago's Billings Hospital, with its focus on teaching and academic medicine, Mullan wanted to get closer to the kind of public hospital he believed in: "As ardent a critic as I had become of the medical care rendered the poor, I had never worked in an institution whose primary goal was the provision of that care."[1]

What he found at Jacobi was in many ways a disappointment: another excellent teaching hospital that, while it served many poor patients from New York City, remained utterly detached from their cultures and communities. Understanding a patient's background and medical beliefs was, for Mullan, an essential part of medical practice, because these beliefs could impact health care outcomes. Such understanding could also make a hospital into part of a community, rather than a last resort in case of emergency on that community's margins. When Mullan moved to Lincoln Hospital for the final year of his residency, he and other staff members sought to address this situation, reaching out to the hospital's community in order to give it a say in, and a living connection to, the hospital whose mission was to care for it.

Mullan recounts the experiences of his student and resident years in *White Coat, Clenched Fist: The Political Education of an American Physician*, first published in 1976 and reissued with a new preface in 2006. It was this period in his life more than any other that, Mullan says, gave shape to his career as a whole:

> I made a career of melding a social mission, which at times is more strident—the clenched fist side of things—with a traditional service profession, medicine. Those two came together during that civil rights summer and have stayed together in various expressions ever since.

"I THOUGHT I'D DIED AND GONE TO HEAVEN": PUBLIC SERVICE AND THE NHSC

To fulfill his draft obligation, Mullan had joined the U.S. Public Health Service as a commissioned officer, allowing him to complete his residency before beginning service. It was a choice, he explains, that allowed him both to avoid complicity with what he felt to be an unjust war while also working towards some of the same ideals he had fought for as a student:

> I was very much against the war. I wasn't a pacifist, I wasn't against fighting,
> I wasn't against the military—but I thought what we were doing in Vietnam
> was a travesty, and I didn't want to go support it. The Public Health Service
> was government service, but it didn't involve killing the people of Vietnam.
> In fact, it involved going to underserved communities and helping. It was
> perfect for me.

After staying on at Lincoln for a year past his residency as a pediatrics instructor, Mullan was assigned to work in New Mexico in 1972 as a member
of the first class in a new program within the PHS, the National Health Service Corps. The NHSC deploys primary care physicians, nurses, pharmacists
and other health professionals to areas of the United States most in need of
them. Mullan's service in the program lived up to his expectations. It was, he
says, "like exactly what we had dreamed of as students...I thought I'd died
and gone to heaven."

His dedication to the program translated into advancement within it.
Mullan went on to become director of the NHSC from 1977 until the beginning of 1981, under the Carter administration. In 1972, the NHSC had
begun offering scholarships to health professionals willing to commit to a
period of service in primary care, even if they planned to specialize later
on—the scholarship program exists to this day. Mullan became director just
as the first class of scholarship students completed their education; the corps
thus quadrupled in size during his tenure, from roughly five hundred to two
thousand. Mullan presided over what he calls the high point of the scholarship program; in the 1978-1979 academic year, it funded over nine percent
of the nation's medical students.

A program that harmonized so well with Mullan's ideals was, perhaps,
bound to conflict with ideals originating at the other side of the political
spectrum. As a government program dedicated to the direct remediation
of societal inequalities, the NHSC was, Mullan says, "clearly a political program, and it was controversial, particularly in those first few years." With
Ronald Reagan poised for victory, Mullan foresaw hard times ahead for the
NHSC and a difficult position for himself:

> When Reagan came to town, with his very articulate, militant conservative
> ideas and team, it was clear they wanted to get rid of the National Service
> Corps. They didn't like federal docs, they didn't like federal subsidies. Al-
> though the president couldn't simply abort the program because the law was
> on the books, he could certainly put a lot of budgetary and management con-
> straints on it. And having spent almost a decade of my life in practice in the
> corps, managing the corps, as chief medical officer for a while, I didn't want
> to do the things I knew I was going to be asked to do.

Wishing to avoid such an awkward position without leaving the PHS, Mullan requested a "detail" or sabbatical, which he used to accept a position as scholar-in-residence at the Institute of Medicine, the medical branch of the National Academy of Sciences.

"MEMORIES OF PURGATORY": SURVIVING CANCER

If working with the NHSC was, for Mullan, like dying and going to heaven, it was interrupted by a much more literal brush with death. In 1975, near the end of his time in New Mexico and before becoming director of the NHSC, Mullan was diagnosed with cancer. For the next year and a half, he was constantly in and out of the hospital for surgery, radiation and chemotherapy. "I was," Mullan recalls wryly, "really in the crapper most of the time healthwise."

That blunt, terse phrase covers over a long period of varied and intense suffering. What Mullan discovered during his time as a cancer patient was that the effects of cancer extend well beyond a tumor that needs to be removed. Treatment itself led to more treatment: Mullan spent as much time dealing with the complications of surgery and therapy, including an esophagus burned by radiation therapy and a chest infection resulting from contamination during surgery, as he did with direct effects of the cancer itself.

Mullan planned to cope with his disease in part by writing about it, and went into treatment with what even his literary agent felt to be a somewhat morbid exuberance:

> I called him to let him know I was in the hospital...I said, "Hey, we're going to get a good story out of this!" And I remember him going, "You've got to be kidding. You're telling me this is a good deal!"

Mullan persevered for a while in his plan to write about the experience. His parents bought him a Dictaphone—in part, he recalls, "because they thought I might die and wanted a record"—but he soon found the brutal reality of his condition overwhelming his ability to reflect on it:

> I just was so angry, so upset, so sick. The notion of trying to make sense of it, to speak in some kind of prudent, dispassionate fashion... I said to myself, "I don't want to write about it. I don't want to think about medicine. If I come out of this, I probably don't want to practice medicine again."

Mullan did, eventually, write the book he had planned. *Vital Signs: A Young Doctor's Struggle with Cancer* (1983) is a memoir that also makes an implicit case for a new understanding of cancer and the needs of cancer patients. Mullan would later describe his experience as "a purgatory that was touched by sickness in all its aspects but was neither death nor care. It was survival..."[2]

After advocating for more patient input into health care institutions in New York City, Mullan had now become an advocate for a group of which he himself was a part. In the decade following his treatment, he worked with other cancer survivors and experts to give that group an institutional center and a permanent, credible voice in health care policy decisions. In 1986, Mullan became founding president of the National Coalition for Cancer Survivorship. Central to the coalition's mission was the redefinition of cancer not as a disease with a cure, but rather as a condition to be survived, from the moment of diagnosis through the remainder of the patient's life. Complications such as those experienced by Mullan had to be recognized by the health care community, the coalition argued, as an unfortunate but regular consequence of the more narrowly defined disease.

MAKING PRIMARY CARE PRIMARY AGAIN: THE IOM AND BEYOND

Mullan went on to serve in a number of high-level positions as an officer in the Public Health Service, including secretary of the Department of Health and Environment for the state of New Mexico, director of the Bureau of Health Professions, and as an advisor on President Clinton's Health Care Task Force. From 1991 to 1996, Mullan was assistant surgeon general, after which he retired from the Public Health Service. Since 1996, he has been a contributing editor of the "Narrative Matters" section for the journal *Health Affairs*,[3] and a professor of medicine and health policy at George Washington University.

It was his time as a scholar-in-residence at the Institute of Medicine from 1981 to 1982, though, that in many ways laid the foundation for much of the work that followed. Based in Washington, D.C. and fresh from leading the NHSC, Mullan was especially attuned to the relationship between the corps's scholarship program and nearby medical schools. In part because of high tuition rates and in part because they drew students interested in government, medical schools at Georgetown and George Washington University had unusually high numbers of students on NHSC scholarships.

Mullan saw a clear gap in the medical school curriculum: with so many students prepared to serve at least temporarily in poor communities, there was still no curriculum designed to prepare them for this kind of work. Mullan had approached the schools about developing such a curriculum while still heading NHSC, but administrators were wary: "We were basically told, 'Get out of town; the feds aren't going to tell us how to run our curriculum. This is academic freedom here.'" The issue remained foremost in Mullan's mind as he began his work at the IOM:

> I wanted to figure out what community medicine was, and what a curriculum
> for it ought to be that could be taught in general, and certainly to people who

were going to work in underserved areas. In the military you send people through ROTC and teach them how to march, how to salute and wear a uniform, and by the way they're getting their tuition paid. So what is the analogue for that for community medicine, and how do you do it?

COMMUNITY-ORIENTED PRIMARY CARE

The answer, Mullan knew already from his work with NHSC, lay in an emphasis upon primary care, which he describes as "the currency of practice in underserved areas":

> It's not that underserved people don't need a dermatologist or a neurosurgeon part of the time, but when you've got nothing, what you're going to build is your primary care system—that's your platform—and then you're going to worry about your referrals after that.

In discussing his ideas with other interested physicians at the IOM, Mullan was introduced to the work of Sidney and Emily Kark and their concept of Community-Oriented Primary Care (COPC). Sidney Kark had been trained as an epidemiologist, but as health care workers in rural South Africa in the 1930s and '40s, Mullan explains, Kark and his wife "were the only show in town. So they did water management and census taking and infant mortality reduction; they delivered babies and set bones and took care of the sniffles. They did everything."

Doing everything, and trying to do it as efficiently as possible, meant focusing on communities rather than exclusively on individual cases, and thus expanding the scope of the primary care physician's responsibilities to include work traditionally in the province of public health workers. The Karks were as concerned with communally shared causal factors like malnutrition as they were with the diseases resulting from them, and taught contour ploughing and composting as well as prescribing drugs.

The Karks had left South Africa under apartheid and emigrated to Jerusalem. Mullan became interested enough in their ideas so that he went to visit them there, and at the end of his year at the IOM put together a conference to encourage discussion of how COPC might be applied to new contexts. The conference, explains Mullan, "kind of got the idea planted, and I've been kind of in and out of the idea ever since then." As the Karks' example attests, though, the idea is not an easy one to put into practice, because it requires more and different kinds of effort than primary care physicians are traditionally trained for:

> It requires a clinician or a clinical practice to spend extra time enumerating its population, defining its problems, doing that in collaboration with the community, and then undertaking a pretty good campaign to focus on re-

dressing a certain problem—and evaluating the outcome and starting it all over again.

Thus it remains for Mullan, who teaches a curricular track based on COPC and is one of the foremost experts on it in the U.S., "both a great love and a great frustration." Yet Mullan firmly believes that contemporary health care concerns can be addressed by COPC, and sees it converging with other emergent approaches to health care management:

> Movements such as total quality management and continuous quality improvement have migrated from the industrial sector to the health care sector. Both of these movements have a great deal in common with COPC, resting as they do on basic principles of data development, data analysis by all involved…and reforms based on those analyses. In contemporary terms, COPC has the potential to be an instrument of quality management in health care.

COPC is also a continuation of the ideals Mullan began his career struggling towards. It stresses the need for communities to participate in their own health care, and thus "provides the essential, conceptual machinery for managing care in a democratic fashion."[4]

FAIRNESS OF THE SYSTEM:
PRIMARY CARE NATIONALLY AND GLOBALLY

While Mullan's teaching has focused on transformative models of primary care, perhaps more urgent for him has been the need to re-emphasize primary care itself within the U.S. health care system. In *Big Doctoring: Profiles in Primary Care*, Mullan situates the biographies of a diverse array of practicing generalists in the context of what he sees as "both a good time and a difficult time" for primary care. The subject of both renewed interest for its potential to make medical care efficient and humane, and of renewed criticism for its perceived gate-keeping role in profit-driven managed care organizations, primary care is, Mullan argues, undergoing a period of transition—though in what direction remains unclear.

While he emphasizes the diversity of the physicians that he interviewed, he also notes some recurring themes. One is a shared feeling that primary care physicians are underdogs in the prevailing medical culture; Mullan has often expressed concern at the fact that financial incentives, including the structure of Medicare and other insurance reimbursements, so heavily favor specialization. Another recurring element that he notes among generalists is their sense of serving a community. This is one priority that Mullan worries has lost out to what he sees as "the distorted sense of health value which we have in this country"—an infatuation with expensive technology and interventionist medicine:

> In recent years we doubled the NIH budget, effectively diverting funds from other key public health agencies such as the Centers for Disease Control, the Health Services and Resources Administration, and the Agency for Healthcare Research and Quality. Our investments in translation science, in clinical evaluative research, and in broadening coverage to all Americans, are trivial by comparison to the fiscal homage we pay to the NIH. The U.S. rates 37th in the world in overall health system effectiveness. To address this painful fact, we need a public commitment to efficiency and fairness—not more bench research.

Mullan adds that his attitudes towards research are "complicated, including great respect for the people who do it." Yet he believes the commercial motive for much clinical research has distorted national priorities, and he has pointed out that while there are national institutes for cancer and arthritis, there is not yet one for the study of primary care.

He also argues that a medical culture dominated by specialization and interventionist techniques is not only expensive but sometimes leads to less than optimal patient care. Mullan understands the end-of-life care given to his father as a particularly immediate example of this paradox. Admitted to the hospital for abdominal pain shortly after his longtime internist had retired, Mullan's father was cared for by half a dozen competent specialists, but had no single physician coordinating his care. These physicians, writes Mullan, "did creditable jobs, but their communications with one another and with us, his family, were haphazard at best." It was also, in financial terms, "patently inefficient," and Mullan believes that his father, himself a physician who understood the scarcity of medical resources, would have been displeased at the unnecessary tests and consultations paid for by fee-for-service Medicare. "Fairness of the system," he writes, "was at the top of Dad's concerns."[5]

Mullan's research and writing have encouraged health care policy makers to consider "fairness of the system" on an ever more comprehensive scale, increasingly global as well as national. In articles seeking to understand global health care problems in terms of an increasingly mobile international workforce, he has argued that one of the most important things the U.S. can do to improve worldwide healthcare is to educate enough physicians to care for its own population; approximately one quarter of the physicians practicing in the U.S. are immigrants, many from countries with severe shortages of health care professionals.

As the lead editor of the IOM's 2005 report on U.S. health care workers' response to the global AIDS crisis, Mullan has argued that the will to help among U.S. physicians and medical students exceeds opportunities to do so, and has advocated the creation of a federally coordinated U.S. Global Health Service to channel this untapped resource.[6]

Reflections and Legacies

Mullan's career has encompassed an unusual variety of roles: activist, writer, government official and policy expert, teacher, scholar, and cancer survivor. Yet the role he identifies with most, and believes to be fundamental to all the others, is simply that of physician:

> In spite of being an anti-medical student at times and critical of my profession over the years, I'm very much imprinted on being a physician. When people ask me what I do, I say I'm a physician. I don't feel like a writer; I feel like a physician who writes.

This is in spite of the fact that what Mullan is most proud of—other than his children, he says—are the books he has written. Beginning with his activist work in Mississippi, Mullan believes that his role as a physician has enabled much of his other work. This was especially true during his battle with cancer. Mullan speculates that he might have tried to found an advocacy group for survivors even had he not been a physician. Yet his M.D., he says, allowed him to accomplish more than he otherwise could have:

> Being a dual agent—a patient and a physician—was particularly effective in getting the national coalition going because I could walk both sides of the street. I could go into a cancer center and relate to their directors, doc to doc, even though I was really a patient, and in the early years that was very helpful in recruiting people to the board, and getting credibility.

As important as being a physician was to him, Mullan was largely forced to give up clinical practice from 1976 to 1996, when administrative work and writing absorbed his time and energy. Missing clinical work, Mullan undertook three months of retraining at Children's National Medical Center in Washington, D.C. when he retired from the PHS in 1996. Since then, has been practicing pediatrics part-time at Children's and at the Upper Cardozo Community Health Center, also in Washington:

> Going back to pediatrics has been wonderful. I enjoy kids even more now than before. They're endlessly entertaining and gratifying and your allies are moms and families. With most kids, even sick kids, you're dealing with the robustness of life. It's really fun.

Still, Mullan believes that he has found the right balance in practicing part-time while giving the majority of his time to writing and teaching. Mullan has especially come to value the latter since beginning work at George Washington:

> There are students who trained with me who are now working their way up through the system. I just take great pride that I gave them a little policy education along the way. My first resident is a full-time physician/manager at a

community health center, and I feel really good about that.

Asked if he has any regrets, the one thing that comes to mind for Mullan is that he hasn't lived and worked abroad. "The health inequities in the U.S. are small in comparison to global health disparities. I would like to have spent more time abroad working on the issues of global health and poverty."

Mullan connects his work with students, residents, his young patients, and his own children alike: "I love working with young people. They're a legacy. They're the future. They've got a bit of me in them—it's a very rudimentary kind of instinct. But the future is theirs, too," adds Mullan, "and it is full of challenges":

> The world is getting smaller and if it doesn't become fairer, if resources and opportunities are not available in a more equal way, war, terrorism, civil and global strife will be the way of the future. Pragmatism and principle argue vociferously for building a more equitable America and a fairer world.

Mullan's work at the Upper Cardozo Clinic, often with the children of recent immigrants, places him in the center of the struggle between the poverty of Third World children and the wealth of the country to which they have come. His clinical work there reprises the central theme of his career and bears witness to his continued determination to provide health care for all.

Notes

1   This and the preceding quotation are from *White Coat, Clenched Fist: The Political Education of an American Physician* (Ann Arbor: University of Michigan Press, 2006), 70.

2   "Seasons of Survival: Reflections of a Physician with Cancer," *New England Journal of Medicine*, July 1985. This article is quoted in the NCCS's 2005 annual report, "Pioneering Survivorship," available through the coalition's website at www.canceradvocacy.org.

3   Many of the essays from this section, including several written by Mullan himself, have been collected into a book: Fitzhugh Mullan, Ellen Ficklen, and Kyna Rubin, eds., *Narrative Matters: The Power of the Personal Essay in Health Policy* (Baltimore: Johns Hopkins University Press, 2005).

4   This and the preceding quote are from Fitzhugh Mullan and Leon Epstein, "Community-oriented primary care: new relevance in a changing world," *American Journal of Public Health* 92 (2002): 1748-1755. For more on the theory of continuous quality improvement, see Donald Berwick's profile on page 52.

5   "My Dad Was Not A Prepaid Group Practice Patient," *Health Affairs*, Web Exclusive, Feb. 4, 2004.

6   For a summary of the conclusions Mullan draws from the IOM report, see "Responding to the Global HIV/AIDS Crisis," *Journal of the American Medical Association* 297 (2007): 744-6.

SELECTED PUBLICATIONS

Narrative Matters: The Power of the Personal Essay in Health Policy. Ed. Fitzhugh Mullan, Ellen Ficklen, and Kyna Rubin. Baltimore: Johns Hopkins University Press, 2005.

White Coat, Clenched Fist: The Political Education of an American Physician. Ann Arbor: University of Michigan Press, 2006.

Big Doctoring: Profiles in Primary Care. Berkeley: University of California Press, 2002.

Plagues and Politics: The Story of the United Sates Public Health Service. New York: Basic Books, 1989.

Vital Signs: A Young Doctor's Struggle with Cancer. New York: Farrar Straus & Giroux, 1982.

Joseph P. Newhouse

MacArthur Professor of Health Policy and Management, and Director, Interfaculty Initiative on Health Care Policy, Harvard University

One of the founders of the field of health economics, Joseph Newhouse made his career leading the RAND Corporation's landmark $82 million, fifteen-year Health Insurance Experiment, which remains the definitive work on the elasticity of demand in health care. In this profile, he discusses the evolution of his interest in economics and health care, the challenges of doing pioneering work in a relatively new field, and the way in which his interdisciplinary approach has shaped the field of health services research.

Education & Training

1959–1963	A.B., Harvard University (Economics)
1963–1964	Fulbright Scholar, Goethe University, Germany
1964–1969	Ph.D., Harvard University (Economics)

Career Path

1968–1972	Staff Economist, The RAND Corporation
1972–1981	Senior Staff Economist, The RAND Corporation
1981–1985	Head, Economics Department, The RAND Corporation
1981–	Founding Editor, *Journal of Health Economics*
1985–1988	Senior Corporate Fellow, The RAND Corporation
1988–	John D. MacArthur Professor of Health Policy and Management, Kennedy School of Government, Harvard University

Selected Publications

Free for All?: Lessons from the RAND Health Insurance Experiment. Cambridge, MA: Harvard University Press, 1996.

Pricing the Priceless: A Health Care Conundrum. Cambridge, MA: MIT Press, 2002.

"Medicare." In *American Economic Policy in the 1990s.* Cambridge, MA: MIT Press, 2002.

"Reimbursing Health Plans and Health Providers: Selection versus Efficiency in Production." *Journal of Economic Literature.* 1996 Sept.; 34(3):1236–1263.

McClellan M, McNeil BJ, and Newhouse JP. "Does More Intensive Treatment of Acute Myocardial Infarction Reduce Mortality?" *Journal of the American Medical Association.* 1994 Sept. 21; 272(11):859–866.

When I began my career, I thought about the economics of an issue; then I began to think about the politics as well. Moreover, my first instincts as a young researcher were to think about what the researchable question was and where the publishable paper was. But then I began to think about how policy might be improved.

—*Joseph Newhouse*

Joseph Newhouse's pioneering studies of the economics of health insurance helped to establish and expand the specialized field of health care economics. Perhaps most notably, Newhouse was the principal investigator for the Health Insurance Experiment, a fifteen-year, $82 million study that established the elasticity of demand in health care, and laid the foundation for co-payments and other pricing mechanisms in the health care sector. Newhouse is editor and founder of the *Journal of Health Economics*, and as the MacArthur professor of health policy and management he has been responsible for integrating health care research and training across many of Harvard's schools and departments.[1]

INTRODUCTION TO ECONOMICS

While growing up in Iowa in the 1950s and 1960s, Newhouse was not aware of public policy as a discipline: "It certainly wasn't a subject in high school," he says. He began his freshman year at Harvard College, intending to pursue a degree in mathematics. He quickly became disenchanted with the math department's focus on molding students into future professors, however, and switched his sights to the sciences. He enrolled in an honors chemistry sequence, only to find that he disliked lab work. He fared no better with history and government, each of which he felt presumed a level of knowledge that he did not possess.

As freshman spring arrived and the deadline for choosing a major approached, Newhouse faced a dilemma: "And I put down economics," he says, "not really understanding what economics was, but thinking that it sounded interesting." His introductory economics class confirmed his instinctive attraction to the subject:

I understood it, which I couldn't say about all of my math classes. And then I thought it was very insightful. It was a set of phenomena that I hadn't encountered in high school, but economics seemed very transparent.

SPECIALIZING IN HEALTH ECONOMICS

An interfaculty seminar in health care during his senior year at Harvard provided Newhouse with his first exposure to health economics as a distinct discipline within the larger field. It was a visionary course, tying together issues related to business and public health long before most researchers saw any interconnections between the two fields. As a result, Newhouse ended up writing his senior thesis on the labor market for nurses.

After completing his thesis, though, Newhouse thought that he had finished his work on health issues; health economics was not an established career path, and it was not clear what he would do with it. Newhouse earned a Fulbright Scholarship after graduation, and spent a year in Germany at Goethe University in Frankfurt. Still undecided about his future after he returned to the U.S., he applied to graduate programs in law, business and economics.

Looking for a path that balanced academia with industry, business, and "the real world," Newhouse turned to his mentor, John Dunlop, whom he believed had achieved a desirable balance among these three fields. After listening to Newhouse's concerns, Dunlop told him that he did not think it mattered much which path he pursued. But since Newhouse wanted to follow in Dunlop's footsteps, he decided to pursue a Ph.D. in economics. "I liked it," he says, "and I just kept going."

Newhouse remained at Harvard for his doctoral work. At the end of his second year, he again found himself writing about health economics. Although he found health economics interesting, he describes his choice to immerse himself in it for his dissertation as "the path of least resistance," since Dunlop had secured dissertation grants for him in the subject. Through an opportunity with The Commonwealth Fund, he pursued a research project studying non-profit institutions in health care and other sectors.[2] The end product of his dissertation, a lengthy article entitled "Toward a Theory of Nonprofit Institutions: an Economic Model of a Hospital," was published in the *American Economic Review* and is still often cited.

The summer after his third year in graduate school, Newhouse interned at the RAND Corporation, a non-profit think tank in Los Angeles conducting research on topics including defense, social welfare, education and health care. He had first been exposed to RAND as an undergraduate:

As it happened, following Richard Zeckhauser's advice, I had taken Tom Schelling's seminar in defense economics as a junior in college. Numerous works from RAND were on the reading list. Moreover, Richard and Tom had both spent several summers at RAND and spoke of it as nirvana on the Pacific. I was sufficiently impressed that, even though I had never set foot in Los Angeles County, I told an interviewer for a foreign fellowship in my senior year of college that what I wanted to do when I grew up was to be an economist at RAND.

Newhouse jumped at the opportunity to spend a summer during graduate school at RAND. At the end of that summer, he was invited to return as a full-time economist upon completion of his Ph.D. Newhouse declined, however, since like many of his colleagues at the time he assumed that he would stay at Harvard as an assistant professor after graduate school. Much to his surprise, though, this turned out not to be the case:

> Unbeknownst to me, however, a new economics department chair had come in that fall and decreed that henceforth no new Harvard Ph.D.'s would be hired. I was slow to hear about this edict, finally getting the news around December 20, about a day before my fiancée and I were to drive to Iowa to spend Christmas with my family. Rather than turn right around on the day after Christmas and drive to New York City to interview at the economics meetings, which would have crushed my mother, I called RAND and asked if they were still interested in hiring me. If they were, I was now interested in coming.

Just a few hours after defending his dissertation, he and his wife packed their bags and moved to California. He intended to stay at RAND three years—five at most. He ended up staying for twenty.

HEALTH POLICY AT RAND

Newhouse was RAND's second employee specializing in health care. Since the think tank was just starting to branch out from its focus on military policy into health care and education, he did not expect to devote more than half of his time to health care economics. Newhouse had also been influenced by his graduate training to think of himself as an applied microeconomist, and not specifically a "health economist":

> I thought that I should not spend all my time in health, or any other applied field, but should carry my toolkit around from one different applied field to another. So, it was somewhat unusual to specialize to the degree I wound up specializing in health care.

As he spent more time working on health care issues, Newhouse became particularly interested in a central problem he saw in the economics of the health care system. He believed that widespread indemnity health insurance—insurance that covers all of a patient's eligible medical costs—was neutralizing the market forces that would normally regulate consumer decisions. Indemnity health coverage shielded patients from the price of their health care, leaving them with little incentive not to be wasteful. Furthermore, because patients could decide where to seek care while insurers paid the cost, health care providers could charge high prices without losing patients. "Because consumers saved little or no money by seeking out a cheaper physician or hospital," Newhouse explains, "prices were not set in the usual fashion."

This problem led Newhouse and one of his RAND colleagues to develop the concept of "Variable Cost Insurance," insurance with premiums that vary according to the cost of the health care provider chosen by a patient. While the idea did not gain much momentum at the time, it would later evolve into the framework for the preferred provider organizations (PPOs) that became widespread in the 1990s.

Newhouse's work on Variable Cost Insurance focused on the relationship between price and choice of provider. Closely related to this, however, was price's impact on overall demand—on which services patients decided to use, and how often they used them. The relationship between price and demand, which economists refer to as the "elasticity of demand," became Newhouse's next subject of inquiry. His preliminary research showed that there was no consensus on the subject, and at a time of growing concern about the overall cost of the health care system, it was clearly worthy of study. Newhouse first submitted a grant proposal to the National Center for Health Services Research, but ultimately received funding from elsewhere:

> At about that time an economist at the Office of Economic Opportunity (OEO), Larry Orr, had been named to an interagency task force on Medicaid reform. One of the issues before the task force was the role of consumer cost sharing in Medicaid. Larry came to the same conclusion I had; the literature was of no help in addressing this issue, although he did discover that opinions were strongly held. Somehow he had seen my work or my proposal, so he came out to talk. At the time the OEO was carrying out the New Jersey Negative Income Tax Experiment, and Larry raised the question with me of whether an analogous project in health insurance was sensible. I subsequently received a grant from OEO to spend the next several months both analyzing what I later termed "non-experimental data" as well as designing an experiment in health insurance.

EXPANDING HIS AUDIENCE

At the same time, a series of events led Newhouse to begin work with a colleague on an article on medical demand for the *New England Journal of Medicine*:

> One day about this time a prominent academic physician, William Schwartz,

came into my office. He wanted to turn his attention to health policy, but he knew no economics and wanted me to teach him and also collaborate with him. I tried to brush him off, but he was persistent. He wanted to write a synthesis article on demand for medical care for the *New England Journal of Medicine*; moreover, he said this paper should be the definitive article on the subject for the next decade. The idea of a definitive article appealed to me, so he, a new RAND colleague, Charles Phelps, and I set out to write it.

Writing this article was a challenge, first of all because Newhouse had never before written for a clinical journal. He was unaccustomed to the emphasis on empirical data over theoretical modeling that this new field required—the priority in the economics journals in which he had published before was typically the reverse.

Newhouse and his two partners worked on the article on and off for a total of two years. At the one-year mark he began counting drafts: there were 72 in the second year alone—all handwritten, as Newhouse notes. The finished article was quickly accepted, and took up fifteen journal pages in print—the longest article the *New England Journal of Medicine* had ever published.[3]

Difficult as it had been, the experience proved invaluable, fundamentally changing the way that Newhouse thought about his writing, his audience, and the importance of his message:

> The experience raised my sights in several ways. Earlier my test for investing in a paper was whether a good economics journal would publish it. But frequently technique seemed as important as the substance of what one had to say in generating the all-important acceptance letter. Now I viewed the task not as getting a letter of acceptance from an editor but having an impact on both my fellow economists and actual policy once the paper was published. Moreover, I now began to want to write for both my fellow economists and also for others. The non-economists were definitely not interested in technical flourishes that contributed little overall to how they looked at an issue.

THE HEALTH INSURANCE EXPERIMENT

The research project that OEO had funded during the period when Newhouse was working on his article became known simply as the "Health Insurance Experiment." Its objective was to measure the elasticity of demand in health care and the effect of variation in demand for health care services on health care outcomes. RAND was selected for the job, and Newhouse was named principal investigator.

The Health Insurance Experiment was an enormous undertaking: the U.S. Department of Health, Education and Welfare (HEW) ended up granting a total of $82 million for the study, which produced more than 250 publications. Modeled partially on the New Jersey Negative Income Tax Experiment, the study looked at the way in which consumer demand for health care was related to out-of-pocket payment. 5,800 people were randomly assigned to either a group that received free health care or one of several groups in which the participants had to pay for varying proportions of each service they used. The experiment proved to be a learning experience for Newhouse:

> For a while all went smoothly, and after a successful pilot sample, we prepared to enroll the regular sample. At this time, however, the Nixon administration decided the Office of Economic Opportunity was a relic of Johnson's Great Society, and should be abolished. To complicate matters, the experiment was also attacked by the right wing of the Republican Party, who asserted that it was "the Nixon administration plot to introduce national health insurance." The idea that my fine-tuned design was an administration plot was at first laughable, but I wasn't laughing when I was summoned to explain to then Secretary of HEW Casper Weinberger why this project should be allowed to proceed.

Secretary Weinberger allowed the project to continue, although it encountered further roadblocks and review processes until President Ford himself ultimately gave it a go-ahead. In total, fifteen years were spent on the project.

The Health Insurance Experiment was monumental both in its methods and its findings. It was the first study to apply a randomized trial to health economics, an innovation that greatly expanded the scope of subsequent health services research. Its findings formed the basis upon which co-payments and preferred provider organizations (PPOs) were built.

The Health Insurance Experiment found that, as classic economic theory predicts, people reduce their use of health care services when accountable for a co-payment; this confirmed Newhouse's hypothesis that shielding consumers from cost had created a lack of incentive to limit use appropriately. The monumental importance of the study, however, lay in its other key finding: variation in the use of services did not affect the quality of health care services. Prices could be set such that patients would reduce utilization that was medically unnecessary without affecting their health outcomes. This principle, which became the foundation of the now ubiquitous co-payment system, was of enormous significance in reducing health care costs.

The project had a personal effect on Newhouse, as well. He recalls how much it taught him about management:

> I was receiving on-the-job training in management, since in effect I was simultaneously running a small insurance company and a large survey operation, as well as managing a subcontractor for physical examinations of the participants, a large data processing staff, and a multidisciplinary staff

of economists, statisticians, physicians, psychologists and survey methodologists. At times I wondered how these skills could have been taught didactically. I remain skeptical that there is any good substitute for on-the-job training.

As for the direction of his career at the time, Newhouse considered himself to be "happily in golden handcuffs." Although various universities were offering him jobs, he had invested so much time and energy in the RAND study that he would not consider leaving it unfinished. The admonition of an official at HEW and former colleague had also remained with Newhouse: "You bear responsibility for carrying this project out well, because otherwise there will be no similar future projects."

Returning to Harvard

As the Health Insurance Experiment was being completed in the mid- to late 1980s, Newhouse found himself with a wealth of career options, including offers from Harvard and Stanford. There were many reasons not to uproot himself, though. The health group at RAND, largely through Newhouse's contributions, had become one of the premier health care research groups in the nation; the atmosphere there encouraged the type of collegial thinking that he enjoyed, and he still felt professionally productive. Additionally, he and his wife had adolescent children who did not want to leave their schools and friends. He found himself facing a difficult decision:

> For the first time, I found that I could not decide whether I wanted to stay at RAND or accept one of the offers. I also realized that contrary to economists' usual assumptions, preferences are not always well-defined. My wife and I kept walking around our neighborhood, endlessly going over the pros and cons of the three options—Boston, Palo Alto, or staying in Los Angeles.

After agonizing until the last possible moment, Newhouse decided to accept Harvard's offer of the John D. MacArthur Professorship of Health Policy and Management, a three-faculty joint appointment to the Harvard Medical School, the Harvard School of Public Health, and the Kennedy School of Government.

Newhouse took the position for several reasons, but principally because he was attracted to the breadth of its mission: it required him to work in health policy across the entire university, trying to integrate its various schools into a cohesive whole. Under his leadership, to take just one example of this integration, Harvard founded an interfaculty Ph.D. program in health policy.

In addition to his work at Harvard, Newhouse has served in numerous positions on boards, journals, and commissions. In 1981 he founded the

Journal of Health Economics, which he continues to edit. From 1993 to 1996, he served as commissioner of the Physician Payment Review Commission, which sets Medicare payment levels for physicians. In 1996 he was asked to chair the Prospective Payment Advisory Commission, which served a similar function for hospitals. These commissions were merged to become the Medicare Payment Advisory Commission in 1997, on which he served until 2004. Since the end of the Health Insurance Experiment, Newhouse has also served as the principal investigator for additional research projects totaling more than $50 million in grants, including serving as co-principal investigator for the Harvard Medical Practice Study, two studies on outcomes in myocardial infarction, the role of private health insurance plans in Medicare, and more than twenty other studies on various aspects of health economics and policy.

REFLECTIONS ON A CAREER

Newhouse considers himself extremely fortunate in his career; his move to RAND, made when the expectation of a junior professorship at Harvard failed to be realized, ultimately led him back to where he had wanted to be at the beginning. Looking back on the path he has taken, he marvels at how unpredictable it seems in retrospect:

> When I was in graduate school, if someone would have told me I would ultimately become a professor of health policy and management, I would have thought they were hallucinating. This would have been doubly the case if I had been told that I would begin my academic life as a full professor and skip the junior faculty stage. Thinking back to graduate school, I don't see how I could possibly have planned my career the way it happened. Indeed, I wouldn't have even foreseen that what happened was a possible option.

Notes

1   Parts of this profile were borrowed from Newhouse's autobiographical essay, "A Non-Traditional Way Up the Academic Ladder," in *Career Moves*, ed. John H. Noble. Copyright 2001, President and Fellows of Harvard College.

2   For more information on The Commonwealth Fund please see the profiles of Karen Davis on page 152 and David Blumenthal on page 84.

3   Newhouse J.P., Phelps C.E., Schwartz W.B., "Policy Options and the Impact of National Health Insurance," *New England Journal of Medicine* 290 (1974): 1345-59.

JUDY NORSIGIAN

Executive Director, Our Bodies Ourselves

An internationally acclaimed leader in women's health, Judy Norsigian was one of the founding authors of the *Our Bodies, Ourselves*, the bestselling manual of women's health. In this profile, Judy Norsigian discusses the series of events that led to the publication and growing repute of *Our Bodies, Ourselves*, and the organization which has grown up around it. She also discusses her desire for social change, and why women's health is an effective platform from which to advocate for it. She also explores her role as a translator of medical information and her organization's efforts to make this information accessible to women across the globe. Finally, she comments on her role as a mentor, and on issues surrounding her work and family.

EDUCATION & TRAINING
    1966–1970   B.A., Radcliffe College

CAREER PATH
    1971–1998   Board Member, Boston Women's Health Book Collective
    1976–1992   Board Member, National Women's Health Network
    1984–   Board Member, Public Responsibility in Medicine and Research
    1992–   Executive Director, Our Bodies Ourselves

PUBLICATIONS
Our Bodies, Ourselves. New York: Simon & Schuster, 1973.

The New Our Bodies, Ourselves. New York: Simon & Schuster, 1984.

Our Bodies, Ourselves for the New Century. New York: Simon & Schuster, 1998.

Our Bodies, Ourselves: A New Edition for a New Era. New York: Simon & Schuster, 2005.

Our Bodies, Ourselves. 9th revised edition. New York: Simon & Schuster, 2011.

FURTHER INFORMATION
Our Bodies, Ourselves: www.ourbodiesourselves.org
The Work of Irving Zola: www.irvingzola.com
Community Works: www.communityworks.com

The closest I ever came to making a conscious decision to be a women's health advocate was thinking about becoming a physician. I even took the MCATs. But I got derailed when I became involved with *Our Bodies, Ourselves.* I got very interested in the concept of lay women educating ourselves without professional degrees—having a good basic education and discovering that you can, in fact, read and even understand medical literature and get what you need to know to put information in clear, lay language.

— *Judy Norsigian*

Judy Norsigian is the executive director of Our Bodies Ourselves (OBOS), a Boston-based independent women's health advocacy organization formerly called the Boston Women's Health Book Collective. In addition to producing the women's health text *Our Bodies, Ourselves*, which has been published in nineteen different languages, this organization worked with more than twenty women's groups in Latin America to produce the Spanish language adaptation of OBOS, *Nuestros Cuerpos, Nuestras Vidas.* Among Norsigian's many interests relating to women and health care are hormone replacement therapy, direct-to-consumer advertising of prescription drugs, midwifery, reproductive health, reproductive and genetic technologies, tobacco usage in young women, and the medicalization of women's lives.

Acquiring the Language

During the late 1960s the women's movement was gaining strength in Boston, but Judy Norsigian, at the time an undergraduate at Radcliffe College (Harvard University), knew nothing about it. She was instead involved in playing the cello and very engaged with the math, science and education courses she was studying in school. In fact, in 1969 there was a women's liberation conference at Emmanuel College in Boston where several of the women who later collaborated on *Our Bodies, Ourselves* met, and Norsigian did not even know about the event. It was not until she became involved with the intentional community movement that she was made aware of the great variety of social change movements happening around her.

During her senior year at Radcliffe, Norsigian lived in a group house off campus and began meeting with others from both New York and Boston to plan a rural commune. Shortly after graduation, she moved to upstate New

York to be part of an intentional commune of nine adults and two children; the commune was interested in practicing and promoting organic farming, social change, and alternative lifestyles. Norsigian's year-long stay at this commune proved to be a formative experience for her future in social activism:

> We began to travel around to different college campuses and discuss value systems and the many things that were wrong with the way the world was heading. That included the environment, family structures, the limitations of the monogamous family where there wasn't enough social support. I later found these things consonant with what *Our Bodies, Ourselves* was all about.

The group Norsigian was living with eventually broke up due to personality conflicts, but the experience left her focused on social change: "I had a general inclination towards wanting to make the world a better place, I had the instincts. I just didn't have the language yet."

In an effort to involve herself in both social change and teaching, an interest that stemmed from courses she had taken at Harvard's Graduate School of Education, Norsigian moved back to Boston in late 1971 and started working with teenagers at a housing development in North Cambridge. She and a colleague co-directed a teen center and worked with one of the newly established juvenile delinquency prevention projects funded by the federal Law Enforcement Assistance Administration.

She recalls that her work at this time took place in the midst of sometimes extreme social and racial tensions: "There was a lot of conflict, not just between communities but between the kids and the police. During one confrontation, there were packs of kids lighting fires and turning over cars in the street. There were also protests against police brutality." It was here that Norsigian first took on a role that she would play many times in the future: that of the translator. One of her responsibilities at the center was organizing and leading group discussions on "everything from sexuality to stealing cars." Leading these talks meant figuring out what information she needed to impart, and then determining the best way to make herself heard and her message effective.

Our Bodies, Ourselves: An Introduction

In September of 1971, Norsigian met the group of women who had produced the first small newsprint edition of what would become *Our Bodies, Ourselves*—the book's first edition was called *Women and Their Bodies*, and published by the New England Free Press in 1970. Norsigian wanted to get involved after realizing that there was no chapter on nutrition, a subject she had become interested in through exposure to organic farming during her time at the commune. In 1974, she became a staff member of the Boston Women's Health Book Collective, which in 2002 changed its name to Our Bodies Ourselves:

> I met the women through a friend of a friend. I loved them. Some of them were musicians and I'm a cellist, so we'd play music together. And we just grew closer over the years, both as a personal support group and as a work group that put out one edition of the book after another.

The book was originally conceived as a resource for women to learn about their own bodies. Many of the original authors felt that medicine was being practiced in a judgmental and paternalistic manner, and that their doctors were not providing them with the information that they needed to make good decisions about their health.

In 1973, Simon & Schuster published the first commercial edition of the book. The group chose a mainstream publisher to help widen both the audience for the book and the scope of their political work:

> One of the most important things about our work is that we understand that the personal is the political, and if you want to create a movement for change, you've got to start where people are at. And where people are is often struggling with immediate personal problems, like health problems. You start from there and provide concrete help, but you also help people think about *why* they have these problems and whether larger societal changes could prevent such problems. So our approach is to raise consciousness about these links wherever we can.

One aspect of OBOS's work that Norsigian believes sets them apart from most other women's health advocacy groups is the political criticism that has been at the core of the group: "We are explicitly feminist and explicitly political. We have a consumer oriented feminist critique that looks at the power relations involved and who's really benefiting from a particular policy." She believes that this kind of critique does not always happen at other organizations, sometimes because of concerns regarding funding sources. One of the things she and OBOS have firmly maintained is their refusal of any funding from pharmaceutical companies:

> We are relatively poor, despite the success of the book, because we haven't gotten many large grants. Nor do we receive many large individual donations. In the end, we believe that you can't refrain from biting the hand that feeds you, no matter how good you are, so we don't want to take any funding from drug companies. Such funding would also compromise our integrity, and possibly cause our constituents to doubt the legitimacy of our words. In the years since first being published, *Our Bodies, Ourselves* has been translated into nineteen different languages. In fact, the organization worked with more than twenty women's groups in Latin America to pro-

duce the Spanish language adaptation of OBOS, *Nuestros Cuerpos, Nuestras Vidas.*

WOMEN'S HEALTH AS A PLATFORM

Norsigian sees herself in the role of creating greater access to information and critiques not necessarily articulated by the mainstream media. Although she had considered furthering her education and going back to school for an M.P.H., she ultimately decided not to. She says she is best at packaging messages and translating them for a lay public—and this doesn't require a master's degree. "Besides," she adds, "something that was more important than graduate school always came up."

But it is not just in the field of health that Norsigian feels she can function as a translator. She has also tried to raise people's consciousness about other social problems. "We need more in-depth critiques of the information we get from mainstream media, which is frequently distorted or inaccurate. Even though these critiques may be available, we may not necessarily know where to find them." She believes that women's health works as a platform because it is central to people's lives:

> People care about their health. There are billions spent on improving health, but often not on things that actually have the most impact on your health, like the water you drink, the food you eat, the air you breathe, occupational and environmental safety. And then, of course, there is the profound impact of violence: street violence, family violence, neighborhood violence. Around the world women often identify violence in their lives as the single greatest health risk. They're not worried about breast cancer; they're worried about whether they're going to get beaten or shot or raped.

Norsigian has thus been instrumental in trying to redefine health as a public issue in a way that includes much more than just how the physical body is functioning. She mentions environmental problems, occupational health hazards, violence prevention and information blockages as problems to which she has responded: "We're not just concerned about access, because if you have access to a bad system, what good will that do?"

A MONITORING ROLE

One of the other roles that Norsigian has often played is that of the monitor. She believes that one of the largest problems with today's medical system is the lack of monitoring and appropriate accountability. At the government level, agencies like the Food and Drug Administration have experienced large budget cuts or inappropriate interference from influential politicians that sometimes compromise the work of the agency, such as the vetting and halting of misleading drug advertisements. Through her role as an advisor with organizations such as the Contraceptive Research and Development Program, the National Institutes of Health (NIH) and the World Health Organization, Norsigian has been able to point out specific problems with current medical approaches, new technologies, and informational materials. Her vantage point as a member of an independent activist group has enabled her to be a whistleblower while remaining largely immune from backlash:

> The reality is that if you work in an industry and you blow the whistle, chances are you're not going to find a job somewhere else. I play a role that insiders often can't play, if they don't want to risk their livelihood. It's an interesting part of our work, and it shows that sometimes to be effective advocates, you need people like us on the outside.

Still, Norsigian does not feel as if she chose to do her work in women's health and social change specifically as an outside activist:

> I came into social justice work without much awareness of previous health activism. It wasn't like we had this wonderful array of beautifully written materials, and we could read them and say, "Ok, do I want to be in a public interest group, a non-profit? Do I want to be at the NIH where there's a department for women's health research?" There wasn't even that choice back then. I just as well could have worked on the inside, but circumstances led me here.

INTERSECTION: WORK AND PERSONAL TIME

As Norsigian speaks about work and personal time, she swings her leg up over the armchair that sits in the middle of her spotlessly clean but thoroughly disorganized kitchen. Wearing her husband's old cotton shirt and green leggings, she talks candidly about the trade-offs that those who immerse themselves in their work might expect: "When you feel passionate about your work, you sometimes let personal relationships slide, and you don't spend as much time with the people you love." Here she is interrupted by Tricia, her housemate, who is busy cleaning out the basement. Tricia interjects, "You're always on the phone," and Norsigian laughs, acknowledging the acuity of Tricia's comment:

> I've stretched myself over and over again to stay up late, work long hours and frequently don't get enough downtime. I don't need to be socializing all the time; in fact, I get a lot of personal contact through work because some of my closest friends are the women I work with. But you sometimes don't pay attention to little things that go on in your family. You miss a non-verbal cue because you're going 90 miles an hour. But the people that know you well know that they can just stop you.

Adding that the OBOS atmosphere has always promoted parenthood and the experience of mothering, Norsigian nonetheless acknowledges that she personally has not been able to achieve the best balance of work, play, parenting and family life. In part, this is because of the often precarious financial state of her organization and the resulting urgency of fundraising efforts. This has been in many respects the greatest challenge in her professional life. Because of chronic funding problems, OBOS has never had a staff large enough to allow her to take more time off.

Norsigian says that her greatest personal regret is not having taken more time off after her husband, Irving Zola, passed away in 1994:

> There are things that I would do over, especially after my husband passed away. I wish that I had taken a good six months off from work, because that was an incredibly traumatic experience. I don't think I handled it well, and work problems were also severe at that time. He was a much beloved man, and a thousand people came to his memorial service. I was visited for years after he died. I got hundreds of letters, and there was a way in which having to greet people in their pain meant that I relived my own grief a lot, more than I think was good for me. But at the same time, I was trying to function. I did end up with a huge gap in my memory; that piece of my life is a haze and it didn't have to be, if I'd taken some time off.

Norsigian considers herself lucky to have spent fourteen years with Zola: "I am one of the lucky people that had one of those matches made in heaven. It was an incredible love affair, one that some people don't even have for a year."

THE PRESENT AND FUTURE

Today Norsigian lives in a large house in Newton, Massachusetts with several housemates, including her grown daughter, her close friend Tricia, and Tricia's teenage daughter. Other friends and colleagues stay there as well, for both longer and shorter periods. In addition to her position as executive director with OBOS, she serves on the board of Community Works, which raises funds for social change organizations through workplace payroll deduction programs, and has also served on the board of the Greater Boston Youth Symphony Orchestras for the last 25 years: "I am deeply committed to that organization—I think that music is very important in people's lives."

Her goal for the next ten years is to transition OBOS to an organization with totally new leadership. Norsigian believes that it has to be run by younger women that are in touch with current societal pressures and health issues, and maybe even some men, too:

> In the end, these solutions that we're talking about have to be crafted with both sexes working together. We won't succeed if just half the population feels invested in that personal way.

NANCY E. ORIOL

Dean for Students, Harvard Medical School
Associate Professor of Anesthesia, Harvard Medical School

An anesthesiologist by training, Nancy Oriol has been involved in clinical medicine, public health, and medical education. In this profile, she discusses how her love for obstetric anesthesiology translated into the invention of the "walking epidural," a procedure now used around the world for women in childbirth, and how her desire to help underserved communities led to the establishment of the Family Van, a mobile clinic in Boston. She also discusses her experience as an African American woman in medicine, her reasons for supporting affirmative action, and the changes she has perceived in medical students' values over the past 25 years.

EDUCATION & TRAINING
1964–1967	B.A., Boston University
1975–1979	M.D., Harvard Medical School (HMS)
1979–1983	Resident, Anesthesiology, Beth Israel Hospital (Boston)

CAREER PATH
1983–1996	Director of Obstetric Anesthesia, Beth Israel Hospital
1992–2001	Executive Director and Founder, The Family Van
1997–2001	Associate Master, Oliver Wendell Holmes Society, HMS
1998–	Associate Dean of Student Affairs (1998–2004) and Dean for Students (2004–), HMS
1999–	Associate Professor of Anesthesia, HMS
2000–2009	Director of Faculty Development, Department of Anesthesia and Critical Care, Beth Israel Deaconess Medical Center
2008–	Co-Executive Director, Harvard MEDscience Curriculum for High School Students, and Co-Founder and Co-Executive Director, Harvard Summer Premedical Institute

SELECTED PUBLICATIONS

Breen TW, Shapiro T, Glass B, Foster-Payne D, Oriol NE. "Epidural anesthesia for labor in an ambulatory patient." *Anesthesia and Analgesia*. 1993 Nov; 77(5):919–924.

Hawkins JL, et al. "Practice guidelines for obstetrical anesthesia: a report by the American Society for Anesthesiologists Task Force on Obstetrical Anesthesia." *Anesthesiology*. 1999 Feb; 90(2):600–11.

Gordon JA, Oriol NE, Cooper JB. "Bringing Good Teaching Cases 'To Life' in Undergraduate Medical Education." *Academic Medicine*. 2004; 79(1):23–31.

Bachrach Photographers

Medicine is the perfect mix of science and service and for the creative mind offers endless opportunities to realize both goals.

— *Nancy Oriol*

On the floor of Nancy Oriol's office at Harvard Medical School sits an odd-looking gadget—"essentially a turned-around vacuum cleaner," she explains. The device, which intrigues Oriol on many levels, is an early anesthesia ventilator, which helped patients breathe during long operations and thus made major operations such as chest surgery possible. She recounts in great detail the object's physics and history, from the underlying principle of the potential energy of compressed air to the numerous blunders that preceded its adoption. What becomes clear as she walks you through the details is that Oriol has a profound passion for two things: understanding how things work, and helping people, particularly those in need or in pain. Her career has been driven by these two passions, and has provided her with some unique opportunities to combine them.

Her chosen specialty, anesthesiology, is the perfect example of such a combination: at its core is the patient's comfort—both physical and emotional, Oriol emphasizes. Yet she was initially drawn to the field for its involvement with the "entire human body"—as if she were too excited about each organ system, too fascinated with the interactions among them all, to give up studying any of them. Her contributions to this field include, most prominently, the development and advocacy of the "walking epidural," which has given women the option of pain relief during childbirth without temporary paralysis. She is also founder of the Family Van, a community-based public health program that annually provides free health care to as many as seven thousand residents of Boston's disadvantaged neighborhoods. Finally, in her role as a dean for Harvard Medical School, she serves as an administrator and teacher, and as a trusted advisor to many of Harvard's medical students.

THE PLEASURE OF FIXING THINGS:
AN APPROACH TO LIFE AND MEDICINE

From as far back as she can recall, Oriol has always enjoyed the science and challenge of fixing things, and still enjoys taking clocks apart to understand how they work. Unlike carpentry or engineering, however, medicine was particularly appealing because it involved healing a living being:

> If you look at the things I have chosen to do, it always began with a problem that intrigued me that I thought I could solve; then I would solve it, and go on to the next problem. Even as a child I really liked thinking about the way animals worked. The science of it attracted me, and the process of making something better. You know, you find something broken, and you try to make it better.

Yet while she was certain of her resolve to pursue medicine, medical school remained an unpleasant prospect: "I always thought I wanted to be a doctor, but during college I knew that I did not want to be a medical student." Accordingly, Oriol took on a range of different jobs after college: one as a teacher, another as a construction worker. (Oriol has a lifelong love of construction, and admits that when she walks past the construction projects that are ubiquitous in today's hospitals, she feels a certain longing to join in.)

However, about six years after graduating from college and three years after her first child was born, something changed. Suddenly, school looked like fun—even the pre-medical course work:

> All of a sudden, I felt, "Tomorrow I want to get up and study again," even though it meant I had to start from the very beginning—with all the premed requirements—starting with introductory biology. This time school looked like a good idea. So that's what I did. In an instant I decided that the whole process of education was attractive. And I had to decide that the effort was worth the risk of failure, as there was no guarantee I would get into medical school, especially given that I was an older student and a mother.

Oriol was accepted to Harvard Medical School. Once there, she recalls having an interest in "everything." However, surgery stood out for her, and she decided to pursue that as her specialty. After completion of her surgical internship at Beth Israel Hospital, Oriol did a year of research:

> I was working on hypovolemic shock, massive blood loss, which is a severe physiological insult [i.e. an event causing tissue or organ damage]. During that time I decided that I really wanted a career that was steeped in physiology. Physiology is just a brilliant science—it's lovely—it is the core of medicine. Physiology explains how your body works. When you think about the human body, first you have the anatomy—the parts. Surgery is about putting the anatomy back together correctly. Physiology is about the process of how the parts function, and how they work together.

Anesthesiology and the (Entire) Human Body

After spending a year in physiology research, Oriol decided to pursue a residency in anesthesia instead of surgery. As a specialty, anesthesia offered the opportunity to focus on the entire human body:

> Prior to this I had very little understanding of what anesthesia was really about. I hadn't ever been given anesthesia as a patient. As a medical student I'd only had a one-week rotation during which I'd mostly learned how to place an IV and how to intubate [i.e. insert a breathing tube into a patient's trachea]. In one week you just cannot learn to appreciate the specialty of anesthesia; nothing in medical school even begins to explain its breadth. It was only when I was a surgical intern and spent a month on the anesthesia service that I discovered that at its core anesthesia was really great science, and I liked that.

The anesthesiologist is usually the first physician a patient sees on the day of an operation, and thus often plays a particularly important role in the patient's emotional experience. As Oriol explains:

> Most patients are very scared, and it helps if you can gain their confidence in the few short moments you have with them before surgery. This requires being able to very quickly establish a relationship of trust with your patients.

Oriol strongly valued these "intense" doctor-patient relationships. At the same time, the intellectual component of the specialty kept her riveted; anesthesia combined her interest in physiological systems with her love of problem-solving.

Tackling New Problems:
Public Health, Fetal Monitoring, and Childbirth

Oriol's skill as an anesthesiologist was recognized by the staff at Beth Israel Hospital, where she was asked to stay on as an attending physician and faculty member after her residency. Her mentor and department chair, John Hedley-Whyte, was looking for a director of the obstetric division of anesthesiology and offered Oriol the position. Since Oriol had "actively decided" against specialization in an area like obstetric anesthesiology, preferring a broader base of experience, she initially felt conflicted about the offer. However, the challenge of leading a division proved much too intriguing for her to reject:

> Leading a division has a lot of administrative responsibilities. You have to solve problems, design systems and communicate with a wide range of colleagues. But it also gave me freedom to invent things, start research projects or emphasize anything that I was interested in. During my time as the director of the division, I would see a problem and design a solution. It was very rewarding.

With this approach, she began tackling other unsolved health care problems. She saw considerable deficiencies in patient education and access to health care in some of the poorer neighborhoods of Boston. To help meet this need, in 1992 she developed the Family Van, a mobile health center dedicated to serving these neighborhoods. The Van, which is actually a 35-foot-long Winnebago, regularly travels to seven locations in some of Boston's most vulnerable communities, where it offers curbside assistance including confidential medical screenings, health education, and referrals to appropriate health and community services. When fully operational, it provides care to seven thousand at-risk individuals each year.

Her favorite quote from their original mission statement captures what Oriol sees as the reason for the program's success. As she explains it, "the Family Van listens":

> The issue for most of our clients is not simply insurance or transportation. It is, broadly speaking, a sense that institutions designed to serve them are unwelcoming or even hostile. It is the unease of the outsider looking into a fast-paced world that cannot hear the whole story or begin to address the holes that a lifetime of deprivation has created in the ability to manage the business of life. It is our mission to welcome in our neighbors, listen to their story, share our resources and open the doors to Boston's wealth of institutions.[1]

As questions about the value of care provided by the Family Van and other mobile clinics have arisen, Oriol has played a leading role in empirical studies of the program's costs and benefits. She co-authored a two-year longitudinal study of Family Van patients that established that substantial health benefits and health care cost reductions are associated with just one of the Van's services, diagnosing and treating high blood pressure.[2] She was also co-principal investigator in developing a return-on-investment calculator for mobile clinics; taking into account the savings from preventive care and decreased emergency room visits in the areas served, the calculator showed an impressive ROI of 36:1 for the Family Van.[3] To facilitate similar demonstrations of value and information-sharing among mobile clinic programs from across the country, she also teamed with Anthony Vavasis to found the website mobilehealthmap.org. In 2009, the American Medical Association honored Oriol's leadership of the Family Van project with its "Pride in the Profession" award, which recognizes outstanding work on behalf of underserved patients.

In her work in obstetric anesthesia, Oriol focused on improving the quality of pain relief in childbirth. She also invented both the NEO-VAC Meconium Suction Catheter for newborn resuscitation, which made mouth-to-mouth meconium resuscitation of newborns unnecessary, and a fetal monitoring system that identifies fetuses at risk for birth asphyxia by ana-lyzing fetal heart rates during labor.[4] During this time she developed a deep appreciation for what she had initially considered a "narrow" field:

> In obstetric anesthesia you have two patients—and one of them you cannot even see. So you have these two physiologies interacting simultaneously—it's fascinating. Anything you do to the mother will affect the fetus. It is another level of complexity that I found fascinating.

Perhaps her most significant contribution to the specialty of obstetric anesthesiology is her creation and advocacy of what has become known as the "walking epidural." The epidural normally used to provide pain relief during childbirth left a woman numb and unable to move from her waist down. The walking epidural provided pain relief, but without the physical and psychological distress caused by partial paralysis:

> What a horrible feeling—no control and no feeling. They used to get a high dose of medication for labor pain. What I did was to try giving a smaller dose. To me, it seemed so simple—who wouldn't want to have more control and feel more like yourself? It was unfortunate that it got named the "walking epi-dural," because the point was not that you had to walk—which many women in labor do not want to do—but rather that you *could* walk if you wanted to. The fact that you weren't paralyzed from the waist down was the big deal.

Many of Oriol's colleagues had doubts at first that such a low dose would provide effective pain relief. It did, however, and as the evidence of its effi-cacy grew, the procedure became widely used around the world.

EDUCATIONAL LEADERSHIP AND INNOVATION

As the reputation of her obstetric anesthesia division at Beth Israel grew, Oriol expanded its reach. She ran a clerkship for students, taught residents and started an obstetric anesthesia fellowship. One of her fellows developed an earlier idea of Oriol's and created a patient education video about pain relief for childbirth, further raising awareness of the discipline and educat-ing women.

During this period, Oriol also served on the admissions committee at Har-vard Medical School (HMS) and was elected vice chair of the Faculty Council for four consecutive years—an unprecedented length of term. This led to new opportunities, including teaching the school's "New Pathway" medical educa-tion system, participating on numerous strategic planning committees, and helping to create the Division of Service Learning, which has helped to make community service a part of academic medical training. She was later invited to become the associate master of one of HMS's academic societies, and was eventually appointed associate dean for student affairs and, in 2004, dean for students. In this position, Oriol and her staff focus on promoting the individual and professional development of students at HMS.

Oriol has also been a leader in developing Harvard Medical School's MEDscience curriculum for high school students, an innovative program that allows students, with the help of teachers and a sophisticated mannequin known as "Stan," to apply classroom science in simulated clinical situations. The program's goal, writes Oriol, is to make "the joy of play, experimentation and inquiry" a part of the learning experience for students interested in clinical care.[5] The curriculum, in place at three Boston-area high schools and in a summer school program at HMS, has also been adapted for use with college and non-clinical graduate students. The program is perhaps a way for Oriol to bring within the reach of young students the hands-on pleasure in fixing things that led her to medicine in the first place.

RISING TO THE CHALLENGE: RESISTING THE "RUMORS OF INFERIORITY"[6]

As an African American woman, Oriol's achievements and appointments have often been undermined in the eyes of her peers, and to some extent in her own eyes, by the nagging suspicion that a determining factor for many of her distinctions and opportunities may have been her status as a woman and a minority:

> When I was asked to be a trustee of my hospital it was quite an honor. For many people, that would have been just that, a feeling that somebody respects my judgment. For me, when a colleague quipped, "You were selected just because you are a woman and a minority—by choosing you, they got two for one," I would silently wonder, "I hope it isn't true." Our world often sees achievement through the lens of affirmative action and therefore anything you achieve, you might not really deserve. Was it a gift? Was it more than you deserved? Or were you really the most qualified? You never know.

She notes that while affirmative action has wrought tangible benefits for minorities, "the world still has problems." She points out the many examples she has seen where minorities or women are not seen as individuals, but rather as representatives of an entire group. Their success or failure is not theirs alone, but rather a reflection on the group to which they belong: "If they fail, it just proves that people like them—African Americans, women—just can't do it. And if they succeed, then their success is questioned as the result of affirmative action." She believes that negative attitudes towards affirmative action, which she supports, are the result of an unreasonably limited perspective on the causes of inequality:

> People take a snapshot in time and believe that what they see is the whole story—they take the moment out of context: "If I'm sitting here, you're sitting

there, we both have a number 2 pencil, we're both taking the same test, so right now we're equals." The fact that one person had a hearty breakfast and was driven to the test in a car while the other person maybe had to work all night and had nothing to eat, they are not really in equal worlds. At that one moment in time, they may look the same—taking the test—but one actually has an advantage. To ignore that advantage is unfair.

Oriol believes that to portray the equalization that affirmative action seeks to provide as a diminishment of someone's achievements can be very damaging. She sees a sense of self-doubt in many medical students: regardless of gender or ethnicity, many of them "believe they got in through the back door—they think they don't belong here." When you take that underlying insecurity, she explains, and add the doubts fostered by the anti-affirmative action perspective, it confirms the student's worst fears and leads to a potentially destructive loss of self-confidence. Her advice to those facing similar issues is that they should "develop a thick skin, and learn to see such undermining comments for what they are." This is part of her larger philosophy of confronting failure and self-doubt:

> Part of the solution is working hard, taking pride in your effort and accepting and learning from your failures. Self-confidence is important—for all of us. When you go through life, the things that undermine your self-confidence can truly hurt you and diminish even your best abilities. The fact is no one is perfect, yet everyone needs to have the self-confidence to accept the risk of failure and move on.

LEARNING AND PRACTICING MEDICINE IN THE 21ST CENTURY

In many ways, Oriol believes that the medical profession is not much different now than when she entered it three decades ago. The motivations of most students are the same: a dedication to service and science. Medical students still tend to be academically talented and extraordinarily hardworking. Nonetheless, she believes that physicians' expectations about quality of life are quite different today than they were when she first entered medical school:

> Physicians are expecting to have a life while they're doctors. I don't know that people even talked about that twenty years ago; you were expected to practice medicine a certain way, everyone had an image of what that meant. It was something out of the movie *The Interns*—you lived at the hospital all the time. We did not hear doctors expressing a desire to spend more time with their families or pursuing outside interests—that sentiment was not expressed publicly even if it was held. But now it's a common discussion by everybody, men and women. Many medical students come through wanting to have a meaningful private life—in addition to a successful professional life.

This is interpreted by some as wanting to work less hard, but often it is just really wanting more balance.

Oriol thinks this new attitude may be due to the growing presence of women in medicine. Women may have at first been more willing to express this sentiment publicly, but she notes that men are now equally open about it.

Another change she has noticed is an increasing tendency for physicians to use their training in affiliated careers. She does not take issue with this at all, and does not believe medical school was a mistake for these people: "Having a medical education is a valuable knowledge-base for many careers. And I think that whatever you're going into, the clinical training adds a perspective you couldn't get anywhere else." Oriol believes it is particularly useful for those who are going into public health, health policy or health care management:

> I wish we could sign doctors up to be the CEOs of every hospital and insurance company, and in elected positions—then maybe we'd have laws and policies that were better informed. When you look at some laws put in place by people who have no understanding of our health care system, you see a lot of harmful unintended consequences. The confidentiality aspect of HIPAA [the Health Insurance Portability and Accountability Act] is an example—it's not clear how much benefit it has provided, and it's been at an enormous cost.

Oriol is particularly convinced that people outside of the medical field can lack an understanding of the diversity of issues that affect health care:

> Many policies try to accommodate every possible situation and in the compromise end up not particularly worthwhile in any situation. Having physicians knowledgeable about policy and practice would be a good starting point.

Looking Back and Thinking Forward

Oriol's understanding of what it means to be a physician has changed dramatically since she first decided to pursue a career in medicine. She believes that the field provides immense opportunity, but is difficult to understand until you enter it:

> I think that when you decide you want to be a doctor—since I now know that being a doctor is absolutely nothing like anything you can imagine before you get there—you do so on faith. But I don't think that matters. We are being drawn to a vision, and for most of us, the rewards of the profession are as great as our vision—even if the details of the reality are not quite what we expected.

For Oriol, both the vision and its rewards have been immense, and her love for medicine is as strong as ever; seeing her inventions and goals realized has given her a sense of pride and accomplishment. She explains that she has inhabited many different worlds in her career, and that each has had its own highlights and satisfactions. In the three areas this profile has focused on—obstetric anesthesia, public health and medical education—Oriol names the walking epidural, the Family Van, and the Division of Service Learning at HMS, respectively, as the achievements of which she is most proud.

When Oriol reflects on her career, she projects a sense of passion for each of the things she has done. While each new challenge has involved giving up old ones, she has no regrets about the trade-offs she has made:

> Anything that I love, but am not doing right now, I miss. But since I also love what I am doing now, and I know that you can't do everything all of the time, I have no regrets.

She explains that the choices she has made in her career were the right ones for her, and that her tendency is to think more about the future than the past:

> I think forward, not backward. I'm always wondering, "What can I do now, what looks like a good challenge for tomorrow?" And certainly there are times when I say, "I can't stand this anymore." Academic medicine can be frustrating, and I sometimes long for the concrete rewards of my days as a builder. But the uncertainty of tomorrow draws me. And because I don't believe that I know where some other path might have taken me anyway, how can I have regrets?

Notes

1 Oriol NE, Bennett F, inventors: Fetal data processing system and method. U.S. Patent 5,596,993. 1997 January 27.

2 Oriol and her colleagues have articulated this philosophy of care in more detail in "Knowledgeable Neighbors: A Mobile Clinic Model for Disease Prevention and Screening in Underserved Communities," *American Journal of Public Health* 102.3 (March 2012): 406–409.

3 Zirui Song et al, "Mobile Clinic in Massachusetts Associated with Savings from Lowering Blood Pressure and Emergency Department Use," *Health Affairs* 32.1 (2013): 36–44.

4 Nancy Oriol et al, "Calculating the Return on Investment for Mobile Healthcare," *BMC Medicine* 7.27 (2009).

5 Nancy Oriol et al, "Using Immersive Healthcare Simulation for Physiology Education: Initial Experience in High School, College, and Graduate School Curricula," *Advances in Physiological Education* 35 (2011): 252–259.

6 The term "Rumors of Inferiority" is borrowed from Jeff Howard and Ray Hammond, "Rumors of Inferiority: The Hidden Obstacles to Black Success," *Change/ Education*, Issues in Perspective, 2nd ed., (1995): 51–8.

John W. Rowe

Professor of Health Policy and Management, Columbia University
Former Chairman and CEO, Aetna, Inc.
Former President, Mount Sinai Medical Center and School of Medicine

John Rowe's career has spanned the fields of clinical research, academic administration and health insurance. In this profile he discusses what motivated the decisions bridging these segments of his career and how he became interested in gerontology, a field Rowe redefined most notably through his leadership of the MacArthur Foundation's landmark study of "healthy aging." Finally, Rowe reflects on his complex decision to leave the non-profit world and move to Aetna, where he became one of the sector's most prominent executives. He explains why he believes it is not only acceptable but vital that physicians be involved in this arena.

Education & Training

1962–1966	B.S., Canisius College
1966–1970	M.D., University of Rochester School of Medicine and Dentistry
1970–1972	Resident, Medicine, Beth Israel Hospital (Boston)
1974–1975	Fellow, Nephrology, Massachusetts General Hospital
1975–1976	Chief Resident, Internal Medicine, Beth Israel Hospital (Boston)

Career Path

1975–1988	Professor of Medicine, Harvard Medical School
1980–1988	Director, Division of Aging, Harvard Medical School
1988–2000	President, Mount Sinai Medical Center and School of Medicine
1998–2000	Chief Executive Officer, Mount Sinai-New York University Health
2000–2006	Chairman and CEO, Aetna Inc.
2006–	Professor of Health Policy and Management, Columbia University

Selected Publications

Rowe JW, Kahn RL. *Successful Aging*. New York: Pantheon Books, 1998.

Rowe JW, Besdine RW, eds. *Geriatric Medicine*. Boston: Little, Brown and Company, 1988.

One thing I would say is that I think it's important to be opportunistic. That is kind of a bad word—and people think that's bad—but I think it's good. I think an opportunist is a guy who steals home plate from third base when the pitcher throws the ball at the catcher's head. And if you sit there on third base and don't steal home, you are not being opportunistic and you're not taking advantage of the opportunities in front of you. You're not serving anybody well.

—John W. Rowe

For John Rowe, running Aetna presented a set of challenges different from anything he had ever faced before. Rowe will tell you that the greatest difference was that, as chairman and CEO of a publicly traded company, he held his position at the will of the shareholders, and was constantly aware of how his decisions affected them. As comfortable as Rowe appeared in his role at the head of Aetna, a for-profit insurance company, it was the first position of its kind that he had held. His decision to accept the job, after being approached by an unsolicited headhunter, was made only after much deliberation:

> The reason I took the job was because it seemed to me that managed care was not doing well, and that it had been driven from the field by the managed care backlash. It was in an adversarial position with physicians and hospitals and policy makers. There was going to be another phase of health insurance in the U.S.—I wasn't sure what that was going to look like—but that it would have to be part of the solution rather than the problem. And I was being offered the position to lead a company that would participate in that discussion. I felt that, while I didn't know anything about insurance and I was far from a businessman, I certainly understood health care.

Rowe's leadership of Aetna, which he successfully brought out of its crisis, was a new kind of success for him. His career up to that point had been defined by his tenure as president of Mount Sinai Medical Center, and by his groundbreaking research in the field of gerontology.

FIRST ENCOUNTERS WITH GERONTOLOGY

Rowe's career in medicine began in 1966 when he started medical school at the University of Rochester. Although what initially attracted him to medicine was an interest in applied science, he became increasingly interested in research: "I did research nights, weekends, summers, published a couple of papers—and found that I really enjoyed the academic aspects of medicine." Rowe studied many topics, but found that it was nephrology, the study of kidney disease, and endocrinology, the study of the hormonal system, that most excited him. His interest in nephrology led him to the Gerontology Research Center in Baltimore, and he found the research being undertaken there immensely compelling:

> The scientists had a technique there that they were using called the Glucose Clamp technique. I could envision ways in which this technique—which was to study humans by infusion of glucose and different hormones and apply mathematical models to study the regulation of hormones and their effects— could be modified and applied along my interests. So I decided to go there to learn about this technique.

At this juncture in Rowe's career he had no interest in the main focus of the Gerontology Research Center—aging. Surrounded by colleagues who studied aging, he nevertheless continued to see nephrology as his focus. Rowe left the research center, completed a fellowship in nephrology at Massachusetts General Hospital, worked as chief resident in medicine at Beth Israel Hospital, and began to receive job offers in nephrology from various medical centers. Only at this stage did he realize that his interests lay, not with kidneys or endocrinology, but with aging itself:

> Nobody in academic medicine that I knew was paying any attention to the science of aging. The ones that I could find that were interested in aging, in American medicine, they were all geriatricians. They were interested in taking care of old people that were sick, and I wasn't. I was interested in studying aging—in studying how a healthy old person is different from a healthy young person, because I saw those physiological differences to be precursors of the influence of age on the presentation of disease and its response to treatment and the complications that ensue.

The turn to gerontology—as distinct from geriatrics—proved "obvious" to Rowe, who went to Franklin Epstein, the chair of medicine at Beth Israel, and told him that he wanted to be a gerontologist. Epstein had been expecting Rowe to stay on the faculty at Harvard University as a nephrologist. While surprised at Rowe's desire to change fields, Epstein did not want to lose him to another institution, so he arranged for Rowe to set up a lab for research on aging. "I think that Epstein felt that I would get over it and then I would be there and he could put me in the kidney department," recalls Rowe.

Developing a New Field of Knowledge

During this time, two critical events advanced Rowe's career. First, the

National Institutes of Health (NIH) accepted a grant proposal he had written. Though he had never written a grant, Rowe chose to bypass the smaller grants typically applied for by young researchers. Instead, he proposed a large, multi-disciplinary, multi-investigator project with himself as the principal investigator. The grant focused on unanswered questions about the physiology of normal aging:

> It's kind of intuitive, but I said no one's ever studied in real detail what the immune system changes and the pulmonary system changes and the cardiovascular system changes are specifically in this 80-year-old man versus his 20-year-old grandson. And how preventable are they, and how variable are they from one person to another? It's one thing to study pneumonia or influenza, but shouldn't we understand the changes in the physiological substrate?

The grant generated a lot of interest from both the medical community at large and especially at Beth Israel, where Rowe had given a talk on the methodology of practicing gerontological clinical research. Rowe ultimately published a single-author article on the subject in the *New England Journal of Medicine*.

This early work in gerontology led to a second pivotal event for Rowe. Mitch Spellman, a dean at Harvard University, decided to start a program that would examine some of the very issues that Rowe was concerned with:

> They tried to decide what the right approach to aging was at Harvard. Should they set up a division, have a department, or do nothing? Should it be at the school of public health, the med school, or in Cambridge? They were trying to figure out what to do around the social, political, economic and medical issues.

Rowe was asked to participate in the discussion and implementation of Harvard's interdisciplinary research program on aging.

In conjunction with his work at Harvard, Rowe began consulting, writing and researching with several different groups on gerontologic topics. He developed relationships with the Veterans Administration Geriatric Research Education Clinical Centers, the Hebrew Rehab Center on Aging, and finally the MacArthur Foundation, a private institution with the broadly defined mission of awarding grants to improve the human condition. The MacArthur Foundation gave Rowe a $50,000 grant in 1984 to "think about what the field of aging means." He spent six months meeting with a group of people he had recruited to discuss the issue:

> After these meetings I felt that what the field of gerontology needed was a change in focus. There was a preoccupation with disease and disability and the risk factors for Alzheimer's and hip fracture, causes of hospitalization and

nursing home admission and all of that. What was neglected was the study of what were the factors that drove successful aging—what permitted so many people to do so well.

Confident about the potential of his ideas, Rowe approached the chairman of the health committee at MacArthur and convinced him to fund a study based on a paper Rowe had written for *Science* called "Human Aging: Usual versus Success." The chairman loved the idea, and ultimately MacArthur ended up committing over $15 million to fund the work, a study that the foundation has cited as one of its most successful grants.

Mount Sinai: A Change in Focus

By 1988 Rowe was a full professor at Harvard University, and his efforts to make aging a more central issue in the discourse of medicine had succeeded. That year, the theme of the Gerontological Society of America's annual meeting was successful aging, and the NIH had given several grants on the topic. "All of a sudden I was not alone!" remarks Rowe. Despite his success in academic medicine, the offer of the presidency of Mount Sinai School of Medicine and Mount Sinai Medical Center from a colleague of his came as a surprise:

> I said to my colleague, "I never ran anything. How can I run something like this, a huge thing, one of the biggest academic medical centers of the United States? I've never even been a dean, I've never been a hospital director, I've never even been a department chair." So they hired me. I was 43.

For Rowe, the position was an opportunity to have a significant impact on a broader scale. Although his research at Harvard was going well, he felt he could continue to supervise it even while taking on his new position. Rowe found that he had an affinity for management and administration, and he remained president at Mount Sinai for twelve years.

Aetna and the For-Profit Question

Rowe's tenure at Mount Sinai was interrupted in 2000 by a phone call that was, to say the least, unexpected:

> The headhunter said, "How would you like to run Aetna?" And my response was, "I'm suing Aetna. I'm not a businessman, I've never had a for-profit job, I've never done anything with insurance. What did you have in mind?" And he said, "chairman and CEO." I mean, how could you possibly hire a guy out of academic medicine to run a Fortune 500 company?

When Rowe decided to take the position, Aetna was failing. Due to a long history of bad relations with doctors, hospitals and medical centers; seemingly arbitrary claim denials; poor customer relations; and the high cost of medical care, Aetna was facing lawsuits from 20 different medical societies and scores of doctors, patients and hospitals:

> Right around the time when they hired me the wheels came off. It was all terrible; the stock prices fell dramatically. We started working on turning the company around: building a new senior management team, developing a new strategic direction, fundamentally revising our operating models, and strengthening our balance sheet.

Rowe sees Aetna, and other health plans like it, as part of the solution to the rising cost of health care in the United States. He recognizes that some physicians and other health care providers do not always view insurance companies in this light: "They see us as part of a controlling, limiting and regulating environment. I certainly saw some of those problems in the past. But these things needed to change and have changed." He believes that health plans can help regulate and standardize the quality of care that Americans receive. In this same way, Rowe does not differentiate between his roles leading the non-profit Mount Sinai and the for-profit Aetna:

> At Mount Sinai I was trying to increase cost-effectiveness and increase quality and safety. So I'm trying to do it now from a different point of view, but it's still all about the doctor and the patient. Ninety percent of my expenses at Mount Sinai were driven by decisions out of my control that were made by doctors about patients—and it's the same situation here. We now understand that the quality of those decisions aren't always good, that there are racial and ethnic disparities that are rampant in our health care system, there are costs that are wasted; it's not safe. I think we're part of trying to rationalize the system.

For those who would question Rowe's choice to depart from a strictly academic and non-profit medical path, he offers an anecdote:

> There are a lot of people who started asking me why I went to the "dark side." One of them said to me, "Why did you go work for a managed care company?" And I said, "Well, what do you think their problem is?" And he said, "Their problem is they just don't have people there who understand us doctors and health care." And then he said, "Ohhh, I get it."

Rowe used his experience as a physician to turn Aetna around, in terms of both financial performance and physician relations. In 2003, the company settled a very large class action lawsuit with its physicians. Under Rowe's leadership, the company pledged to make its business practices more reasonable for patients and physicians—a pledge hailed as a turning point in health care history and managed care-physician relations.[1]

By 2006, when he chose to step down from his position at Aetna, Rowe had transformed the company's image, reoriented its business model towards quality of care, and placed it on a financially sound footing: the company was valued at $27 billion in 2006, compared to $3.3 billion in 2001.

After leaving Aetna, Rowe accepted a position as professor of health policy and management at Columbia University's Mailman School of Public Health. In addition to his teaching and research at Columbia, Rowe serves as a trustee of the Arthur P. Gold Foundation, which is dedicated to fostering "humanism," respectful and compassionate treatment, in patient care.

Reflecting on his career thus far, Rowe believes his intervention in the medical discourse on aging has been his most significant contribution. He recognizes the importance of gerontology in the field of medicine as a whole, and is proud of his influence on how the elderly are cared for in our society:

> Health care is supposed to be taking care of people who are sick. And who's sick? Old people. These are the burdens of illness and this is what we have to focus on, so it's critical to the success of health care in America to take care of those who are really sick. This is a group of people who were being relatively neglected. We weren't studying them.

Note

1.   For a more detailed account of Aetna's turnaround under Rowe, see the following articles: Jessi Hempel, with Diane Brady, "Aetna: Succession at Full Speed," *Businessweek*, Jan. 15, 2006; Brian Moriarty and R. Edward Freedman, "Case in Point: To Go From Worst to First, Alter the Business Model," *Washington Post*, June 12, 2011.

Robert L. Ryan

Former Senior Vice President and Chief Financial Officer,
Medtronic, Inc.

As CFO of Medtronic from 1993 until 2005, Robert Ryan oversaw the finances of
one of the world's largest and most prestigious medical device companies across
a period which included a ten-fold increase in both the company's revenues and
stock price. In this profile, Ryan talks about how he became involved in the health
care industry from a background in finance. His story illustrates the role of diverse
learning experiences in defining a career path and captures his perspective as an
African American working in executive level management positions.

Education & Training
1961–1966	B.S., Wayne State University (Electrical Engineering)
1966–1968	M.S., Cornell University (Electrical Engineering)
1968–1970	M.B.A., Harvard Business School

Career Path
1970–1975	Engagement Manager, McKinsey & Company
1975–1982	Vice President, Citicorp Inc.
1982–1984	Treasurer, Controller, Union Texas Petroleum Corporation
1984–1993	Vice President, Finance, Union Texas Petroleum Corporation
1993–2005	Senior Vice President and Chief Financial Officer, Medtronic, Inc.

Board Memberships
Hewlett-Packard Company
Black & Decker
General Mills
Citigroup

Further Information
Medtronic, Inc.: www.medtronic.com

It's easy to get hooked on health care. I get health care from a lot of different perspectives—you see it from the HMO services side, from the hospital's side, from the physician's side. Health care is just full of issues, and it's an industry that really needs much better management talent than it currently has.

—Robert L. Ryan

Robert Ryan was the senior vice president and chief financial officer at Medtronic, Inc. Medtronic has long been viewed as a leader in medical technology, and its products range from cardiac resynchronization devices for heart failure patients to drug pumps that more efficiently deliver insulin to diabetics. Ryan has also served on the board of directors for two other health care organizations, Abbott Northwestern Hospital and UnitedHealth Group. In his capacity as a board member, Ryan used his financial and administrative expertise to impact different dimensions of the health care system, like hospital management and insurance provision. Ryan is perhaps best known for his work as a finance executive, and he is an example of someone who brought the business skills he learned in other industries to health care.

EARLY MOTIVATIONS, TRIAL AND ERROR

While Ryan was growing up in Detroit, his parents stressed the importance of a good education:

I'm from a family where no one had ever gone to college. My dad was the fifteenth of sixteen children. His parents were both dead by the time he was thirteen and he only went to the fifth grade. So he moved to Detroit, where one of his favorite sisters lived, and he tried to get a job working in the auto industry. Working in an auto plant on the assembly floor was a relatively high paying job that did not require a high level of education or technical skill. So he went around to all the auto plants telling them that he was eighteen when he was really only thirteen. Clearly a thirteen-year-old doesn't look like an eighteen-year-old. It wasn't until he was sixteen that he was big enough that they finally believed he was eighteen. He worked at Chrysler for 43 years. My mother was a wonderful student, but her father felt that women shouldn't go to college so he wouldn't agree to that. He sent her to a school to become a beautician. She hated it, but that was her only choice.

Aware of the difficulties they had faced because of their lack of educational opportunities, Ryan's parents urged him to seek success in his own schooling. When he was a child, they enrolled him in a Catholic elementary school. Later, he was accepted at a well-respected public high school in the center of Detroit. As African-Americans, both Ryan and his parents also knew that racism would be an obstacle in his path. To illustrate the degree of overt racism African-Americans growing up in the middle part of the twentieth century faced, Ryan relates an anecdote about his wife:

> My wife's parents put a very strong value on education. Her father graduated from the University of Pittsburgh School of Pharmacy in 1928, one of the first African-American graduates of that program. For college, my wife applied to Boston University, but didn't get a response back. Finally, she got a response back that she was not accepted. My mother-in-law knew a man named Jack Butler, who was probably one of the first African-Americans at the Harvard Business School. So she asked him to go over to BU and find out what had happened—because my wife was a great student, her grades were good, everything. When he got over there, he found out that my wife's high school had refused to send in letters of recommendation or transcripts. So my mother-in-law went to the school and the school counselor said, "Well, that's not a school black people should attend." She then went to see the superintendent of schools and my wife's transcript was sent, and the school accepted her. My wife graduated from BU, and is now on the Board of Trustees, and my daughter is also now a BU graduate.

The racial climate and the experience of his parents greatly influenced Ryan's initial approach to his career:

> As I talked to my parents about schools and choices, their advice was that you should look for three things in a career—and we later came to feel differently about this. Number one, you should look for a career in which you make the most money; number two, have the greatest amount of job security; number three, the least amount of racism.

Engineering seemed like a good fit for all of these criteria. In addition, the historical events of the time pushed Ryan in this direction: "The Russians had put up a satellite called Sputnik and there was a great cry in this country for engineers." With that in mind, he enrolled at Wayne State University, where he did very well as an engineering major, and then went on to Cornell, intending to pursue a doctorate in the same field. What he discovered in the course of his studies, however, made him change his path. Although he did quite well in the Ph.D. program, after the first year he realized that he did not like the work:

> I had a NASA fellowship that paid $3,000 a year, which at the time was a lot of money. My tuition and fees and room and board were covered, because I

had a teaching assistant job. I bought a brand new car, and on top of that I had a student deferment, which back in the days of Vietnam was very important. But I really got to thinking, "If I get this degree, what am I going to do with it? I'm either going to be a teacher or a researcher." And if I didn't get the degree, I didn't want to be a plant engineer. I didn't want to do any of those things.

In addition to his dissatisfaction with the options he would have as an engineer, Ryan found that the others in the program had very different professional personalities than he did:

The engineering grad students loved to talk about technical projects. I would come in and want to talk about current events, business, or law, and no one was interested in talking about those subjects.

THE DECISION TO ATTEND BUSINESS SCHOOL

As he got further into his Ph.D. program, Ryan knew he did not want "to live a life of regret," meaning he did not want to look back in 25 years and regret not taking advantage of this time when he could make a career change. He had always liked business but felt that path was not an option because of barriers like discrimination. Realizing that work was something he ultimately wanted to enjoy, Ryan knew it was time to take a risk and change his career path. He decided that business school would be a better match for both his working temperament and his academic interests, so he applied solely to Harvard Business School (HBS): "I really thought that I had a lot of obstacles being African-American, and I said, 'I've got to pick the best business school.'" He was also concerned about the ongoing draft for the Vietnam War, and this at first complicated his decision to attend when he was accepted to Harvard in 1968:

So I decided to go to Harvard kind of in steps. I went and visited with my draft board and said, "If I make this decision I would at least like to be able to get through the first year before I get drafted." They said, "We can't tell you that we will or won't draft you, but what we will tell you is that you're the only student in this draft district that will be a student at the Harvard Business School, and we'll let you interpret what you think that means...."

Increasingly confident that he was making the right choice, Ryan now had to break the news to his family:

I read this article on HBS from the *New York Times,* and the classroom experience sounded great. I remember sending the article to my parents, because even though I had been accepted, I hadn't made the decision to go, and I still hadn't told my parents that I'd applied. My mother read the article and said, "Boy, this just seems like such an awful place." What she saw in the article was the competitive nature of the HBS classroom. What I saw was the free debate and interchange of ideas among students in the classroom. Everything that I picked up as positive she thought was negative. So to make a long story short, I decided I would go and I absolutely loved it.

Once at HBS, Ryan was overjoyed to find that he was excited by the work and at home among the people: "I loved the students, I loved the way the school was run, I loved the material. I was transformed in that process from a very detailed person—as an engineer you're very detailed and meticulous—into someone who liked a lot of the broader, more strategic issues."

EARLY CAREER MOVES AFTER BUSINESS SCHOOL

After completing his M.B.A., Ryan accepted an offer to work at McKinsey & Company. At McKinsey, he rapidly acquired practical knowledge about the business world: "You learn how companies work at a high level, you learn how to conduct yourself with CEOs, you learn not to be intimidated, and you learn to try to figure out what's important." Despite learning so much, he was very discouraged by the amount of time he had to spend away from home. "My wife literally saw me most of the day Sunday and every other Saturday, which was tough," he remembers.

Ryan decided to search for other work and took a job at Citicorp in 1975. He started in a staff job, but wanted to get involved "in the mainstream of what the bank did." He approached the bank's chairman, Walt Wriston, who asked Ryan what skills he thought he needed. Feeling he lacked accounting skills, Ryan asked to take Citicorp's intensive accounting course for new employees. His initiative paid off when he was promoted to head up the corporate lending department, which was responsible for lending to cable and broadcast television clients.

At Citicorp, Ryan started building his finance résumé. He enjoyed learning the craft of lending in the fast-paced and growing cable industry. The work was exciting and interesting. As Ryan recalls, "It wasn't unusual that I would get a call from a customer who would say, 'I want to bid on a cable TV franchise. I need you in Anchorage, Alaska tomorrow.'"

After seven years and numerous financing deals, Ryan accepted an offer to work at Union Texas Petroleum in Houston. Union Texas Petroleum, the largest independent oil and gas company in the U.S., was a wholly owned subsidiary of Allied Corporation and accounted for 80 percent of Allied's earnings. He accepted the offer in 1982, with the understanding that he would move to Allied itself in three to four years as treasurer. In 1985, though, Allied decided to sell Union Texas and Ryan was asked to stay with Union Texas as part of a leveraged buyout. At the time the buyout was completed, oil prices were nearly $30 per barrel. Within nine months of the deal, oil prices fell to less than $10 per barrel, throwing the company into a major cash flow crisis.

What started out as a two- to three-year adventure in a leveraged buyout based on financial opportunity turned into eight years of incredible learning opportunities for Ryan. With Union Texas, Ryan's range of experiences grew to include company downsizing, equity and debt deals, investing road shows, the creation of an investor relations department, and work with Wall Street's investment banks and major merger and acquisitions law firms. The tumultuous atmosphere at Union Texas provided the greatest learning platform for Ryan and solidified his path in finance.

By the early 1990s, however, the company had sold many of its assets and was dramatically smaller in size. Ryan decided it was time to pursue other opportunities. In addition, his wife was unhappy in Houston, where the company was based, so he made the decision to leave. Ryan had done well financially in the leveraged buyout and wanted to take a year off before searching for his next position, but then an unexpected offer came his way. A headhunter for Medtronic had heard of Ryan's impressive track record as chief financial officer, and asked him to come to Minnesota to interview for the same position at Medtronic. Initially, he was not very interested: "Every time I'd been to Minnesota was on a road show, and it always seemed like it was cold—I didn't have a very favorable impression. But the headhunter must have called me five times, and finally he convinced me to go look." Ryan was pleased with what he found when he got there. Medtronic CEO Bill George was equally pleased:

> He started telling me about Medtronic and what the company was and what it did. Then he said, "Well, tell me what you've done?" So I went back to the mid-1980s, and I said, "I'll walk you through, year by year." I'd only gotten about a third of the way through when he said, "Wow, that's more experience than anyone I've talked to."

The offer was attractive, but Ryan was still struggling with ties and transactions at Union Texas. He initially declined, feeling a responsibility to see Union Texas through a secondary public offering, but Medtronic offered to keep the position open until he could tie up his loose ends in Houston. After a few more months, Ryan relocated his family to Minneapolis and joined the company.

MANAGING MEDTRONIC'S MONEY

During his tenure, Ryan oversaw all financial operations at Medtronic. In 2005, his final year in the position, the company had revenues exceeding $10 billion and earnings of more than $2 billion, as well as the largest market capitalization of any company in Minnesota at just more than $65 billion. The company has been a household name in health care for years, and its medical technology products can be found practically anywhere in most hospitals: defibrillators in emergency rooms, angioplasty catheters used in heart surgery, technology for people suffering from neurological disorders, and therapies for controlling chronic pain.

Though his responsibilities were similar to those of his prior positions—he acted as treasurer and tax controller, and was responsible for the company's internal auditing and investor relations—Ryan enjoyed the new experience of working in the health care industry:

> What I like about Medtronic is that you can really see the issues in health care and the people are great here: very non-political, very focused on the patient. As the CEO used to always say, "Everybody wants to talk to me about maximizing shareholder return, and the way I look at it is you maximize what you do for the patient and what you do for the physician, who is our customer. And if you do all those things really well, all the financial success will follow those things." So they have a really good value system and I just think it's inherently a very interesting company. I spend a lot of time talking with physicians, and I go in the operating room a lot. So I get to see who we affect.

Ryan came to Medtronic because of his past experiences in finance. For those interested in combining business and health care, he believes it is possible to become involved in the field for both financial and altruistic reasons:

> What Medtronic tries to do, with all the therapies that we come forward with, is to make health care better, to make it less invasive and to make the total procedures less costly. So look for companies that are trying to do those things, and if you want to have fun in the job and enjoy the job, but also do well financially, look for something with great growth opportunities. The growth opportunities here are just great. You have to think health care is interesting and to a degree you have to be interested in people, otherwise you won't be interested in health care.

REFLECTIONS ON DISCRIMINATION

Considering his experience as an African-American corporate executive, Ryan feels lucky not to have felt the effects of racism in an overt way. He believes that once you make it to an executive level, people judge you on your skills, past accomplishments and whether or not you can do the job—not on the color of your skin or your gender. Because he started in upper-level management roles relatively early in his career and never really worked under a lower-level supervisor, he escaped much of the discrimination he sees against other African-Americans working in similar corporate contexts:

I didn't think about where you'd meet discrimination and where you wouldn't…but I do think about it when I look at so many people who are having trouble, even today, 30 years later.

Ryan notes that he has most often seen discrimination "at the lower levels in organizations—at middle management levels and below." He feels that many managers and supervisors are uncomfortable with employees who are members of minority groups because of a "lack of connection," either real or imagined, to those individuals:

What happens is that you'll have a manager that doesn't relate, a manager who won't give truly honest feedback. Some of it is race and some of it is perceived race, but no matter what, it's an issue that's there.

Reflecting on his success despite these obstacles, Ryan comments: "I think the thing I did well from early on was that I loved what I did. So I made the most of the opportunities that I had."

Donna E. Shalala

Former Secretary, U.S. Department of Health and Human Services
Former President, University of Miami
Former President and CEO, The Clinton Foundation

Donna Shalala has served in a wide array of leadership positions in health care and government, most prominently as secretary of health and human services during the Clinton administration. In this profile, she discusses the career path that led to her cabinet appointment, including her initially reluctant move into administration from a more research-oriented academic career. Shalala reflects on her successes and disappointments at HHS. She also talks about the experience of moving between government and academia, and explains the skills that have made her an effective manager in each.

Education & Training

1958–1962	A.B., Western College for Women (History)
1964–1970	Ph.D., Syracuse University (Social Sciences)

Career Path

1962–1964	Volunteer, U.S. Peace Corps, Iran
1972–1979	Associate Professor and Chair, Program in Politics and Education, Teachers College, Columbia University
1975–1977	Director and Treasurer of the Municipal Assistance Corporation for the City of New York
1977–1980	Assistant Secretary, Policy Development and Research, U.S. Department of Housing and Urban Development
1980–1987	Professor of Political Science and President, Hunter College of the City University of New York
1987–1993	Professor of Political Science and Chancellor, University of Wisconsin-Madison
1993–2001	Secretary, U.S. Department of Health and Human Services
2001–2015	Professor of Political Science and President, University of Miami
2015–2017	President and CEO, The Clinton Foundation

Additional Information

Department of Health & Human Services: www.os.dhhs.gov

University of Miami: www.miami.edu

The fact is that being the head of a university—particularly a research university—gives you a wide range of expertise on a lot of central issues. You're an employer, so you see the health care system from that point of view. You have a major hospital and a medical school, so you see all of the allied health professions. You deal with the nursing crisis. You deal with the aging crisis. Universities are in many ways one of the best places to get trained for heading a major health care agency.

—Donna Shalala

When asked what her career path can teach younger people, Donna Shalala replies rather modestly. "I guess what my career reveals is that you can actually bounce around a little bit." Coming from Shalala, this is an understatement. She has been moving between government and academia for the past 25 years, and has been successful in some of the most challenging management positions in either sphere—most notably, of course, as the longest-serving U.S. secretary of health and human services. As secretary, Shalala was responsible for the expansion and improvement of numerous government health initiatives, and presided over a vast increase in funding for the National Institutes of Health designed to spur nationwide biomedical research. She became the president of the University of Miami in 2001, and has also served as chancellor of the University of Wisconsin-Madison and president of Hunter College. She has a distinguished track record as a professor and researcher in political science and social policy, and has taught these subjects throughout most of her career. In 2008 Shalala was awarded the nation's highest civilian honor, the Presidential Medal of Freedom, by President George W. Bush.

A STUDENT AND PRACTITIONER OF PUBLIC POLICY

Born in Cleveland, Shalala received her A.B. in history from Western College for Women in Oxford, Ohio. After college, she became one of the first volunteers in the recently formed Peace Corps and went to work in Iran. This decision was decidedly not a career move: "I wasn't looking at a career then—I just wanted an adventure after college."

After returning from the Peace Corps, Shalala began her Ph.D. at the Maxwell School of Citizenship and Public Affairs at Syracuse University. She had wanted to be a journalist before graduate school, so after she graduated she gave journalism one more try:

> When I finished my Ph.D., I applied for a job at the *New York Times,* but they didn't have any openings, and suggested I go to a smaller newspaper. I wanted to go to New York City, however, so I went to teach at Columbia.

At that point, she had a vision for her career that involved service in both government and academia. Shalala wanted to influence public policy, and thought she could best achieve that goal through a career that would let her see the issues from a variety of professional perspectives:

> I wanted to go in and out of government, in and out of being involved in major policy decisions. I wanted to be a student of public policy, and I wanted to be a practitioner of public policy.

Her role in academia, she figured, would be as a researcher: "I never thought I was going to be managing research institutions...I thought I'd be doing research."

EARLY EXPERIENCE IN MANAGEMENT

During the seven years she taught at Columbia, a number of management opportunities presented themselves to Shalala. Intent on pursuing a successful career as a scholar, she turned most of them down. She did, however, accept a position as chair of her department—a move which prompted her colleagues to suggest she take on higher levels of responsibility within the university's administration:

> People were talking to me about being an assistant dean and things like that. But what I really liked to do was to go in and out of government, so being a professor was the best way to do that, from my point of view. It never occurred to me that I was going to go manage large institutions.

At one point, Shalala was even offered the chance to move into government, an opportunity that she eventually wanted, but had to decline because the timing was wrong: "The governor had offered me the budget director's job in New York State, but I was just about to get tenure at Columbia." However, she did agree to accept a part-time appointment instead, as a director of the Municipal Assistance Corporation (Big MAC) for the City of New York. This position was pivotal in launching her future career:

> I was the treasurer of Big MAC—part of the team that saved New York City. I had done the budget transition for the governor of New York, which is how I got on the Big MAC board. I was part of a team with a number of prominent Wall Street people. That got me noticed by the people in Washington when Carter got elected.

On the basis of both her policy expertise and her government experience with Big MAC, Shalala was considered for two different positions in the

Carter administration in 1977. Characteristically, Shalala took on the more difficult of the two:

> The Carter administration was trying to recruit women. Stu Eisenstat had tried to recruit me as associate director of the Domestic Policy Council, and at the same time Pat Harris interviewed me for assistant secretary for policy at Housing and Urban Development (HUD). Everybody told me not to go to HUD, but it looked more interesting. Being an assistant secretary at that age—I was in my early thirties—I thought was more important. It turned out probably to be the right decision.

This position offered Shalala invaluable managerial experience. The secretary of HUD under Carter, Patricia Roberts Harris, recognized Shalala's capability and efficiency and entrusted her with higher levels of oversight:

> When I was an assistant secretary at HUD, the secretary—because I was well-organized—kept giving me more and more responsibility. She kept trying to get me to do more in terms of managing the department, and setting up decision-making processes.

Shalala's competence in this high-level position played a major role in advancing her career.

FROM GOVERNMENT BACK TO EDUCATION:
HUNTER AND WISCONSIN

In 1980, the election of Ronald Reagan put an end to the Carter administration. Shalala was planning to return to academia when a surprising opportunity arose:

> I was on my way to Harvard to teach at the Kennedy School after coming out of government. And by chance, the Hunter presidency was available. While I had been at HUD, a cabinet official had told me I should take on some significant management experience to boost my credentials. So I decided to take the Hunter presidency. I was in no way qualified—I hadn't even been a dean. I had been a department chair at Columbia, but I had never been a dean.

Shalala's decision to accept the presidency of Hunter College, the largest college of the City University of New York, was particularly significant because it meant an end to the kind of academic career in research that she had foreseen. If she had returned to a teaching position after HUD, she would have been doing what she had planned—going back and forth between studying and practicing public policy. By taking on the presidency of Hunter, though, she was launching herself quite deliberately into a career as an institutional manager. Shalala made the decision for a number of reasons:

> I just had enjoyed the managerial part, and a chance to be a college president at my age was a wonderful opportunity, even though I was clearly going to

be over my head for a while. And I just loved Hunter. It was an interesting, diverse, large public college in the middle of the city I loved. I just took a shot at it; it was high-risk for me and for them.

Shalala remained president of Hunter for seven years, and then left to take on an even larger role: chancellor of the University of Wisconsin-Madison. As chancellor, Shalala led what was then the nation's largest public research university. She arrived with limited relevant experience, and as a result many people doubted her abilities at first—something she says people did at the start of each of her jobs before her appointment to the cabinet under President Clinton.

She credits her success as chancellor at Madison to her willingness to listen to people who knew more about particular subjects than she did— something she would rely on heavily in her future positions as well: "I sort of listened to the people who knew what they were doing." She explains how she managed to establish her credibility with athletics—an important part of the university at Madison, and an area where a woman's credibility is often pre-judged:

> Well, I may have been a woman, but I fired the football coach. I fired the football coach and the athletic director, and hired new people for those positions, both of whom were very powerful, and took the university to three Rose Bowls. So, I immediately established myself as widely knowledgeable about athletics. Of course, I didn't actually have a clue.

At the end of her time at Wisconsin, in 1992, *Business Week* named Shalala one of the top five managers in higher education.

JOINING THE PRESIDENT'S CABINET

In 1992, the newly elected Clinton administration wanted Shalala to join the cabinet. At that point, since Shalala had thirteen years of experience running two different universities, and seven more as a professor, secretary of education was a logical position for her. Still, the position did not appeal:

> Secretary of education is not at the center of Washington politics. It's basically educational finance. Education is primarily a state function, not a federal function. I sent a very clear message to the Clinton people that if he wanted to talk to me about education, I wasn't interested.

Although health policy had not been the focus of her career thus far, Shalala expressed a strong preference for the position of secretary of health and human services. HHS was the largest and most complex of the domestic federal agencies, and Shalala believed that she could have a greater impact on public policy at HHS: "All of the action was going to be at HHS," she explains. At the time of her appointment in 1993, HHS controlled roughly 40 percent of the federal budget, and demographic changes were creating ever more demand for federally funded health care programs:

> I thought those were the central issues, because of what was happening to the population, and because of the nature and the power of those government programs. There are only a handful of cabinet-level jobs that are significant in Washington, and very few of them are domestic. The major domestic agency in the federal government is HHS.

In 1993, President Clinton invited her to serve as the nation's eighteenth secretary of HHS.

Learning to Manage Health Care

Shalala has never considered herself a "health care person." She has spent time in several different areas of public policy and would classify herself as, if anything, a "manager of large complex institutions." Shalala explains that her lack of specific health care experience was not a problem in her selection for secretary at HHS:

> The president didn't care how much I knew about health care. What he cared about was whether I could manage a large, complex agency, through both the political and the budgetary processes. He knew that I had a background in science and that I knew enough about health care—but he was much more concerned with getting someone who could manage HHS.

Furthermore, Shalala's experience in managing academic research institutions was a distinct advantage at HHS because it allowed her to look at health care issues from several perspectives. Managing a university, she explains, had given her experience with an extraordinarily diverse range of health care perspectives:

> The fact is that being the head of a university—particularly a research university—gives you a wide range of expertise on a lot of central issues. You're an employer, so you see the health care system from that point of view. You have a major hospital and a medical school, so you see all of the allied health professions. You deal with the nursing crisis. You deal with the aging crisis. Universities are in many ways one of the best places to get trained for heading a major health care agency.

Recognizing that she was not a health care expert, one of Shalala's top priorities after joining HHS was to hire people with the knowledge she needed:

> I hired people assuming I had a lack of expertise in a whole set of areas. I was committed to hiring people that knew a lot more than I did in every area.... My skill is going out and finding people that know a lot more than I do, and hiring them. So, by the time I got finished with my hires, people were pretty calmed down.

She says that the people who proved the most helpful to her were those who had diverse backgrounds, with both health care expertise and operational or management experience:

> The people who were the most useful to me at the highest levels were people who had had a variety of experiences in the health care system. For instance, we had policy people who had been in state insurance departments...the fact that they had this mixed background—with both policy and operational experience—made them particularly useful to me.

She values people with such diverse experiences for the different kinds of knowledge they have acquired, and perhaps still more for the adaptability they have demonstrated. People who have been confined to a single field, explains Shalala, "can't adjust very well to new jobs. I like people that have had four or five different jobs as part of their careers."

After assembling a staff with diverse experiences in the health care industry, Shalala made sure that this diversity also informed HHS's work at every level. In formulating policy at HHS, she made it a priority to have representatives from all of the relevant areas at the table. Since any policy will involve those responsible for supervising and implementing it, she sought out the input of health care managers and practitioners to supplement that of policy experts:

> I always wanted the operating people, and the policy people, and the management people all in the same room to discuss a major policy issue. I was as interested in the inspector general's opinion as I was in the health care policy people, as I was in the people that actually ran the health care system. I think you have to mix all three, and my skill was my ability to be secure enough to bring them all to the table so I could hear from different points of view.

The perspectives of these different groups balanced each other out, she says, and provided a range of perspectives from which well-rounded policies and programs could be developed.

The Highs and Lows at HHS

When Shalala took over at HHS, she and the Clinton administration had a vision of what they wanted to achieve: "When we left after eight years we wanted to fundamentally be able to say that Americans were healthier, and that the United States was on the cutting edge, was in the middle of this golden age of biomedical research." During her tenure at HHS, she feels that the department was able to achieve a great deal, including welfare reform, the development of new health policies and programs and the strengthening of many existing ones. They vastly expanded the number of children who receive routine immunizations, and they doubled the budget of the National Institutes of Health (NIH), the largest federal benefactor of biomedical research. She also led the agency in developing the Human Genome Project, strengthening AIDS policy, and addressing bioterrorism.

Her one major disappointment at HHS, however, was the failure of the Clinton Plan, the proposal for universal health care that Clinton had put forth shortly after taking office. Shalala blames the plan's downfall on poor management. She notes that the proposal was a "big, complex system" and that, in retrospect, it could have been structured more simply. Moreover, the architects of the plan could have generated more support from policy makers early on by involving a congressional committee in writing the bill.

Shalala was put in a difficult position by the plan. While she strongly supported its central ideas, she had reservations about the administration's political handling of the plan. While at the time she felt there was little she could do about this, she emphatically states her willingness to accept responsibility for it: "I'll take as much responsibility as anyone wants to give me." She says that if she had it to do over again, she would take a more aggressive approach:

> I thought a mistake was being made. I don't think I knew quite how to effect that kind of change, because the president had made up his mind...but if given the chance to do it again, I would have organized the entire cabinet and marched in there to see him.

Shalala served as secretary during the entire Clinton administration, leaving only in 2000 when George W. Bush was elected; this made her the longest-serving HHS secretary in U.S. history. At the end of her tenure, the *Washington Post* described her as "one of the most successful government managers of modern times."

In 2001, Shalala returned to academic administration as president of the University of Miami. Under Shalala's leadership, Miami raised its profile as a research institution and had enormous success in fundraising, exceeding its initial goals in two campaigns that raised over $1 billion each. At Miami, she also continued to be involved in health care. In addition to her responsibilities as president, she held professorships in the department of epidemiology and public health and in the department of political science, and taught a large undergraduate class in the politics and economics of health care. In 2015, Shalala stepped down from her position at Miami to become president and CEO of the Clinton Foundation.

MANAGING INSTITUTIONS AND THE IMPORTANCE OF INSTITUTIONAL CULTURE

While Shalala has brought her past experience to bear on each new position she has held, what she has learned above all is that no single methodology will allow her to manage an institution as complicated as a university or a cabinet department:

> I understand that large complex institutions have very different cultures, and therefore cannot be led like cookie cutters. You can't use the same approach with every part of your organization, and some need more flexibility than others.

Shalala has seen such broad differences of culture and structure between academic and government institutions, and believes that her experience of these differences has helped her to manage both kinds of institution effectively:

> Most universities are non-hierarchical. They're very flat; deans are very powerful. When you get to cabinet-level departments, while they have powerful sections, like Social Security or Medicare, they actually are quite command-and-control. And the fact that I basically was skilled at running decentralized organizations helped me actually to move a hierarchical organization along, because I was so collegial and secure.

Interestingly, the personal attributes that Shalala says have contributed most to her success as a manager have more to do with receptivity and flexibility than authority—she speaks of effective management as a process of understanding:

> I'm not rigid, and I'm not compulsive, and I'm patient. So if you know how to listen, you can figure it out eventually. People are always asking me for some grand scheme, but it actually evolves.

Given Shalala's history of being recruited to come in from the outside to run an organization, one might be tempted to think of her as a "hired gun," an executive hired to implement existing goals for the institutions she manages. She feels, however, that this has been far from her only function, and that she has played a more active and creative role in the identification and resolution of problems. In many cases, Shalala says, "there was consensus on the problem, but it was my idea to go after it, and my idea how to approach it."

Solving a problem at the institutional level, however, is never a one-person task, and Shalala emphasizes that her motivational abilities have been crucial to making the institutions she has led successful: "I think it was my ability to effect change by getting everybody to buy into what needed to be done, and by people feeling like they were part of the success story."

LESSONS, REGRETS, AND THE IMPORTANCE
OF RECOGNIZING OPPORTUNITIES

Shalala has few regrets, but she does sometimes miss her work as a traditional academic scholar and teacher. Her last full-time academic research position was at Columbia, but she does try to remain connected with teaching as much as possible: "I've tried to stay in the classroom. I taught every year, all of those years. I tried to stay in the classroom, and I did write a few things—mostly endowed lectures, and I did get a few articles published."

Shalala believes that the key to a successful career lies in recognizing opportunities—in being in the right place at the right time, and knowing it. Accepting job offers in widely varying fields has required Shalala to hone this skill, and each new position has in turn allowed her to practice it in a new field. Shalala observes that, in a career that has repeatedly involved the willingness to adapt and take risks, she has planned very little ahead of time:

I never decided I wanted to be a cabinet officer, or president of a major research university. I don't make decisions that far ahead; I'm just there. If it walks in the door, I may or may not jump.

PETER L. SLAVIN

President, Massachusetts General Hospital
Professor, Health Care Policy, Harvard Medical School

A physician by training, since completing his residency Peter Slavin has been on a steep path of increasingly senior management roles leading to his current position as president of Massachusetts General Hospital. In this profile, he recounts the experiences that first interested him in health care management, and discusses the challenges of pursuing rigorous training in business when such a path was still relatively rare for a physician. Slavin also explains his philosophy as a manager, and reflects on the events of an especially difficult beginning to his tenure as president of MGH.

EDUCATION & TRAINING
1975–1979   A.B., Harvard University (Biochemical Sciences)
1980–1984   M.D., Harvard Medical School
1984–1987   Resident, Medicine, Massachusetts General Hospital (MGH)
1988–1990   M.B.A., Harvard Business School

CAREER PATH
1987–1997   Instructor in Medicine, Harvard Medical School
1994–1997   Senior Vice President and Chief Medical Officer, MGH
1997–1999   President, Barnes-Jewish Hospital (St. Louis, MO), and Assistant Clinical Professor of Medicine, Washington University School of Medicine
1999–2002   Chief Executive Officer, Massachusetts General Physicians Organization
2002–2006   Senior Lecturer, Department of Health Care Policy, HMS
2003–   President, Massachusetts General Hospital
2006–   Professor, Department of Health Care Policy, HMS

ADDITIONAL INFORMATION
Massachusetts General Hospital: www.mgh.harvard.edu
Partners HealthCare, Inc.:   www.partners.org

I always try to take the high road rather than playing games with people, or dumping things on them that they really don't want to do. I think that in medicine we have a very sacred relationship with our patients—we need to treat them in a very professional way—and I think you need to behave similarly in a management setting. I don't think managers in health care who are beating each other up and treating each other rudely can expect that our nurses and doctors are going to be taking great care of patients. We have to set an example at the top of these organizations, and emulate the same behaviors that we want from our caregivers.

–*Peter Slavin*

When Slavin was five years old, he was diagnosed with pneumonia. His illness was serious enough to land him in the intensive care unit at Children's Hospital of Boston for several days. What he remembers most vividly about the experience is not so much the fear or pain of being sick, but his amazement at "the technical wizardries that the doctors used and the compassion of the doctors and nurses." It was this experience that turned him on to health care.

Slavin also came from a family that was both politically conscious and politically active. His early interest in politics was further solidified by an internship in the mid-1970s with Congressman Ed Markey, who was at the time a member of the Health Subcommittee in the House. During the internship, Slavin learned about issues such as food regulation and national health insurance. Although it did not become clear to him until much later in his career, it was during this summer that he began to see how he would be able to combine his interest in medicine with his growing desire to be involved with public policy.

With this goal in mind, Slavin began Harvard Medical School in 1984. "I thought I would be a clinician," he remarks, "but still spend time doing health policy research or be involved in policy at some level. My thoughts about what exactly my career would be were pretty vague at the time."

As Slavin progressed through medical school, he found that he was most interested in internal medicine:

I thought the breadth of internal medicine was very challenging and stimulating. I found the people who gravitated to internal medicine to be the people

I enjoyed working with. I also thought that internal medicine provided me with the opportunity to develop long-standing relationships with patients.

He attributes the decision to forego a more specialized area of medicine to his desire to "take a broad view" in his career: "By the time I was considering a subspecialty, it was either do that or get some training to help with other parts of my career." He decided to pursue the latter option.

As an internal medicine resident at Massachusetts General Hospital, Slavin remembers becoming increasingly conscious of the hospital's management: "Very few of the people in leadership roles were physicians, and I was struck that those people had the same opportunities to influence the same issues that I cared about while I was in Washington: cost, quality, access to health care services." Excited by the possibilities, Slavin began to look for roles that would give him the chance to take on managerial responsibilities.

Directly after his residency, he approached the chief of medicine at MGH, John Potts, to discuss his new interest in health care management:

I really wanted to get a sense if this was something I'd really enjoy doing on a day-to-day basis. I was concerned when I went to see the chief that he would be agape that one of his trainees would want to go into this unusual field of health care management. I was concerned that he wouldn't be supportive, but, as it turned out, he couldn't have been more supportive

Potts was so accommodating, in fact, that he gave Slavin his first management job, as special assistant for fiscal affairs and management for the medical services at MGH, a position which he started immediately after completing his residency.

As Slavin began actually working in health care management, it became clear to him that he wanted more formal training in business: "Someone suggested business school in an almost off-handed way. At first, I thought it was a crazy idea, but the more I thought about it, the more it made sense." Business school was an unusual choice among his peers at MGH and HMS, and was even actively discouraged by some of the physicians there. Slavin considered pursuing some of the graduate programs more traditionally pursued by physicians, such as a masters in public policy or in public health, but ultimately decided that his learning curve would be steepest in business school, and that what he learned there would be most useful over the long term.

Despite feeling good about the decision to pursue "as rigorous training in business as [he] did in medicine," Slavin felt some doubt about the path he chose:

What was the most unsettling part of it was just the fact that there were all these other people going on these well-trodden career paths—cardiology fellowships, endocrine fellowships—and here I was, just making it up as I went along, without any clear idea about what this was going to lead to.

With these thoughts in the back of his mind, Slavin enrolled in Harvard Business School in 1988 and completed his M.B.A. in 1990.

FROM STUDENT TO MANAGER

After graduating from HBS, Slavin returned to the hospital and medical practice with a significantly enhanced awareness of the infrastructure in which he and his colleagues provided patient care. Across the next few years he took on a series of positions of greater responsibility in the MGH leadership, culminating in his appointment as a senior vice president and chief medical officer (CMO)—the hospital's top physician. During this time he also pursued several other professional activities, including publishing several articles on medicine and health care policy, serving as a member of the medical staff for the New England Patriots, and as a reviewer for the *New England Journal of Medicine*.

Among these roles, however, Slavin singles out his three years as senior vice president and chief medical officer at MGH as one of the most formative periods of his career, and also one of the most challenging:

> Chief medical officer at MGH was my first senior management role, so I had to learn very quickly about supervising other people, other managers. I had to learn about managing a sizeable operating capital budget, how to set management priorities, and how to pursue them on a day-to-day basis.

Slavin appreciated the "steep learning curve" that came with the position, and feels that what he learned in that role has stayed with him ever since.

Slavin enjoyed his work at Harvard and MGH, as well as life in the Boston area. In 1997, though, he got an unexpected offer from Barnes Jewish Hospital in St. Louis, Missouri:

> I wasn't looking to leave at that point. I was sitting in my office on a beautiful spring day, and got a call from a recruiter. I had been out to Washington University on several occasions for conferences and meetings and always thought it was a terrific medical center, so I decided to explore it. Before I knew it, they had offered me the job.

The offer, in fact, was to become president of Barnes-Jewish Hospital. It was a difficult decision for Slavin, but the position was an excellent chance for him to further test his management skills, and he was excited by the opportunity to experience a new professional community. Ultimately, after much discussion with his wife, he accepted the position.

During his two years in St. Louis, he continued his work as a practicing physician and taught classes at the Washington University School of Medicine. Slavin found that one of the challenges of working in a new community was that he did not "know the players" in the same way. To succeed in a managerial context, he had to work hard to become familiar with new policies, procedures, and personalities—an experience which ultimately proved to be difficult but satisfying.

His next move, back to Boston, came as unexpectedly as the initial decision to move to St. Louis. "Again," he notes, "I wasn't looking for a job, I was quite happy doing what I was doing out there." But in 1999, MGH asked him to become the chief executive officer of the Massachusetts General Physicians Organization, the entity that employs the majority of the medical staff, and a position which has often served as a stepping stone to the hospital's presidency. It was an attractive offer, and combined with his quietly mounting homesickness for the city of Boston and the extended family he had left there, it was enough to persuade him to go back. He continued in this capacity for three years, and was subsequently offered the presidency of MGH.

LOOKING BACK ON A REWARDING PATH

Slavin's position as president of MGH, which began in early 2003, requires him to draw on the knowledge and experience that he has acquired throughout his management career. He spent years before his current position learning to adjust to different organizations and management styles, and this has helped him to become a flexible leader, able to work with and motivate the people around him:

> I guess that what I've learned over the years is, the more positive energy put out, the more positive energy you're likely to get back. I'm not someone who likes to rant and rave, or carry on, or intimidate people; that's certainly not my management style. What motivates me are some very value-driven things: intense desire to make a difference in other people's lives, and the hope that other people around me will see that and will be equally motivated by it.

Slavin stresses how important it is for developing leaders to remain open-minded about their career paths, so that they are not afraid to adjust to new opportunities or their own changing preferences. Just as people who set out to become practicing physicians sometimes find that they are better suited for management, those who set out to become managers sometimes find that what appeals to them instead is the personal interaction of clinical practice. Though he values discipline and determination, Slavin thinks this flexibility is vital to career satisfaction:

> We do need doctors to take care of patients and do research, so if [doctors who had aspired to management roles] fall in love along the way with cardiology, emergency medicine or OBGYN and want to practice that for the rest of their lives, they shouldn't view it as a tragedy.

Slavin also feels that there is no fixed path to becoming a successful manager in health care:

> Some of the best managers I've ever met in health care never spent a day in business school, a school of public health, or a public policy school. They just have a natural feel for it.

In the long term, Slavin believes that experience on the job can make up for limitations in one's early training. He urges people not to feel constrained by having chosen an educational path that does not lead to the "perfect first job," because there is so much to be learned along the way:

> I think over time what kind of formal training you have becomes secondary to what you've accomplished, and what kinds of impressions you have made on other people. I think those kinds of issues become more important over time than what degrees you have, what letters you have after your name.

REFLECTING ON A MANAGEMENT CAREER

When Slavin looks at his career today, he can sum it up with a noun and an adjective: "The noun would be 'physician' and the adjective would be 'socially-minded.'" In fact, as the title "socially-minded physician" suggests, one of Slavin's greatest joys is the interaction he has with the people he encounters, and the feedback he receives from them:

> In a management role you get to interact with lots of people. I enjoy the incredible richness of the issues and diversity of the issues you get to deal with on a day-to-day basis. That was clearly one of the things that attracted me more to management than a career in research. I just didn't have the patience to write a grant application over several months, wait to see if it got funded, do the research over years, write it up.... It seemed like it was going to be a multi-year feedback loop. In management there are lots of feedback loops going on simultaneously and they're usually much shorter in their duration. There is a rapid cycle time where you see the effects of your work.

Slavin is quick to point out that the achievement in his life that he is most proud of is his family—his wife and two sons. However, he feels that his greatest professional accomplishment is the quality and utilization management program that he has established at MGH. "When I started, people were skeptical that this institution would tolerate a program like that because we had all these independent-minded doctors, and suggesting that care could be better was sort of revolutionary," he explains. But he adds that this is the kind of managerial situation he thrives on:

> Trying to get physicians, nurses, and other care-givers to think about ways to improve the care that they deliver—that is the one area of management

that I find the most interesting and challenging, because it combines medical thinking and management thinking in a very real way.

Soon after assuming the role of president of MGH, Slavin found himself navigating the hospital through an especially difficult period. In the span of one year, tragedy struck the hospital three times with the murder of a staff cardiologist, the accidental death of a custodial worker, and a fire in a Rhode Island nightclub, the Station House, that killed over one hundred people and taxed the resources of MGH when twelve critically injured people were sent there simultaneously for treatment. Slavin acknowledges that nothing could have altogether prepared him for these events—and that getting the hospital through them was not something he could have accomplished alone: "You don't learn how to manage these sorts of things in business school or in medical school for that matter. It took a lot of thought, a lot of energy, and the work of a lot of people to get this organization through those tragedies."

Guiding MGH through this period, in Slavin's mind, was "one of the most important things [he has] done." But he believes that he made an even larger impact on the field of health care by paving the way for other physicians to seek training in business. As one of the first to have done so, he recognizes the contribution that physicians with management training can make:

> I would hope that I proved that in health care management, it is possible for a well-trained physician to make a difference. There are a lot of people who go into health care management—who get M.B.A.'s—principally because they want to make money, and they aren't really all that interested in health care or medicine. Whereas I respect people who go into health care management with a genuine interest to improve the delivery of health care.

Val W. Slayton

East Region Medical Director, Humana
Former Medical Director, Molina Healthcare
Former CMO, UMass Memorial HealthAlliance Hospital

Though he is a clinician by training, Val Slayton's interest in quality improvement in health care systems has led him to tackle increasingly senior roles in hospital and health care system administration. In this profile, Slayton discusses his decision to move from clinical practice into medical administration, and the importance of his early clinical experience for the administrative work that followed. He also reflects on the personal and professional values that have led him to seek out not only new professional challenges, but also a balance between work and family.

Education & Training

1977–1981	A.B., Harvard College
1982–1987	M.D., Harvard Medical School
1985–1987	M.P.P., Harvard Kennedy School of Government
1987-1990	Resident (Internal Medicine), Massachusetts General Hospital,
2004–2007	M.B.A., Isenberg School of Management (University of Massachusetts at Amherst)

Career Path

1990–1995	Staff Internist, The Permanente Medical Group
1990–1995	Assistant Clinical Professor, Department of Internal Medicine, University of California, Davis Medical Center
1992–1995	Co-Director, Preventive Care Program, Kaiser Permanente Health Plan
1996–1997	Associate Medical Director, HealthAmerica
1997–2000	Vice President, Medical Affairs, HealthAmerica
2000–2003	Chief Medical Officer, Fallon Community Health Plan
2004–2005	Chief Medical Officer, Tewksbury Hospital
2005–2010	Chief Medical Officer, HealthAlliance Hospital
2010–2013	Vice President Medical Affairs/Vice President Medical Informatics, Jewish Hospital and St. Mary's Heathcare/ KentuckyOne Health
2013	Vice President, The Camden Group
2013–	Principal, VWS Consulting
2014–	Medical Director, Molina Healthcare

I knew I wanted to have a role in medicine that would allow me to influence patients or populations at a level above the individual doctor-patient relationship. At the same time, I wanted a career path that was going to be challenging—intellectually challenging, challenging in terms of time and effort—but that was also really broad-based and required me to function effectively across a wide range of skills. I think the career path I've ultimately chosen—and I'm not quite sure how much it was a career path I chose as opposed to a career path I took—has allowed me to then have an influence on a larger scale and, at the same time, to be continuously challenged.

—Val Slayton

Throughout his more than thirty years in medicine, Val Slayton's interests and training have taken him from medical school to business school, from Massachusetts to California to Kentucky, and from work as a practicing internist to the executive suites of several different health care systems. A generalist by inclination, Slayton has repeatedly sought out administrative roles that were also learning opportunities, increasing the breadth of his knowledge with each step in his career. His career decisions have also been motivated by a desire to work for organizations whose vision of health care coincides with his own. As chief medical officer of the not-for-profit Fallon Community Health Plan, the first federally funded health maintenance organization in central Massachusetts, Slayton focused on the best ways to provide health care coverage to the plan's 200,000 members. In 2005, he became chief medical officer for HealthAlliance Hospital, a member hospital of UMass Memorial Health Care.

CAREER INTERESTS: FROM BROAD-BRUSH TO GRANULAR

Born and raised in the small town of Monticello, New York, in the lower Catskill Mountains, Slayton arrived at Harvard University as a freshman with a strong academic background and a set of career interests that were, he says, "very broad-brush—medicine, law, business—nothing more granular than that." By his second year at Harvard, however, he had decided to apply to medical school.

Immediately after receiving his undergraduate degree, Slayton went to Harvard Medical School, initially hoping to become a neurologist. A disappointing early lab experience and his growing preference for a career that would allow him to participate in medical administration and policy ultimately steered him away from this specialty:

> I was attracted to internal medicine, really because of the breadth of the field. In terms of many of the challenges that were then facing medicine—and many of those challenges were the same as they are now—I really felt as though a background in internal medicine would give me the broadest possible perspective from which to pursue further career advancement. I knew at that point I had what I would say were ill-defined interests in terms of wanting to work in medicine on a macro basis.

In the middle of Slayton's third-year clinical rotations, a group of students from Harvard's Kennedy School of Government came to the medical school to give a presentation on the joint M.D.-M.P.P. program. "As I thought about what my career path might be and my interests," remarks Slayton, "it really made a lot of sense." After further researching the program, Slayton enrolled and studied public policy alongside medicine.

In 1987, he graduated from Harvard Medical School and the Kennedy School of Government with the dual degree. This choice broadened his options beyond clinical practice, and was instrumental in his ability to take advantage of opportunities in administration.

From Coast to Coast, and From the Clinic to Administration

After graduation, Slayton accepted an internship and residency in internal medicine at Massachusetts General Hospital (MGH). He views this as a valuable period in which he observed a wide range of clinical cases and treatment scenarios. As he developed his clinical skills, though, he became increasingly interested in health care on a macroscopic and systemic level; the questions that seemed most pressing to him concerned how his clinical experience was affected by the policies and organizational networks underpinning it. Pursuing these questions would have to wait, however, until the intensive training of his residency was over: "It was enough to do to stay focused on what was occurring in terms of all of the pressures of clinical medicine," he says.

In 1990, after completing his residency at MGH, Slayton accepted an offer to go into group practice in Sacramento with the Permanente Medical Group, affiliated with the Kaiser Permanente Health Plan. By then, Slayton was married, and a position in northern California suited him for personal as well as professional reasons. He held a teaching appointment at the University of California's Davis Medical Center while working for Permanente, and he also hoped his new position would allow him to pursue his interests in health care policy and administration:

> I decided that I wanted to be in an organized system. I didn't want to go out and just start a practice. I wanted to be in an area where I could do some teaching; I liked the idea of being in a system where research was going on, although I was not doing much research, and I didn't think I was going to be a researcher. And I wanted a system where I could pick up administrative opportunities as they came along.

With Kaiser, Slayton was forthright about his desire to develop his administrative skills. He joined multiple health care committees within the Kaiser network while building his clinical practice as an internist.

CHANGING PRIORITIES

Slayton split his time between clinical and administrative responsibilities for five years, finding the work to be satisfying but the pace and time commitment hectic. As the stress from his dual role became greater, he realized that the hours he spent at work were limiting his time with family. He wanted to be a bigger part of his children's lives, and he wanted to be closer to his parents, who were still living in upstate New York. "At that point," he comments, "I began to recognize my changing priorities and my increasing frustration with trade-offs of clinical, administrative, and family time." These feelings, coupled with a growing sense that his ideal service model was in conflict with Kaiser's, pushed him to make a change.

In 1995, Slayton found himself browsing the *New England Journal of Medicine*, where he stumbled across a listing for what seemed like an ideal administrative position. HealthAmerica, a division of Coventry HealthCare and an early-generation HMO in Pittsburgh, was looking for an associate medical director with experience in credentialing, utilization management, and quality improvement. To Slayton, the experience in the field of health insurance offered by the position seemed like a fresh opportunity to improve care for large groups of people: "It's an administration position," he recalls thinking at the time, "it gets me closer to the East Coast, you know, I'll put my CV together—what's there to lose?"

Slayton was the right person at the right time. He had not yet begun a true job search, and the position at HealthAmerica was the only one to which he applied. When HealthAmerica contacted him for an interview, he flew to Pittsburgh, liked what he saw, and accepted the position: "It was a very good segue for me." Slayton remained at HealthAmerica for four years, starting as the associate medical director, a position in which he preauthorized and examined hospital cases, worked with the nurses to authorize care, and monitored all of the organization's case-management needs.

After going through several transitions, HealthAmerica faced a merger that would bring significant changes to its corporate structure and policies—changes about which Slayton found himself increasingly conflicted. "Thinking about all those things you want to do in health care, identifying folks at high risk, and identifying barriers to delivering good care were all priorities for me," says Slayton; he felt that HealthAmerica's restructuring would limit his ability to realize these priorities and limit his growth as an administrator. He ultimately decided to search for another opportunity.

CREATING A MODEL OF SERVICE: FCHP AND BEYOND

Slayton left HealthAmerica to accept a position as the chief medical officer for Fallon Community Health Plan (FCHP) in Worcester, Massachusetts. There, he worked on community-based managed care and assisted with the administrative challenges of providing HMO, Point of Service (POS), Medicare Risk, and Medical Assistance coverage for plan members. He also dealt with the more specific issues related to disease management, a field that has intrigued Slayton since his time in California. Slayton helped to create Fallon's model for service and felt the organization's priorities were similar to his own. The organization did "a phenomenal job with quality," he says. "The Fallon reputation in disease management is very strong and is well-recognized."

In 2003 Slayton left Fallon to pursue clinical interests, subsequently taking on a series of positions as chief medical officer of increasingly large health care systems. In 2004 he became chief medical officer for Tewksbury Hospital in Tewksbury, Massachusetts. In 2005 he became chief medical officer for HealthAlliance Hospital, affiliated with the UMass Memorial Health Care system. Then, in 2010, Slayton moved to Kentucky to initially take on the role of vice president for medical affairs at Jewish Hospital & St. Mary's HealthCare (JHSMH) in Louisville, a regional health network with more than 70 health care facilities and 1,900 patient beds in Kentucky and southern Indiana. He assumed new systemwide responsibilities as vice president medical informatics in 2012, as his organization underwent a merger to form KentuckyOne Health. In 2013 Slayton left JHSMH to become vice president at The Camden Group, a health care consultancy. In 2014, he became medical director for Molina Healthcare in Cincinnati, Ohio.

From 2010 to 2013, Slayton has also been chosen to serve on the Board of Examiners for the Malcolm Baldrige National Quality Award, given annually in recognition of organizational excellence in health care and other fields. Slayton's selection reflects his long-standing interest in quality improvement.

"In Retrospect, A Very Cohesive Path"

While Slayton loves his administrative work, he nonetheless misses some aspects of clinical practice, such as the individual relationships between doctors and patients. Yet his experience with clinical practice, he says, constantly informs his thinking as an administrator; he believes that thinking in terms of individual doctors and patients has shaped his decisions in health care administration.

These decisions have taught him a particular kind of patience. Administrative work in health care, Slayton concedes, entails the same kinds of frustration as other areas of business administration:

> It is a business environment, which means you have a lot of things that are not going to come to fruition. You just have to accept that. It's sort of what they say about marketing: half of the budget is misspent; the trouble is trying to figure out which half. The hope is that some of your projects will have an effect and really make a difference.

That hope has kept Slayton busy with ambitious and ever-changing projects for the past two decades. He believes that his background, by virtue of both breadth and depth, has enabled him to learn about and become an active part of a large number of health care fields and specialties. He both admires those who have devoted their careers to a particular specialty and takes pride in the administrative role of coordinating disparate activities:

> I think what is really important in health care are the dozens or hundreds of people who have got a clear idea of what they're trying to do and are working with a visionary leader who's able to bridge the vision and the operations, and create organized systems so they accomplish things. That ability to lead these people is really critical.

Slayton has not always been able to foresee the next step in his career, but he feels his choices were right for their respective moments. He found an appropriate image for his way of making decisions, he says, while browsing in a bookstore several years ago:

> I picked up a book called *How Would Confucius Ask for a Raise*? It basically was an effort to look at business issues from an Eastern philosophical perspective….It drew an analogy between a career and a river bursting through a mountain-top. The river starts to flow, and it's a beautiful river, and it finds its spot. It stays there for a while and builds up a pool and then bursts through in another direction, flows down the hill, and finds a new spot….The path that the water took could not have been predicted at the beginning, but each step along the way was the right step. From a distance, in retrospect, it looks like a very cohesive path.

ANDREW C. VON ESCHENBACH

Former Commissioner, United States Food and Drug Administration
Former Director, National Cancer Institute, National Institutes of Health

Once focused on practicing oncology full-time, Andrew von Eschenbach has taken on increasing levels of administrative responsibility in his career, gradually putting aside direct patient care altogether. He is a former director of the National Cancer Institute at the National Institutes of Health, and in 2005 was appointed commissioner of the FDA. In this profile, von Eschenbach discusses the rewards and sacrifices associated with his career advancement. He elucidates the ways in which, despite his move away from clinical activities, medical care in general and oncology in particular have remained part of his life, even at the most fundamentally personal levels.

EDUCATION & TRAINING

1959–1963	B.S., St. Joseph's University
1963–1967	M.D., Georgetown University School of Medicine
1967–1968	Intern, Surgery, Philadelphia General Hospital
1976–1977	Fellow, Urologic Oncology, MD Anderson Cancer Center

CAREER PATH

1969–1972	Lieutenant Commander, United States Navy Medical Corps
1972–1976	Faculty, Pennsylvania Hospital/University of Pennsylvania
1978–1999	Faculty, MD Anderson Cancer Center
1999–2001	Executive Vice President and Chief Academic Officer, MD Anderson
2001–2005	Director, National Cancer Institute, National Institutes of Health
2005–2009	Acting Commissioner (2005–2006), Commissioner (2006–2009), U.S. Food and Drug Administration
2009–2010	Senior Advisor, Greenleaf Health, LLC
2011–	President, Samaritan Health Initiatives
2011–	Senior Fellow, Milken Institute
2012–	Director of Project FDA, Manhattan Institute

I love taking care of people. Cancer is an intellectual issue for me, but it also has a human dimension. There's a real topical reality to cancer—people are suffering and dying from the disease. I not only want to solve cancer as a problem, I want those patients to not suffer and die. I have to be "hands-on."

—*Andrew von Eschenbach*

At the end of his freshman year at St. Joseph's University in Philadelphia, Andrew von Eschenbach, who had planned on going into electronic physics, found himself with a 1.56 GPA in the major. He quickly re-evaluated his priorities, and with the encouragement of his father and a summer job that taught him "the realities of life," von Eschenbach returned to school the following year with a newly discovered perspective. He ended up graduating as the president of his class, with several awards for his high grade point average.

This capacity to reinvent himself and to thrive on fresh starts and new challenges has served von Eschenbach well over the course of his career. Von Eschenbach's first rotation in urology, his future specialty, was the result of an administrative error that he accepted and turned into a learning opportunity. After years as a primarily clinical urological oncologist, he successfully made the transition into primarily administrative roles at the University of Texas's MD Anderson Cancer Center, where he rose to the rank of executive vice president and chief academic officer and played a central role in the coordination of over one thousand cancer researchers. Von Eschenbach then made the transition to the national level in 2002, when he was named director of the National Cancer Institute. He was appointed acting commissioner of the U.S. Food and Drug Administration in 2005, and served in that role until 2009.

MEDICAL SCHOOL AND EARLY CAREER

Von Eschenbach's academic success in college paved the way for admission to medical school. After deciding to go to Georgetown because its program emphasized the clinical aspect of medicine, von Eschenbach quickly realized that he had run out of money. To solve the problem, he joined the

U.S. Navy, a move that also fulfilled a lifelong desire to serve his country in the military. Von Eschenbach's commission said, "Go to Medical School." The monthly paycheck and commission largely solved his financial problems, but at the same time three years of continuous active duty in the navy's general facilities disrupted his plans to pursue a surgical residency.

At this point in von Eschenbach's career, chance won out over careful planning. During sign-ups for internship rotations at the University of Pennsylvania, an administrative error changed the schedule that his mentors had handpicked for von Eschenbach: he was mistakenly placed in urology. But since it was a good surgical specialty, von Eschenbach decided to take the placement anyway:

> It was just a random mistake, but the service had a great reputation and it was just one month, one of those thirty-six hours on, twelve hours off internships where you really wondered by the end of it whether you were going to be able to survive. But I ended up swapping one of my easier rotations with someone else so I was able to take another month of urology. There was no question that of all the surgical specialties, that's the one I really was the most fascinated with.

After completing his service in the navy, von Eschenbach returned to his residency in urology, but quickly discovered it was oncology that really excited him. He felt compelled both by the intellectual stimulation that the study of cancer provided and the human drama of those affected by the disease:

> There was a lot about urology that was fun: come in with cystitis and give a patient some sulfa and she's cured. That feels good, but it wasn't terribly profound. It's not as if I was changing the world. With cancer, there are problems that are of such a greater order of magnitude, and the impact it is having on people's lives is of such a greater order of magnitude. If you can make a difference in that field, with those patients, then you are really changing the world.

Von Eschenbach believes he would have ended up in oncology no matter what specialty he pursued. Although he finds surgery somewhat fulfilling, he says it would not have been intellectually satisfying enough for him on its own. He notes that many surgeons focus on the techniques of the actual surgery to improve the outcomes and the process. What he concentrates on has always been slightly different:

> I didn't want to just do more cystectomies, because I wanted to figure out why thirty percent of those cystectomies who got pre-op radiation had no tumor while the other seventy percent still had a tumor. What was the difference? Ultimately, if we could seize upon that knowledge and downstage all of the tumors we could improve all patients' survival and really change the face of bladder cancer.

FAMILY AND CAREER CHOICES

After his residency, von Eschenbach needed a fellowship to continue his medical studies. Only two places in the country then offered a concentration in urology and oncology: Sloan Kettering in New York City and MD Anderson in Houston, Texas. A mentor steered von Eschenbach toward MD Anderson. Von Eschenbach also had to take into account his "four kids and a really big dog" when making the decision. His wife was "not terribly excited about moving into a small apartment in Manhattan with all the kids," so von Eschenbach chose Houston and quickly discovered the merits of the program. MD Anderson's focus on clinical activity seemed a good fit with his ultimate goal of practicing hands-on medicine, and—after working for a year to pay off debts—he moved his family from Philadelphia, where he had been on the faculty at the Pennsylvania Hospital in the University of Pennsylvania Health System. All the while, he was planning on moving back to Philadelphia when the fellowship was through to pursue a position as the urologic oncologist in the Pennsylvania Hospital.

During his fellowship at MD Anderson, however, von Eschenbach received the difficult news that his father, who lived in Philadelphia, had prostate cancer that had become metastatic and hormone-refractory. At the same time, von Eschenbach was offered a faculty position at MD Anderson:

> The opportunity to stay at Anderson was absolutely extraordinary. There wasn't anything you can think or ask about oncology that you couldn't find somebody that was an expert on there. I was immersed in this environment just like a kid in a candy store.

But his father's disease was progressing, and von Eschenbach wanted to be with him in Philadelphia. He struggled with deciding between great opportunity and familial responsibility:

> My father really believed that I could make a contribution by being at MD Anderson. He said to me, "That's what your mother and I have been working all our lives to give you an opportunity to do, so you've got to stay. If you came back to Philadelphia, it would mean a lot to us, but it's not going to change what's going to happen to me."

During that time he entered his father on some of the newest experimental trials of chemotherapy for prostate cancer sponsored by the National Cancer Institute.

Ultimately, von Eschenbach made the choice to stay at MD Anderson for the next five years. Those five years stretched into 26, and his duties expanded well beyond those of a clinical practitioner.

FROM ONCOLOGIC UROLOGY TO UROLOGIC ONCOLOGY

Von Eschenbach found he was able to have a far greater impact on the field of cancer study and treatment at MD Anderson than he had before. For him, there is a difference between being a urologist on an oncology team and an oncologist on a urology team:

> At Penn I would have been the urological oncologist and everybody else would have been doing their thing: the stone guy, the fertility guy. You were a team, but it was a urologic team. At MD Anderson, everybody on the team was an oncologist. You might be the urologic oncologist, they might be the radiation oncologist, but it was an environment that was just pure oncology.

Von Eschenbach was able to focus purely on oncology, without having to take on other types of care, as he would have had to do at a non-cancer-centered clinic. He summarizes the intensity of MD Anderson in this way: "If you made the decision that you really wanted to make a contribution to cancer, you'd say, 'I think I have arrived at the place.'"

MIGRATING FROM CLINICAL CARE TO EXECUTIVE LEADERSHIP

Von Eschenbach says that playing many different roles during his 26 years at MD Anderson allowed him to "bring things together in such a way that the whole is greater than the sum of its parts." Although he focused almost exclusively on patient care, research, and teaching during his early and mid-career, he still found time to get involved in many of the organizational issues at the hospital, where he put his integrative mind to work: "There probably wasn't a committee at Anderson that I didn't, at some time or another, serve on as chairman." Eventually he would leave the operating room for the boardroom on a full-time basis.

Although giving up operating on patients was difficult, von Eschenbach realized that if he wanted to have a larger impact, he could not focus on any one part of medical care:

> There comes a point in time when you realize that you personally are not going to cure cancer, that the cure to cancer is going to depend upon a team, with everybody contributing. Then, as a member of that team, you decide that you're not going to play anymore. You're going to coach. There has to be a decision then as to what's more important: you scoring a touchdown or you doing something that helps the team win.

Even when managing the team, von Eschenbach tried to stay involved in direct care. He frequently talked with patients and did consulting. Yet to balance his larger responsibilities, he did have to give up certain aspects of the clinical experience. Offering the best as a surgeon, he says, means focusing purely on surgery, reading the journals, and being in the operating room every day.

I can't go back to surgery. I don't have the commitment; I don't have the focus. There are too many people asking me too many other questions. There are young people who can do it quicker and better then I can. And it's not about me, and it's not about my ego, and it's not about what I miss. It's about what's in the patients' best interest. I can't offer the best anymore.

Instead, as his focus shifted from individual cases of cancer to the big picture of institutional and national cancer research, von Eschenbach has tried to benefit patients in ways less direct but more broadly influential. This goal was further realized when, in 2001 President George W. Bush asked von Eschenbach to take over as director of the National Cancer Institute (NCI).

ALL CANCER, NOT JUST ONE

Being responsible for "all cancer, not just one," presented a different set of challenges and rewards. The immediate gratification of removing a tumor and hearing a patient say, "'You saved me!'" was replaced by other satisfactions. As von Eschenbach explained a year after taking over the NCI:

We're sitting around talking about our strategic goals for 2015, and I'm thinking, "Heck, I'm not even going to be here!" I'm not going to see the outcome because the timeline's 2015, but I have the opportunity to help put things in place that will ultimately eliminate the suffering of those with cancer. So every time I miss the fact that I don't have a patient that I know sitting in front of me doing well, I keep thinking about a world in 2015 that will be free of the suffering and death due to cancer. I believe that's a reality that's in our grasp.

Even though von Eschenbach's role in cancer had changed, the problem-solving skills that drove him to oncology in the first place remain the same: "It's just as much of a challenge to solve the problem of how the pieces fit together as it is to try to figure out why a tumor metastasizes."

In 2005 President Bush asked von Eschenbach to step in as acting commissioner of the Food and Drug Administration (FDA) after the resignation of the former commissioner. He was later confirmed as the commissioner in 2006, a position in which he continued until 2009. As commissioner, von Eschenbach strove to improve efficiency and transparency at the FDA, and tried to improve its relations with the companies it regulates. Von Eschenbach has continued to focus on these relations since leaving the FDA, serving as a consultant to companies regarding FDA regulations. He has also worked in several think tanks, including Newt Gingrich's Center for Health Transformation, the Milken Insitute, and the Manhattan Institute. At the latter, von Eschenbach chairs Project FDA, developing policies to help the FDA work more productively with corporations inventing new technologies. Von Eschenbach is also an adjunct professor at MD Anderson Cancer Center, and president of Samaritan Health Initiatives, a health care policy consultancy.

Regrets, Reflections, and the Swinging Trapeze

Von Eschenbach attributes some of his success to his ability to let go of the past. As his strengths, aptitudes, and interests have grown and changed, he has pursued new goals while allowing aspects of his job that have become less central to fall away:

> I tell all of the people that I train that life is like a trapeze act, and you swing from one ring to another. When you reach out for that next ring you think is going to take you to a greater height, you've always got to be prepared to let go of the other one. So many people have trouble with that—not reaching for the next ring, but letting go of the last. Bad things happen when you do that. You get spread thin and your priorities, like your family, start falling off your tray. That's a bad scenario. You've got to be able to let go if you want to reach out.

One of von Eschenbach's greatest regrets is that being a clinical provider has kept him out of the lab. Von Eschenbach intended to spend time figuring out some of the medical problems that bothered him in medical school, but he was never able to tear himself away from patient care to do so. "It's not a credential" he's missing, he says. "I think it's a chapter in my life that's sort of missing."

In spite of this missing chapter, von Eschenbach was able to have a major impact on research through his administrative roles, and regards his career's greatest achievement as "the epitome of the integration of basic science and clinical science." Von Eschenbach was in charge of a team that won two SPORE (Special Programs of Research Excellence) awards, which are given to institutions that combine excellent research with clinical application:

> The SPORE program required bringing together two teams and being able to get them working and functioning together in a way that created something that qualified as a specialized program. They are highly competitive awards. Most institutions are knocking themselves out to get one SPORE. Our program had two.

Although von Eschenbach was not the principal investigator of the award, he oversaw the team that did it. He reflects on the accomplishment with his favored metaphor: "It wasn't important that I scored the touchdown; it was only important that the team won."

Von Eschenbach's career path has shifted many times. His experiences as a surgeon, an administrator, and a leader have changed the way he views medicine as well as the way he understands his practice:

I started out with the idea of the "brave warrior." I was going to cure every-body. Death was the enemy and never would it prevail. Cancer really humbled me. I came to realize that there was a difference between the journey and the outcome, that, as a physician, my first and foremost responsibility was to heal. Curing can be an important part of that. But there were a lot of times when I could not cure a patient—that did not mean they couldn't heal.

For von Eschenbach, there is one facet of medical care that can't be ac-counted for by skills and techniques. It is the human part of medicine, which he sees as the most important part of being someone's doctor:

What I did as an oncologist was to engage in a very intimate relationship with another human being who was facing the gravities of the threat of cancer. You'd walk that journey with them, and you'd tell patients, "You know, we're going to go to a dark and scary place here, but I've been through this before. So take my hand, hold on real tight, and we're going to get through this. You focus on the light at the end of the tunnel, and I'll focus on the journey."

Cyril H. Wecht

Forensic Pathologist and Medical-Legal Consultant

As one of the nation's leading forensic pathologists, Cyril Wecht has worked on and formed unwavering conclusions about our nation's most controversial and provocative death cases, including John F. Kennedy's assassination and Elvis Presley's untimely death. In this profile, he provides a detailed description of his field and explains how his law degree has complemented his work as a forensic pathologist.

Education & Training

1948–1952	B.S., University of Pittsburgh
1952–1956	M.D., University of Pittsburgh School of Medicine
1957–1959	J.D., University of Pittsburgh School of Law (conferred 1962)
1957–1959	Resident, Veterans Administration-University of Pittsburgh Law School (Pathology)
1961–1962	Fellowship, Office of the Chief Medical Examiner, Baltimore, MD (Forensic Pathology)

Career Path

1961–1962	Pathologist, North Charles General Hospital (Baltimore, MD)
1964–1978	Director, Pittsburgh Pathology and Toxicology Laboratory
1968–1982	Pathologist and Laboratory Director, Podiatry Hospital of Pittsburgh
1970–1980	County Coroner, Allegheny County Coroner's Office
1973–1999	Chairman, Department of Pathology, St. Francis Central Hospital (Pittsburgh, PA)
1974–	Adjunct Professor of Pathology & Legal Medicine, Duquesne School of Pharmacy
1984–	Adjunct Professor of Law, Duquesne University School of Law
1996–2006	County Coroner, Allegheny County Coroner's Office
1996–	Clinical Professor of Pathology, University of Pittsburgh School of Medicine

Selected Publications

Wecht, Cyril and Dawna Kaufmann. *A Question of Evidence: Compelling Cases from a Famed Forensic Pathologist*. Amherst, NY: Prometheus Books, 2008.

Wecht, Cyril and Greg Saitz, with Mark Curriden. *Mortal Evidence: The Forensics Behind Nine Shocking Cases*. Amherst, NY: Prometheus Books, 2003.

Wecht, Cyril and Charles Bosworth, Jr. *Who Killed JonBenet Ramsey?* New York: Onyx, 1998.

Additional Information

Wecht Institute of Forensic Science & Law: www.forensics.duq.edu
Cyril Wecht's webpage: www.cyrilwecht.com

Our field hasn't changed dramatically. It's not like some surgical or medical specialties with all kinds of new instrumentalities. We have the autopsy, the microscope, the slides, the toxicology testing, the brain examination and so on. DNA, that's a side issue for us. Computers and that stuff may help procedurally but it doesn't help a great deal substantively. The DNA may tell the cops eventually who did it, but it doesn't change things for me in determining if there was evidence of rape.

—*Cyril H. Wecht*

Cyril Wecht's decision early in his career to pursue degrees in both medicine and law was an unusual one, but also a sensible one given his specialization in pathology, which would involve frequent interactions with the justice system. The timing of these studies, though, is what sets Wecht apart and conveys some idea of the abundance of energy and determination that has characterized his career as a whole: Wecht earned his law degree at the same time that he was completing his medical residency, effectively completing two arduous courses of professional training in the time it would normally take to do just one of them. Wecht has been working at a similar rate ever since. A nationally renowned pathologist who has helped to investigate some of the most publicized deaths of the past five decades, from the assassination of President Kennedy to the murders of JonBenet Ramsey and Laci Peterson, Wecht has also served for much of this time as the elected coroner for Allegheny County, Pennsylvania. A politically active Democrat, he has occupied leadership positions with Pennsylvania's Democratic party and was its nominee to become Pennsylvania's U.S. Senator in 1982. Wecht is also a widely respected author of both instructional textbooks related to law and pathology and of several books directed to a general audience about his work as a pathologist.

EARLY EDUCATION AND TRAINING: PACKING TEN YEARS INTO FIVE

Wecht became a doctor because his father told him to be one. The only child of European immigrants, Wecht was an obedient son, a "good kid." "It never occurred to me that I would not go to medical school; it may sound silly, but it is true."

It was not until his third year of medical school at the University of Pittsburgh that he became seriously interested in both law and pathology. To this day, he is not sure why he was attracted to pathology, especially since his medical school did not offer a pathology or forensic pathology rotation. He decided that a law degree would nicely complement a career in forensic pathology because forensic pathologists spend time consulting with attorneys and testifying in courtrooms.

After completing medical school and his compulsory rotating internship, he applied to law school and was accepted to Harvard and Yale, but selected the University of Pittsburgh School of Law because he was offered a full scholarship. At that same time, he began his four-year pathology residency at the Veterans Administration-University of Pittsburgh Medical Center. The chairman of his pathology department allowed him to attend his law school classes as long as he finished his residency work. Because the law school was only a three-minute drive from the medical center, Wecht was able to successfully scuttle back and forth between the two campuses and disciplines.

After he simultaneously finished his first two years of residency and law school, Wecht was required to serve in the military under the Berry Plan, which allowed graduating physicians to do a residency before entering the military in exchange for their service as specialists upon completion of the residency. During his two years of service, he worked as a pathologist at Maxwell Air Force Base in Alabama. While there, he examined surgical specimens sent from 29 airbases throughout the Southeastern United States, and in the process earned credit for the third and fourth years of his residency. After completing his military service, he moved to Baltimore to begin his forensic pathology fellowship at the Baltimore Medical Examiner's Office (BMEO). He chose Baltimore because it had a "top-notch" forensic pathology fellowship program—the University of Pittsburgh did not offer a forensic pathology fellowship—and because the University of Maryland had an accredited law school, which offered evening classes. He trained in forensic pathology by day and attended law school by night.

After one year at the BMEO, Wecht was done with his training: five years of pathology, three years of law school, and two years of military service: "I was fortunate because I packed what would have been ten years into five." He attributes his success in that endeavor to being young, energetic and unmarried:

> I married during my fellowship—but I was eager, and I knew what I wanted to do. I worked hard. I moonlighted during my first two years of residency. I worked an average of three weeknights and two out of every three weekends covering hospital emergency rooms for extra money. I've always been able to work a lot and willing to do so.

FROM STUDENT TO CORONER

Wecht returned to Pittsburgh in July of 1962 and immediately went to work as an Allegheny County assistant district attorney and medical-legal advisor to the district attorney, while he simultaneously worked as a hospital pathologist. Pittsburgh's coroner at the time was a layperson, who was running one of the most backward medical legal investigative offices in the country, according to Wecht. In 1966, the former coroner was replaced by Dr. William A. Hunt, who subsequently asked Wecht to become the county's chief forensic pathologist. Four years later, Wecht was elected county coroner, a position he held from 1970 to 1980 and again from 1996 to 2006. In his role as county coroner, he has been involved in both criminal and civil cases. He performs autopsies, consults with attorneys, testifies in courtrooms, and when a case is complex or especially interesting, investigates crime scenes. Forensic pathologists are trained to investigate crime scenes and to work with detectives, police officers, prosecutors, and criminologists:

> My career is very intellectually provocative and challenging. You think you've seen everything, but there is always something new and different. I just got off the phone with a state trooper who was discussing a case that they thought was suicide. I pointed out that the powder-tattooing pattern shows that the shot was fired from a distance of several inches. While the guy could have reached out with his arm to shoot himself, it's sure not something that ordinarily is done. Now they're going back to the wife and adult son, who were at the scene, to talk about it.

Although he and other American forensic pathologists only examine corpses—in other countries, forensic pathologists are often called upon to examine the living—Wecht also is involved in non-death cases, such as rape and sexual assault. He is given access to the alleged victim's medical examination record and lab reports, and from those reports determines if the person was, in fact, raped. Also, if the attorney requests it, Wecht will interview the alleged victim. According to Wecht, contemporary forensic pathologists are also involved with various traumatic cases because they are specially qualified to deal with the "mechanism of the injury, the etiology of the injury, and the patterns of repetitive nature."

THE PROPER MINDSET

Wecht believes that his rigorous training has enabled him to remain impartial, a necessary trait in a forensic pathologist:

> Certainly, in what you do as a forensic pathologist, as a forensic scientist, as a medical-legal consultant, you must constantly strive to determine things in an objective manner. On the criminal side of things, justice is obviously quite

important. On the civil side, there's justice in another sense. Nothing pleases me more than to have a case where I write a detailed report, give a deposition, and then receive a letter telling me that because of my report and my deposition, they were able to obtain a favorable settlement. That's so satisfying.

Wecht warns, though, that forensic pathologists must be cognizant of their own biases. He has seen them develop prosecutorial biases while working on cases for the district attorney's office. Wecht, who as coroner received his funding from the county executive and the county council, believes that he never ran into a conflict of interest while in office. Along with being objective, he said good forensic pathologists are bold, tenacious, and intelligent, but also patient and understanding:

> The greatest occupational hazard, the most dangerous one in my opinion, because I've seen it played out hundreds of times in four decades, is when forensic pathologists allow themselves to consciously or subconsciously become part of the prosecutorial team. Forensic scientists working in medical legal investigative offices should be independent and should not be part of the prosecutor's office. They have to be objective scientists, medical ombudsmen so to speak. I work and collaborate a lot with law enforcement officers and the district attorney's office. I enjoy good relationships with them, but I'm autonomous and independent. I'm not one of their functionaries.

In the Spotlight

Wecht has also maintained a prominent and successful practice as a private consultant. He is retained for medical malpractice, wrongful death, product liability, and insurance cases. One such case, for example, required Wecht to determine if a truck driver, who died from carbon monoxide poisoning, was killed because of a truck defect.

As a private consultant, he has also worked on many high-profile cases. In 1972, he was the first non-government affiliated forensic pathologist to be granted access to the Kennedy autopsy materials stored in the National Archives Building in Washington, D.C. While conducting the investigation, he learned that the president's brain was missing. He was immediately interviewed by the *New York Times* reporter Fred Graham, who had contacted Wecht prior to his visiting the National Archives. The *Times* ran Graham's exclusive on page one. To this day, Kennedy's brain is still unaccounted for, according to Wecht.

Wecht's involvement in the Kennedy case actually began in 1965 when he gave a presentation to the American Academy of Forensic Sciences about the assassination. In 1966, he was hired as a consultant to Time Life Magazines to study the Zapruder film, the video footage of the Kennedy assassination:

I concluded that the Warren Commission was incorrect, that there were two people shooting. The single bullet theory, which is the *sine qua non* of the Warren Commission report's conclusion regarding the sole assassin, is sheer unadulterated nonsense. Without the single bullet theory, you've got to have two shooters. It's based upon the sequence of the shooting, the correlation of the wounds of Kennedy and Governor John Connelly, the amount of time it takes to shoot the weapon, and the correlation with the Zapruder film.

After Elvis Presley's death in 1977, the television news program *20/20* hired Wecht as a consultant to review the autopsy findings and the toxicology report:

He died from the combination of a dozen central nervous system depressant drugs. He didn't die from any heart disease; it was sheer nonsense. They finessed it from the medical examiner's office, purported that it was a private case, so that they would never have to make the official autopsy report public. He died because his good friend, Dr. Nichopolous, kept on prescribing everything and anything Elvis wanted. He was just loaded up with drugs, and the poor man died from their cumulative effect.

More recently, Wecht worked as a consultant for different news media outlets on the JonBenet Ramsey case. In his book, *Who Killed JonBenet Ramsey?*, he concluded that someone in the household accidentally caused her death during a sex game gone horribly wrong. In 1996 he was also hired by the O.J. Simpson defense team to work as a consultant. He believes that Simpson could not have acted alone in the murder, and that there were therefore two killers.

Wecht attributes his litany of high-profile cases to the fact that he has proven over the years that he is credible and articulate:

I've been around for a long time. I've gotten a lot of experience. Frankly, once you become involved and show that you know your stuff and that you can articulate issues, you can hold up under pressure in deposition or in a trial testimony, that you have credibility and you're not flip-flopping all over the place, that your opinion can't be bought, then the word gets out. You've got to know what you're talking about, you cannot be a bullshit artist, and you can't come up with crazy stories. It's going to catch up with you.

Wecht also believes his law degree has helped him in his career by giving him a better understanding of the legal system and how an attorney's mind works. He said that all forensic pathologists would inevitably end up testifying and working with attorneys:

I am able to anticipate where the opposition is trying to lead me in cross-examination. What traps he's trying to lead me into. I'm able to suggest, before trial, lines of inquiry to the attorney who has consulted me. I'm able to deal with some legal concepts and theories and correlate them with the medical facts, so I can be of much more value to the attorney who has consulted me than I could if I had no legal training.

A FULFILLING LIFE

Beyond his career as a forensic pathologist and the 80-hour workweeks this has typically involved, Wecht has found time to pursue some other key interests, including politics. He served as the chairman of the Allegheny County Democratic Party for six years and in 1982 he unsuccessfully ran for the United States Senate against the Republican incumbent John Heinz, of the Heinz ketchup family. U.S. senator was the only federal position that interested Wecht because, as he said, "U.S. senators deal with pressing international and national issues."

He has also edited numerous technical books and several accounts of his pathological investigations aimed at the general public, including *A Question of Murder* (with Dawna Kaufmann, 2008) and *Mortal Evidence: The Forensics Behind Nine Shocking Cases* (with Greg Saitz and Mark Curriden, 2003). He lectures at the Duquesne University School of Law and at the University of Pittsburgh School of Medicine. In 2000, Duquesne, which is located in Pittsburgh, honored Wecht by establishing the Cyril H. Wecht Institute of Forensic Science and Law. The institute is the first forensic science program to work in conjunction with a law school (Duquesne School of Law).

Wecht has no plans to retire from his work as a pathologist, and has continued to serve as a consultant for numerous investigations and trials, including nationally known cases such as the murder of Laci Peterson as well as lower-profile cases in his home state of Pennsylvania. Looking back on his career, Wecht feels content with the choices he has made and fortunate in the opportunities that have come his way:

> Not that I ever sat down and thought about it in advance, but I'm glad that I chose this career because I have an inquisitive mind and a broad range of interests. It's not that I get bored easily or I'm a dilettante, but I like things that are intellectually challenging and stimulating, rewarding in many ways. I don't mind saying that I enjoy working with other people, including prominent attorneys, and prominent experts. I like being interviewed and being involved in national television programs. I do enjoy all that and feel I can make a worthwhile contribution to society and the pursuit of justice. I'm damn lucky I went into this field.

GAIL R. WILENSKY

Former Administrator, Health Care Financing Administration
Senior Fellow, Project HOPE

Gail Wilensky is one of the most widely recognized experts on U.S. health care policy and specifically on federal financing and the Medicare and Medicaid systems. She has published hundreds of articles, has testified before Congress on more than ninety occasions, and has delivered hundreds of speeches to professional, business, and consumer groups. This profile traces her career path from academia into government and the highest levels of the health policy sphere.

EDUCATION & TRAINING

1960–1964	B.A., University of Michigan (Psychology)
1964–1965	M.A., University of Michigan (Economics)
1965–1968	Ph.D., University of Michigan (Economics)

CAREER PATH

1968–1969	Staff Economist, President's Commission on Income Maintenance Programs
1969–1971	Executive Director, Maryland Council of Economic Advisers
1971–1973	Senior Research Associate, Urban Institute
1973–1975	Visiting Assistant Professor, University of Michigan
1975–1983	Fellow and Research Manager, National Center for Health Services Research, Department of Health and Human Services
1983–1989	Vice President, Health Affairs, Project HOPE
1989–1990	Commissioner, Physician Payment Review Commission
1990–1992	Administrator, Health Care Financing Administration
1992–1993	Deputy Assistant to the President for Policy Development, The White House
1993–	Senior Fellow, Project HOPE

A list of Wilensky's additional positions appears on the last page of this profile.

ADDITIONAL INFORMATION

Gail Wilensky's website: www.gailwilensky.com

As a physician you have a way to impact the well-being of the individual in the most immediate and direct way, but as a health policy person, I have potentially an ability to impact a community or a state or a nation in a very significant way—never at the level that a clinician will have on a one-to-one basis, but an ability to affect large numbers of people in ways that the clinician who is working one-to-one will never be able to do.

—Gail Wilensky

Gail Wilensky's career, which has taken her from academia to policy think tanks to the highest ranks of government, has been unified by two constant themes: a fascination with human behavior, and a desire to have a direct impact on real health care problems. Her interest in behavior began with her study of psychology as an undergraduate at the University of Michigan, and has extended throughout her career in applied microeconomics. Her desire to directly impact the world, in turn, helped solidify her shift from psychology to economics, and later from a research-oriented career to one more closely involved with policy decisions. After many years as a researcher in the Department of Health and Human Services, Wilensky accepted a senior policy position with the international health care education foundation Project HOPE, an organization to which she returned as a senior fellow in 1993 after a series of high-level positions in government. These included two years of service as the administrator of the Health Care Finance Administration, overseeing both Medicare and Medicaid. In addition, Wilensky has served as commissioner of the World Health Organization's Commission on the Social Determinants of Health in 2005, as co-chair of a Defense Department task force on the future of military health care from 2006–2008, and as president and chair of the Health Care Subcommittee of the Defense Health Board from 2008–2009. In addition to her role at Project Hope she currently serves as a regent of the Uniformed Services University of the Health Sciences, on the board of the Geisinger Health System Foundation and on the Visiting Committee of the Harvard Medical and Dental Schools. She is a former chair of the board of directors of Academy Health, a former trustee of the American Heart Association, as well as a current or former director of several other non-profit organizations. She has also served as a director on several corporate boards including Cephalon, Quest Diagnostics, SRA International, and United HealthGroup.

ANALYSIS AND RIGOROUS THINKING

While growing up, Wilensky did not have a specific career goal: "It never had occurred to me that I wouldn't be actively doing something," she recalls; "I just never thought about what that something would be." During her first year of college at the University of Michigan, her interest in human behavior was piqued by an experience in her introductory psychology class:

> I got into a debate in freshman class with a professor about an answer to an exam question. It was not about whether it was necessarily true or not, but rather about why it logically *couldn't* be true. This was as good an answer on the subject as he had been looking for, and the debate intrigued him enough that he set me up in a lab to try to establish whether or not my answer could be proven correct.

This opportunity provided Wilensky, while still in her first year at college, with access to graduate student labs and research, and as a result she gained a deep appreciation for the scientific method and the analytic process: "It turned out, not surprisingly, that the answer was indeterminate, as many things are, but it made me very interested in the area, and strengthened my appreciation for analytic skills." Intrigued by her new field, she decided to pursue a degree in psychology, with the intent of applying analytic rigor to human behavior as an experimental psychologist.

Wilensky continued on this path through college, and applied for admission to the Ph.D. program in psychology at Michigan. As the end of her senior year drew near, however, she began to have doubts about her chosen field of study:

> In my senior year I decided that I was getting bored with what I was doing. Since I had just gotten married, and my husband was at medical school at Michigan, I could not change schools. I had taken one course in economics as an undergraduate, and I thought it was interesting. But rather than resubmit my application, the university said they would just cross off "psychology" and write "economics" on my application. So my application went to the economics department with my essays about why I wanted to be a Ph.D. psychologist.

Wilensky believes that this decision, while fortuitous in retrospect, was made for "all the wrong reasons." Although she had found her one previous economics class fascinating, she characterizes her career switch as rather brash:

> It was not with a lot of thought and it was almost with no preparation. I entered graduate school having had one economics course as an undergrad. During the summer before, they had suggested that I take a course or two,

although I started my first year as a grad student with no macro or micro background, and no math in college. Today they would never let somebody do that.

Wilensky was allowed to switch fields, but soon found out that catching up on the background she needed would not be easy:

In my first year I was hit with macroeconomic theory, microeconomic theory, mathematical economics and econometrics. And I was like "uh, what happened?" But ultimately, of course, these are the tools that you need in order to be an applied microeconomics person, which is what I ended up becoming.

Despite their somewhat different prerequisites, economics and psychology were, for Wilensky, also closely related fields. First, psychology and economics are both fundamentally about understanding human behavior. While psychology studies how individuals behave under broad sets of circumstances, economics studies how people, either as individuals or as groups, behave under different sets of economic incentives. Wilensky therefore sees economics as big-picture psychology. Furthermore, both fields use testable hypotheses and scientific method to understand human behavior: "It was the rigor of the thinking, and trying to explain behavior in an analytic process, that interested me in psychology and that ultimately interested me in economics, rather than what seemed to be the obvious connections." The interest in health care that would eventually bring these fields still closer together was, at this point in time, not yet a factor in her thinking.

THE SEARCH FOR A BROADER "SO WHAT"

Shortly after beginning her graduate work, Wilensky realized that economics also met another one of her professional needs—the desire to have a direct and tangible impact on the real world:

It was a bit of a shock because economics seemed to have so much real-world, direct application. That had been one of the things that I had been a little frustrated about in my area of psychology. While I liked the rigor and liked the analytic components, I would sometimes be troubled by the distance between the areas I was working on and the actual "so what" part of the question.

A clear "so what" alone was not enough, however. Wilensky wanted her work to have not just any purpose, but a socially significant one:

The "so what" needed to have a broader application—if I was helping a soap company sell soap flakes, you could say that a sales strategy might answer the "so what" aspect but would have such a narrow consequence that it would not have been very satisfying. It had to be a broader "so what"—in terms of who was affected, how they were affected, and how many people were affected.

Wilensky satisfied this desire to do broadly relevant work by studying the economics of public policy. For her graduate work, she chose to focus on state and local government finance. At first her advisor suggested she work on health care issues, but she refused: "I strongly resisted, first because I thought he was pushing me there because that was a 'female' thing, and second because my husband was a physician, and I thought, one per family in an area was probably enough." She ended up writing her dissertation on financing primary and secondary education, earning her Ph.D. in 1968.

That year Wilensky and her husband moved to Baltimore, where he was beginning his residency in surgery. Wilensky commuted from Baltimore to Washington, D.C. for a position as a staff economist for the President's Commission on Income Maintenance Programs; this new position allowed her to work on welfare reform, which had been another area of interest during graduate school. In this role she set up a micro-simulation model used to estimate the effects of various welfare reform proposals.

Shortly after starting her new job, Wilensky realized she was pregnant and asked about working part-time after her child was born. She was told flatly that professional staff could not work on a part-time basis. The complexity of the analysis and her role in it continued to grow, however, and eventually her boss asked her to return on a part-time basis as soon as she was able. "This was an important lesson," Wilensky concludes. "When employers need flexibility, they are incredibly creative about finding ways to make it happen."

After her maternity leave, however, Wilensky decided to stay closer to home, and joined the newly established Maryland Council of Economic Advisors. The group included very well known economists, but it did not really hold Wilensky's interest: "It was a potent group, but the work was isolated from others and too often boring. I did it for about a year and a half, but then decided that convenience did not outweigh being isolated and bored."

BECOMING A HEALTH CARE ECONOMIST[1]

It was at that point, in 1971, that Wilensky joined the Urban Institute, a decision which began her trajectory into health care economics:

> At the Urban Institute I was initially going to work on welfare reform, but when I went over to talk to them, I met Stuart Altman. He said, "We have so many people working on welfare, and I have no one working on health care. Why don't you work with me on health care?" He said I could do some of the simulations I was doing on income support in health care, and some of the same kinds of modeling behavior. So I agreed to do that. This was my first taste of being in health care.

This was the early 1970s, and the field of health care economics was just becoming a distinct field. Through her work at UI, Wilensky met some of the newly trained economists who were becoming the first generation of modern health care economists, such as Uwe Reinhart and Frank Sloan.

Wilensky initially focused on analyzing the cost distribution effects of a national health insurance; just as Altman had assured her, the work was similar to that involving welfare reform. While her intention was to examine the data at a very analytical and academic level, she found herself increasingly attracted to the underlying policy questions. The implications of the model also spread beyond health care: "Initially it was a quite simple model, but I recognized it could have implications for food stamps, for labor force participation, and for wages." The broad significance of her work at UI left her open to continuing on in health care economics.

Two years later, Wilensky moved back to Michigan with her husband, who had accepted a fellowship there in plastic surgery. Back at Michigan, Wilensky accepted a visiting joint professorship in economics and public policy. She spent her summers at the Survey Research Center, where she developed a new set of interests that would prove important for her future work:

> I became fascinated with survey research as a way of collecting accurate information, as opposed to polling data that provides information on opinions—in how you get unbiased, valid, reliable information through surveys. Until then I hadn't really thought about what it takes to get such information.

In her second year, Wilensky was invited by health care economist Paul Feldstein to base her research at Michigan's school of public health. Through this appointment, Wilensky used her new interest in survey methods to study a personally relevant economic question: how do new physicians decide where to practice after their residencies? Before her study was completed, however, she and her husband moved back to Washington, deciding that Ann Arbor did not need yet one more newly minted plastic surgeon.

Back in Washington, Feldstein put Wilensky in touch with Jerry Rosenthal, who was heading up the National Center for Health Services Research at HHS, and in 1975 she was hired as the first NCHSR health service fellow. At NCHSR Rosenthal put Wilensky and a career government analyst, Dan Walden, in charge of launching a major survey study on health care expenditures, which became the first National Medical Care Expenditure Survey:

> NMCES provided an opportunity to survey individuals about their health expenditures, health insurance, and health care utilization. I had learned how limited the data was, and I was fascinated with surveys as a way of getting good information. I thought this had the potential to let me go back and do what I really had wanted to do at the Urban Institute, when there was inadequate data.

Wilensky and Walden ended up being in charge of a massive $26 million research project with 40,000 survey respondents. At the core of their work lay the central questions of how health care expenditures, coverage, and utilization were related. Similar questions were being asked at the same time by a study known simply as the Health Insurance Experiment, headed up by Joseph Newhouse (page 374) at RAND; Newhouse and Wilensky soon became close colleagues thanks to their common interests.

It was at this point that Wilensky realized that health care had become more than a passing professional interest: "I guess I'm not leaving this area," she recalls thinking, "and that means I'm a health economist." This professional identity was crystallized when George Washington University asked her to teach a course on health care economics after Richard Scheffler, an established expert in the field, left GW for Berkeley. The offer signaled recognition of her accomplishments in the field, and was at the same time a chance to learn more about it:

> The problem was, the only literature I had read was on topics related to my research. That meant I had very big gaps. So, when I was asked if I would like to teach a course of health care economics, I thought, "Sure, that's a good way to learn the literature." So, indeed, I taught a graduate course on health care economics for three years.

At NCHSR, Wilensky also had to hire and manage a very talented group of young Ph.D.'s to assist with the massive study. This provided her with her first significant experience with management, and helped her to realize she had a talent for it—a fact that would later serve her very well. As she explains, the size of the organization is not the most significant factor; once you have five or six people under you, you need to implement a structure, and that is the same no matter how large the organization.

MAKING RESEARCH MATTER: THE TRANSITION INTO POLICY

In 1982, the American Economics Association accepted Wilensky's paper "Government and the Financing of Health Care," a study of the distributional effects of Medicare and Medicaid compared to tax expenditures arising from employer-paid health insurance and other health-related tax deductions. (Tax expenditures are foregone tax revenues, called "expenditures" on the same logic that makes non-collection of a debt equivalent to a payment.) Her paper was only ten double-spaced pages long, and she did not consider its findings extraordinary:

> It had been something economists had talked about for years—how the tax expenditures favored the wealthy, because of their higher marginal tax rate, which could roughly offset the distributions of Medicare and Medicaid at the

low end. It was what economists had presumed, only the paper had much better empirical support than anyone had previously had.

The paper showed, in other words, that if tax expenditures were taken into account, the government was spending roughly as much on health care for the wealthy as it was on the poor. In part because it was released during a slow news cycle and in part thanks to the solid empirical research supporting its conclusions, the paper got national publicity—much to Wilensky's surprise—and changed the course of her career:

> It really propelled me, in a very significant way, into the policy world, as someone who was talking about what were interesting and salient policy issues. I had already been brought into conversations with members of Congress through my work on Medicaid, but this was really on a different level—this was national exposure. A number of people said I was "an overnight success." My response was: "An overnight success…fifteen years in the making!"

After almost eight years at NCHSR, Wilensky was growing somewhat tired of her role as an academic researcher: "I was getting a little bit restless. I had done a lot of writing, a lot of speaking, I had published a lot in this area." The effect of her article on public and legislative debates confirmed her desire for a role with a more immediate impact on policy. It also taught her an important lesson about what it would take for academic research to make this kind of an impact:

> For my work to make a difference, it had to be information that was intuitively understandable, that is able to be explained in a relatively straightforward way. There is a difference between "statistically significant" and "significant." It's fine to use sophisticated statistics to validate what you have seen, but if the only way you can see it is by a very complicated statistical process, it is not likely to be a salient issue. If what you're talking about explains one percent or two percent of an issue, it's not likely to be a big enough deal.

Shortly after this series of events, Wilensky came upon an opportunity for what she felt would be a more direct and meaningful engagement with health policy. During a layover at an airport, she ran into John Iglehart (page 274), the founding editor of *Health Affairs*, a policy journal launched in 1981 as an initiative of the international health education and aid foundation Project HOPE. Iglehart suggested that Wilensky send him a paper she had been working on, and the two of them stayed in touch. Then, in January of 1983, she was asked to interview for a position as vice president for health affairs with Project HOPE, which would make her director of the organization's newly established Health Policy Center. The center was established to conduct research on health policy issues in close partnership with government and non-government organizations, and this move was the next step in her progression towards an increasingly direct application of her interests.

While Project HOPE offered Wilensky a less academic and more policy-oriented role, they lacked the significant funding that she had had at the NCHSR, which posed a new set of challenges. Wilensky had to work hard for funding for the kinds of projects she wanted to research and organize: "You have to come up with the funding yourself. If other people find the funding for you, that has a significant impact on what you can do." As an administrator, she also had to recruit her staff under new kinds of constraint:

> It was a very interesting challenge to try to build a research group that had not existed. I was curious—could I attract a good group of researchers if I didn't have $26 million of data, like I had had back at NCHSR? Being able to attract a first-rate group of researchers is much easier when you don't have to raise money.

Becoming a Government Executive

Throughout her time at Project HOPE, Wilensky had continued to work with the government, frequently testifying before Congress and thus becoming well known to many of its members. Wilensky's approach to health care economics was recognized as preferring "market-oriented" solutions to government regulation, and so Republicans generally found her views consistent with their economic policies. Crucially, however, Wilensky had no clear political affiliation, and was viewed not as a political partisan but simply as a highly qualified expert on health care financing issues.

Wilensky's involvement with government positioned her to move even deeper into the public policy arena. From 1989 to 1992, she took on a series of government positions; these marked her final progression from academic research into roles that gave her a direct impact on policy. In 1989, early in the Bush administration, she was selected to serve as commissioner of the Physician Payment Review Commission, which advises Congress regarding Medicare reimbursement for physicians. Later in 1989, she was nominated to become administrator of the Health Care Financing Administration, and was confirmed by the Senate in 1990; HCFA, renamed the Centers for Medicare and Medicaid Services in 2003, is the agency responsible for the entire Medicare and Medicaid programs. This role put Wilensky in charge of 4,500 employees and a budget of $26 billion.

This position, a political appointment by the president, meant that she was now part of a Republican administration. It was clear, however, that she had been selected for her expertise more than her political affiliations: "After I had been offered the appointment, someone in the White House called me up and asked me if I was registered as a Republican or Democrat."

Interestingly, Wilensky was actually first asked by the Bush administration whether she had an interest in serving as assistant secretary for planning and administration at HHS, a position that involved mostly overseeing policy analysis and planning. She had made it clear, however, that she was not interested in this role—again, due to her desire to have a significant real-world impact: "Being in economic policy is all very nice, but you make policy according to where you spend your money. HCFA therefore had always been a much more attractive place."

Despite Wilenksy's considerable expertise in the field, doubts were raised about her ability to run such a massive agency:

> There were people who raised the question of, "Is this person going to be able to manage an organization like HCFA?" I personally was comfortable that this was not going to be an issue. I was comfortable that I was a good manager and understood how to operate a large organization.

While Wilensky reported to Lou Sullivan, the secretary of HHS, she was quite autonomous in her new role. As she explains, the operating divisions of HHS—such as HCFA, the FDA, and the NIH—are geographically separated and function independently. As the head of HCFA, Wilensky was particularly independent, partly because her expertise was very different from Sullivan's, and partly because she was well connected with members of Congress: "I made his chief of staff and some of the people supporting him very uneasy, because I had more independence than they would have liked." When she came up for confirmation, she was introduced by Senator Lloyd Bentsen, a Democrat from Texas and chairman of the Finance Committee before which Wilensky had often testified: "Well," Wilensky recalls him saying, "we actually think of her as ours…we found her first."

Wilensky's managerial competence soon dispelled all doubts about her ability to run HCFA. Her greatest achievements there, she feels, were making a significant change in how physicians were paid under Medicare and bringing a greater national presence to Medicaid.

A BALANCING ACT AT THE WHITE HOUSE

After two years as administrator of HCFA, Wilensky transitioned to the White House to become deputy assistant to the president for policy development, President Bush's senior health and welfare specialist:

> I left somewhat reluctantly to go to the White House in March at the urging of Clayton Yeutter, who was senior counselor to the president. Effectively, he was convinced that they needed a senior health person in the White House with credibility, and he worked hard to get me to move over. I had said no a couple of times, had raised some concerns, and he resolved these concerns and came back to ask again—this is all in a very short time period—and made me a great offer.

At the White House, Wilensky was given a corner office in the Old Executive Office Building—ironically, the same one later occupied by Ira Magaziner, the architect of the Clinton Health Care Plan.[2]

Overall, Wilenksy loved her new role: "It was wonderful. I got to know the president and to travel with him when he talked about health and welfare issues." At the same time, she missed the autonomy she had had while running her own agency:

> Being at the White House was not as satisfying as being the HCFA administrator, because you're still staff. You're staff to the most important person, but you're staff, and being staff is not as satisfying as running your own operation.

Being on the White House staff also required Wilensky to maintain a delicate balance between her support of the administration and her own professional credibility as an expert, which she recognized as her greatest asset: "I was keenly aware that there was a life after being a political appointee, and I didn't want to do anything to jeopardize it," she explains.

> Many members of Congress knew me as somebody that was respected in my field, and that served me very well. I was very careful to not ever say anything that I thought was not true. You have to support the administration if you are an administration person, but you can always find ways to support the administration without saying something that you believe is not true.

In addition to guarding her reputation as an expert, she also had to be careful to maintain the close and cooperative relationship she had developed with members of Congress:

> If a bill a member of Congress was proposing was not suggested by the administration, I would tell them "It's not consistent with the administration's policy" rather than telling them they were wrong or that it was a bad idea. I think that's a wise thing to do. I think there are instances when people find this is really difficult.

Wilensky left the White House in 1993 when President Clinton took office, and returned to Project HOPE as a senior fellow; she was the John M. Olin senior fellow from 1995 to 2003. At Project HOPE, she developed and analyzed health care and economic policies, and also continued to serve as an advisor to the government as well as in the private sector.

Wilenksy's government roles have included service during the Clinton administration as chair of the Physician Payment Review Commission and then of the Medicare Payment Advisory Commission, which advises Congress about Medicare payments to hospitals. She also served on President George W. Bush's Task Force to Improve Health Care Delivery for Our Nation's Veterans. In the private sector, she has served on several corporate review boards, and she frequently writes and speaks about health care reform for journals including *Health Affairs* and the *New England Journal of Medicine*. She has increasingly become involved in studying health care policy on an international level, and in 2005 to 2008 served as the chair of a major commission for the World Health Organization.

Wilensky sees her role at Project HOPE as increasingly focused on bridging the gap between health policy research and its target audiences: "Being able to translate what you're doing into direct and simple language is very important. Since going to Project HOPE I am much more of a translator of research."[3]

EVOLVING PERSONAL POLITICS

Despite having served as a political appointee, Wilensky has never grounded her identity in a political affiliation. She has instead always prioritized the quality of her work over any political agenda. Recalling her first involvement with government at the NCHSR, Wilensky explains: "I just wanted to know what the answers were. My involvement really was being a technical policy advisor. I was not a political activist."

This had not always been the case. In college she had been a member of the "Clean for Gene" movement, which supported antiwar Democrat Eugene McCarthy's 1968 run for the White House, and she considered herself a Democrat through most of the 1970s.

> I think I switched parties formally in 1984, but sometime during the Carter administration I had decided that what I had previously thought didn't seem to be working out. The mechanisms for change weren't working. I was very disillusioned with how focused people were on regulation—people ignored incentives.

Wilensky's qualified faith in incentives has led her to define herself as "primarily a limited-government market economist." The health care community, she believes, understands that she is fundamentally an empirical social scientist, and that her position is by no means extreme: "Not no government, or no regulation, but limited government. People know that, and they know what I have written, and that makes them comfortable."

AN APPLIED MICROECONOMIST

Overall, Wilensky considers herself an "applied microeconomist"—not a macroeconomist as many may assume because her work involves national health care policy. A macroeconomist studies the economy as a whole, focusing on questions about economic growth, inflation, unemployment, government spending, and tax policy. A microeconomist, however, is focused on the theory of the individual and the firm—how different economic incentives bring about different behaviors. These emphases fit much better than those of macroeconomics with the interest in psychology that drew Wilensky to economics in the first place: "If you're interested in behavior," she explains, "microeconomics is the part you want to be in, because that's where behavior really is explained—at the individual level."

The "applied" part is where health care comes in: Wilensky's work focuses on applying microeconomic theory to people and organizations in health care as it is actually practiced. In thinking through the nation's current struggle with containing health care costs, for example, Wilensky would be more focused on how different payment mechanisms may change physician and patient utilization, rather than on what percentage of GDP should be spent on health care. The microeconomic questions are about how the key players—patients, physicians, and hospitals—will behave given different financial incentives.

COMPARING CLINICAL AND POLICY PERSPECTIVES

The nature of Wilensky's work as an applied microeconomist has been very satisfying to her, though she recognizes the tradeoffs that come with this or any field. The policy expert's impact, she explains, is broader in scope if not as immediate as that of the clinician:

> As a physician you have a way to impact the well-being of the individual in the most immediate and direct way, but as a health policy person, I have potentially an ability to impact a community or a state or a nation in a very significant way.

These differences in scope come along with quite different points of view about health care problems. Most physicians, Wilensky remarks, are trained "to do things for the maximum benefit of the individual." Policy experts more often consider the tradeoffs, for other individuals and for society as a whole, involved in such treatment:

> The sense of the cost of what the services are that are being provided, and how else resources might be used and what you gain from that, is a very different context than most physicians are used to thinking within.

Having a medical degree when talking about health care policy "brings, at least before some audiences, a certain level of credibility that those without a clinical background cannot have," Wilensky believes. This credibility "is about understanding the clinical implications of taking one strategy versus another." While she at times wishes that she had such a background, she believes that being married to a physician has helped to compensate for the limits of her expertise: "Having a spouse that I could talk to about these things is very helpful—just asking him, 'Does this make sense to you as a private practitioner?'"

Policy experts, in turn, have strengths that clinicians sometimes fail to appreciate, in part because policy questions often seem—sometimes deceptively, Wilensky notes—to be a matter of common sense. Having spent her career acquiring an intimate knowledge of the details that matter to health care financing, she emphasizes the importance of such knowledge for a complete and informed debate:

> Just as most non-clinicians wouldn't presume to argue the benefits of one surgical strategy versus another, there are a lot of issues regarding the financial implications of different policy strategies that people who are clinicians might not know or understand or appreciate.

REFLECTIONS ON WOMEN IN HEALTH POLICY

While not denying that gender inequality exists in the health policy sphere, Wilensky does not feel she has suffered significant discrimination as a woman in her career. In her experience, certain branches of medicine, such as surgery, have greater problems in this regard than health policy. She notes, however, that most senior administration posts are held by men: "I don't know if that is an area that has suffered benign neglect from females, in terms of areas of interest, or whether it's something else that is going on."

Wilensky sees her own choices about work-life balance as continuous with the difficult decision-making process involved in any career: "I think I have a more mature understanding that there are tradeoffs we have to make all along life." She credits her own ability to find a satisfying balance while also achieving professional success to the support of her husband:

> I am fortunate to be on my first marriage. I have been married more than 40 years. I have two grown children and three grandchildren. It is hard, and you need proactive support from your spouse as a woman to be able to balance all that and still be successful professionally.

In terms of her own tradeoffs, Wilensky has relatively few regrets. She claims she has never understood why she did not go to law school, given her strong interest in the law, but recognizes that had she done so, she likely would have ended up close to where she is: in some area of economics and law. Her only real regret is not having gone into the Peace Corps when it first started. "That was the one thing I wanted to do that I haven't done."

When asked what she considers her single greatest professional achievement, she explains:

> Making a difference for the most vulnerable populations of Medicare and Medicaid. It was the hardest, most gratifying, and probably most important thing I have done.

Notes

1 The path of an economist specifically becoming a "health care" economist is also discussed in Joseph Newhouse's profile on page 374.

2 The successes and failures of the Clinton Plan are also discussed in the profiles of Donna Shalala (page 418), Richard Corlin (page 128), and David Cutler (page 136).

3 Interestingly, John Iglehart (page 374) discusses his role at Project HOPE and with *Health Affairs* in very similar terms.

ADDITIONAL POSITIONS

1993–	Senior Fellow, Project HOPE
1995–1997	Chair, Physician Payment Review Commission
1997–2001	Chair, Medicare Payment Advisory Commission
2001–2003	Co-chair, President's Task Force to Improve Health Care Delivery for Our Nation's Veterans
2005–2008	Commissioner, WHO Commission on Social Determinants of Health
2006–2008	Co-chair, Department of Defense Task Force on the Future of Military Health Care
2008–2009	President and Chair, Health Care Subcommittee, Defense Health Board
2008–	Regent, Uniformed Services University of the Health Sciences
2010–	Director, Geisinger Health System Foundation

Subject Index

W

W.R. Grace & Co., 160

Wald, George, 188

Walden, Dan, 463

walking epidural, 392–393, 397, 401

Wall Street, 227–228, 230, 275, 280, 415, 420; *also see relevant topics in thematic index*

Wall Street Journal, 228, 230, 280

Walmart, 144

Walsh, William, 278

Walter Reed Army Institute of Research, 112, 115

Ware, John, 63

Warren Commission, 455

Washington, DC, 21, 61, 64, 86–87, 89, 91, 112, 115, 130, 138, 150, 154, 181–182, 185, 187, 195, 199, 206, 208, 215, 250, 255, 276–277, 280, 282–283, 298, 301–302, 308, 310, 318, 348, 351–353, 358–359, 366, 370, 408, 420, 422-423, 425, 428, 430–431, 454, 462–464

Washington Business Group on Health, 208, 215

Washington Post, 280, 283, 408, 425

Wayne State University, 410, 412

Wecht, Cyril H., 450–457

Weinstein, Milton, 58, 199

Weissman, Joel, 177

Welch, Jack, 6, 213

Weld, William, 43

welfare reform, 424, 462–463

Western College for Women, 418–419

Western Samoa, 47

Wharton business school: *see University of Pennsylvania*

whistleblower, 389

White House, 89, 130, 176, 181–182, 348, 352–353, 458, 466–469

Whitehouse Station, New Jersey, 219

Wilensky, Gail R., 150, 458–471

Wilkinson, Lee, 17

Williams, C. K., 210

Winakur, Jerald, 279, 283

Winfrey, Oprah, 173

Wofsy, Constance, 20

Wolf, Marshall, 180

women, 7, 18, 21, 24–27, 37, 54, 84, 89, 155, 162, 172, 176, 179, 232, 234–235, 248–249, 254–255, 268, 289, 292–294, 296, 315, 320, 322, 327, 349, 354, 384–390, 392–393, 397–400, 411, 418–419, 421–422, 471

women's health, 289, 373–377, 381, 384–385, 387–389

Woodward, Bob, 41

workplace safety, 194

World War II, 24, 49, 56–57, 62, 69, 299

Wriston, Walt, 414

writing, 25, 27, 29–30, 33, 41, 56, 64, 66, 68, 85, 88, 90, 93, 115, 118, 120–122, 125–127, 134, 140, 154, 156, 170, 173–174, 190–191, 196, 204, 209–210, 235, 237, 243–244, 269, 275, 277, 282, 288, 323, 327–328, 346, 360, 365, 369–370, 376, 379, 405, 425, 462, 465; *also see thematic index*

Y

Yeutter, Clayton, 467

Z

Zapruder film, 454–455

Zeckhauser, Richard, 86, 376

Zola, Irving, 384, 390

Zolinza, 230

Thematic Index